A-Level

Mathematics

for Edexcel Core 1

The Complete Course for Edexcel C1

Contents

About this book

In this book you'll find...

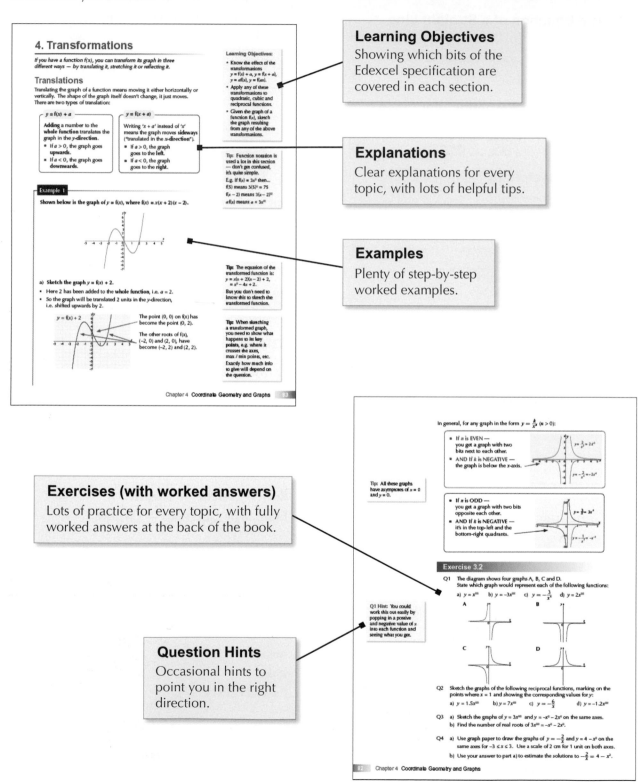

Learning Objectives
Showing which bits of the Edexcel specification are covered in each section.

Explanations
Clear explanations for every topic, with lots of helpful tips.

Examples
Plenty of step-by-step worked examples.

Exercises (with worked answers)
Lots of practice for every topic, with fully worked answers at the back of the book.

Question Hints
Occasional hints to point you in the right direction.

Review Exercise — Chapter 4

Q1 Find the equations of the straight lines that pass through the points
a) $(2, -1)$ and $(-4, -19)$,   b) $\left(0, -\frac{1}{3}\right)$ and $\left(5, \frac{2}{3}\right)$.

Write each of them in the forms:
(i) $y - y_0 = m(x - x_0)$,
(ii) $y = mx + c$,
(iii) $ax + by + c = 0$, where a, b and c are integers.

Q2 a) The line l_u has equation $y = \frac{3}{2}x - \frac{2}{3}$. Find the equation of the line parallel to l_u passing through the point with coordinates $(4, 2)$.

b) The line l_v passes through the point $(6, 1)$ and is perpendicular to $2x - y - 7 = 0$. What is the equation of l_v?

Q3 The coordinates of points R and S are $(1, 9)$ and $(10, 3)$ respectively. Find the equation of the line perpendicular to RS, passing through the point $(1, 9)$.

Q4 Draw rough sketches of the following curves:
a) $y = -2x^9$,   b) $y = \frac{7}{x^2}$,   c) $y = -5x^8$,   d) $y = -\frac{2}{x}$.

Q5 Sketch these cubic graphs:
a) $y = (x - 4)^3$,   b) $y = (3 - x)(x + 2)^2$,
c) $y = (1 - x)(x^2 - 6x + 8)$,   d) $y = (x - 1)(x - 2)(x - 3)$.

Q6 Use the graph of f(x) below to sketch these transformed graphs:

$y = f(x)$

a) $y = f(ax)$, where (i) $a > 1$, (ii) $0 < a < 1$,
b) $y = af(x)$, where (i) $a > 1$, (ii) $0 < a < 1$,
c) (i) $y = f(x + a)$, (ii) $y = f(x - a)$, where $a > 0$,
d) (i) $y = f(x) + a$, (ii) $y = f(x) - a$, where $a > 0$.

Q7 The diagram shows the graph of $y = f(x)$. The curve has a maximum at $(2, 4)$ and meets the x-axis at $(0, 0)$ and $(5, 0)$.

$(2, 4)$

Sketch the graphs of these functions, labelling clearly the coordinates of any maxima or minima and where the curve meets the coordinate axes.
a) $y = f(-x)$ b) $y = -f(x)$ c) $y = 2f(x)$ d) $y = f(2x)$

Review Exercises
Mixed questions covering the whole chapter, with fully worked answers.

Exam-Style Questions — Chapter 4

1 The line PQ has equation $4x + 3y = 15$.

a) Find the gradient of PQ.   *(2 marks)*

b) The point R lies on PQ and has coordinates $(3, 1)$. Find the equation of the line which passes through the point R and is perpendicular to PQ, giving your answer in the form $y = mx + c$.   *(3 marks)*

2 The curve C has the equation
$$y = (2x + 1)(x - 2)^2.$$

Sketch C, clearly showing the points where the curve meets the x- and y-axes.   *(4 marks)*

3

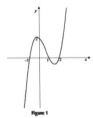

Figure 1

Figure 1 shows a sketch of the function $y = f(x)$. The function crosses the x-axis at $(-1, 0)$, $(1, 0)$ and $(2, 0)$, and crosses the y-axis at $(0, 2)$.

On separate diagrams, sketch the following:
a) $y = f\left(\frac{1}{2}x\right)$.   *(3 marks)*
b) $y = f(x - 4)$.   *(2 marks)*
On each diagram, label any known points of intersection with the x- or y-axes.

Exam-Style Questions
Questions in the same style as the ones you'll get in the exam, with worked solutions and mark schemes.

Formula Sheet
Contains all the formulas you'll be given in the C1 exam.

Glossary
All the definitions you need to know for the exam, plus other useful words.

Practice Exam Papers (on CD-ROM)
Two printable exam papers, with fully worked answers and mark schemes.

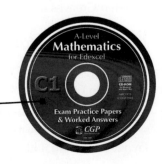
A-Level
Mathematics
for Edexcel
C1
CD-ROM
Exam Practice Papers
& Worked Answers
CGP

Published by CGP

Editors:
Helena Hayes, Sharon Keeley-Holden, Simon Little, Caley Simpson, Charlotte Whiteley.

Contributors:
Jean Blencowe, Josephine Gibbons, Allan Graham, Stephen Green, Phil Harvey,
Alan Mason, Barbara Mascetti, Andy Park, Rosemary Rogers, Janet West.

ISBN: 978 1 84762 811 4

With thanks to Janet Dickinson and Paul Jordin for the proofreading.
With thanks to Helen Greaves for the reviewing.

Groovy website: www.cgpbooks.co.uk

Printed by Elanders Ltd, Newcastle upon Tyne.
Jolly bits of clipart from CorelDRAW®

Photocopying — it's dull, grey and sometimes a bit naughty. Luckily, it's dead cheap, easy and
quick to order more copies of this book from CGP — just call us on 0870 750 1242. Phew!

1. Algebraic Expressions

This first chapter will cover some of the basic algebra skills that you'll need again and again throughout the course — so you'll need to make sure you're completely comfortable with everything here. The good news is you should have seen a lot of it before.

Expanding brackets

Single brackets

When you've got just **one set of brackets** multiplied by a single number or letter — multiply each term in the brackets by the number or letter outside the brackets.

$$a(b + c + d) = ab + ac + ad$$

Learning Objectives:

- Be able to use and expand brackets.
- Be able to identify common factors and take them outside the brackets.
- Be able to simplify complicated expressions including algebraic fractions.

Double brackets

For **two sets** of brackets multiplied together (where there are **two terms** in each) — multiply **each term** in one set of brackets by **each term** in the other. You should **always** get **four terms** from multiplying out double brackets (though sometimes two of the terms will **combine**).

$$(a + b)(c + d) = ac + ad + bc + bd$$

Tip: Remember **FOIL**: First Outside Inside Last as a rule for multiplying out double brackets. It's just an easy way to remember it.

Squared brackets

Squared brackets are just a **special case** of double brackets where both brackets are the **same**. Write them out as two sets of brackets until you're comfortable with it.

$$(a + b)^2 = (a + b)(a + b)$$
$$= a^2 + ab + ba + b^2 = a^2 + 2ab + b^2$$

A common **mistake** is to write $(a + b)^2 = a^2 + b^2$ — you must remember that $(a + b)^2$ is **actually** $(a + b)(a + b)$ to avoid this trap.

Long brackets

Long brackets are brackets with **many terms**. Just like with double brackets, you need to multiply every term in the first set of brackets by every term in the second — you'll just need to do it with more terms.

Write out the expression again with each term from the first set of brackets separately multiplied by the second set of brackets. Always use this middle step so that you can't get confused by all the terms.

$$(x + y + z)(a + b + c + d)$$
$$= x(a + b + c + d) + y(a + b + c + d) + z(a + b + c + d)$$

Then multiply out each of these single brackets, **one at a time**.

Many brackets

When you've got **many sets** of brackets multiplied together — multiply them out **two at a time** treating each set of two as double brackets or long brackets.

Multiply out the first **two** sets of brackets...

$$(a + b)(c + d)(e + f)$$
$$= (ac + ad + bc + bd)(e + f)$$

> **Tip:** Once you've multiplied out the first pair, the resulting terms may cancel or simplify — making the second step easier.

...then multiply out the remaining **two sets**.

$$= ac(e + f) + ad(e + f) + bc(e + f) + bd(e + f)$$

Now multiply out each of these single brackets, **one at a time**.

Examples

Single Brackets Expand $3xy(x^2 + 2x - 8)$.

Multiply each term inside the brackets by the bit outside — separately.

$$(3xy \times x^2) + (3xy \times 2x) + (3xy \times (-8))$$
$$= (3x^3y) + (6x^2y) + (-24xy)$$
$$= \boxed{3x^3y + 6x^2y - 24xy}$$

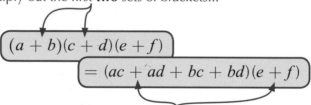

Multiply the numbers first, then put the letters together.

> **Tip:** Putting brackets round each bit makes it easier to read.

Squared Brackets   **Expand $(2y^2 + 3x)^2$.**

Either write it as two sets of
brackets and multiply it out...

$$(2y^2 + 3x)(2y^2 + 3x)$$

$$= 2y^2 \cdot 2y^2 + 2y^2 \cdot 3x + 3x \cdot 2y^2 + 3x \cdot 3x$$

$$= 4y^4 + 6xy^2 + 6xy^2 + 9x^2$$

$$= \boxed{4y^4 + 12xy^2 + 9x^2}$$

...or do it in one go.

$$(2y^2)^2 + 2(2y^2)(3x) + (3x)^2$$

$$\quad a^2 \qquad\quad 2ab \qquad\quad b^2$$

$$= \boxed{4y^4 + 12xy^2 + 9x^2}$$

> **Tip:** The dots used here just mean 'multiplied by' — just like the × sign.

Long Brackets   **Expand $(2x^2 + 3x - 6)(4x^3 + 6x^2 + 3)$.**

Multiply each term in the first set of brackets by the whole second set of brackets;

$$= 2x^2(4x^3 + 6x^2 + 3) + 3x(4x^3 + 6x^2 + 3) + (-6)(4x^3 + 6x^2 + 3)$$

Now multiply out each of these sets of brackets and simplify it all:

$$= (8x^5 + 12x^4 + 6x^2) + (12x^4 + 18x^3 + 9x) + (-24x^3 - 36x^2 - 18)$$

$$= \boxed{8x^5 + 24x^4 - 6x^3 - 30x^2 + 9x - 18}$$

Many Brackets   **Expand $(2x + 5)(x + 2)(x - 3)$.**

Start by expanding the first two sets of brackets.

$$(2x + 5)(x + 2)(x - 3)$$

$$= (2x^2 + 4x + 5x + 10)(x - 3)$$

$$= (2x^2 + 9x + 10)(x - 3)$$

Now expand the long bracket.

$$= 2x^2(x - 3) + 9x(x - 3) + 10(x - 3)$$

Expand the single brackets and simplify.

$$= (2x^3 - 6x^2) + (9x^2 - 27x) + (10x - 30)$$

$$= \boxed{2x^3 + 3x^2 - 17x - 30}$$

Q1 Expand the brackets in these expressions:

a) $5(x + 4)$ b) $a(4 - 2b)$ c) $-2(x^2 + y)$

d) $pq(r - q)$ e) $6mn(m + 1)$ f) $7z^2(2 + z)$

g) $3xy(3 - x^2 - xy)$ h) $-4ht(t^2 - 2ht - 3h^3)$ i) $7xy(x^2 + z^2)$

j) $4(x + 2) + 3(x - 5)$ k) $p(3p^2 - 2q) + (q + 4p^3)$

Q2 Expand and simplify:

a) $(x + 5)(x - 3)$ b) $(2z + 3)(3z - 2)$ c) $(u + 8)^2$

d) $(ab + cd)(ac + bd)$ e) $(10 + f)(2f^2 - 3g)$ f) $(7 + q)(7 - q)$

g) $(2 - 3w)^2$ h) $(4rs^2 + 3)^2$ i) $(5k^2l - 2kn)^2$

Q3 Expand and simplify the following expressions:

a) $(l + 5)(l^2 + 2l + 3)$ b) $(2 + q)(3 - q + 4q^2)$

c) $(m + 1)(m + 2)(m - 4)$ d) $(r + s)^3$

e) $(4 + x + y)(1 - x - y)$ f) $(2c^2 - cd + d)(2d - c - 5c^2)$

Factorising

Common factors

The **factors** of a term are all the bits that **multiply together** to make it up — if something is a factor of a term, the term will be **divisible** by it.

> **Tip:** The definition of a **term** is a collection of numbers, letters and brackets all multiplied or divided together.

For example consider the term **$12xy^2$** — it has many factors including:

- All the **factors of 12** — 1, 2, 3, 4, 6 and 12.
- The variable **x**.
- The variable **y** (and also **y^2**).
- Any combinations of these multiplied together e.g. $3xy$, $12y^2$, $6x$ etc.

Example 1

Find all the factors of 6x.

A good way to do this is to break it up as much as you can:
$$6x = 1 \times 2 \times 3 \times x$$
None of these have any other factors so we can't break it down further.

Now list all possible combinations of 1, 2, 3 and x:

1,   2,   3,   6, x, $2x$, $3x$, $6x$

1 is always a factor.

The term itself is also a factor.

A factor which is in every term of an expression is a called a **common factor**. They can be '**taken out**' and put outside brackets to simplify the expression. When you've taken out **all** possible factors, the expression is **factorised**.

Example 2

Factorise $2x^3z + 4x^2yz + 14x^2y^2z$ completely.

Look for any factors that are in each term.

$$2x^3z + 4x^2yz + 14x^2y^2z$$

<u>Numbers:</u> There's a common factor of 2 here because 2 divides into 2, 4 and 14.

<u>Variables:</u> There's at least an x^2 in each term...

...and there's a z in each term.

So there's a common factor of $2x^2z$ in this expression.

This can be seen more easily if you write each term as $2x^2z \times$ 'something':

$$2x^3z + 4x^2yz + 14x^2y^2z = 2x^2z \cdot x + 2x^2z \cdot 2y + 2x^2z \cdot 7y^2$$

Write the common factor outside a set of brackets...

$$= 2x^2z(x + 2y + 7y^2)$$

...and put what's left of each term inside the brackets.

The three terms in the brackets have no common factors — so this expression is completely factorised.

You can check that you did it right by multiplying it out again and checking you get the original expression:

$$2x^2z(x + 2y + 7y^2) = 2x^3z + 4x^2yz + 14x^2y^2z$$

> **Tip:** The key here is the phrase '**at least**'. There is an x^3 in one term but only an x^2 in the other two, so each term has at least an x^2 in it.

> **Tip:** After factorising, you should always check that your answer multiplies out to give the original expression. (You can do this in your head — if you trust it.)

It's not just numbers and variables that you need to look for — you can sometimes take out **whole sets of brackets** as factors of an expression.

Example 3

Express $(y + a)^2(x - a)^3 + (x - a)^2$ as a product of factors.

This can be written:

$$(y + a)^2(x - a)(x - a)^2 + (x - a)^2$$

$(x - a)^2$ is a common factor — so write the common factor outside a set of brackets and put what's left of each term inside the brackets:

$$(x - a)^2((y + a)^2(x - a) + 1)$$

This term will give $(x - a)^2$.

This term will multiply to give $(y + a)^2(x - a)^3$.

The two terms in the brackets share no common factors so the expression is factorised.

> **Tip:** 'Expressing as a product of factors' just means writing it as numbers, variables or sets of brackets multiplied together. The things you multiply together are the **factors** of the expression.

Difference of two squares

If you expand brackets of the form $(a - b)(a + b)$ the 'ab' terms cancel and you're left with one square minus another:

$$(a - b)(a + b) = a^2 + ab - ba - b^2 = a^2 + ab - ab - b^2 = a^2 - b^2$$

This result is called the **difference of two squares**:

$$\boxed{a^2 - b^2 = (a - b)(a + b)}$$

You need to watch out for it when factorising — if you spot that an expression is just 'something squared' minus 'something else squared', you can use this result to rewrite the expression as a pair of brackets, i.e. to factorise it.

Tip: For more on factorising quadratics see pages 20-23.

Example 4

Factorise $x^2 - 36y^2$.

36 is a square number so $36y^2$ can be written as a square:

$$x^2 - 36y^2 = x^2 - 6^2y^2$$
$$= x^2 - (6y)^2$$
$$= (x - 6y)(x + 6y)$$

This is a difference of two squares.

Exercise 1.2

Q1 Factorise the following expressions completely:

a) $9k + 15l$ b) $u^2 - uv$

c) $10w + 15$ d) $2x^2y - 12xy^2$

e) $f^2g^2 - fg$ f) $3u^2v^2 + 5u^4v^4 + 12u^2v$

g) $p^3 + 3pq^3 + 2p$ h) $abcde - bcdef - cdefg$

i) $11xy^2 - 11x^2y - 11x^2y^2$ j) $mnp^2 + 7m^2np^3$

Q2 Hint: Remember to look for a difference of two squares.

Q2 Write the following expressions as products of factors:

a) $x^2 - y^2$ b) $9a^2 - 4b^2$

c) $25x^2 - 49z^2$ d) $a^2c - 16b^2c$

Q3 Express the following as the product of factors.

a) $(4 - z)^2(2 - z) + p(2 - z)$ b) $(r - d)^3 + 5(r - d)^2$

c) $(b + c)^5(a + b) - (b + c)^5$ d) $l^2m(a - 2x) + rp^2(2x - a)$

Q3d) Hint: Remember that $(b - a) = -(a - b)$.

Q4 Simplify each expression, leaving your answer in its factorised form.

a) $(p + q)^2 + 2q(p + q)$ b) $2(2x - y)^2 - 6x(2x - y)$

c) $(r + 6s)^2 - (r + 6s)(r - s)$ d) $(l + w + h)^2 - l(l + w + h)$

Q5 Hint: Look for common factors first — if you can't see any, try to multiply out the brackets and see if it simplifies that way.

Q5 Simplify these expressions by expanding brackets, factorising or both.

a) $(m + 5)(m^2 - 5m + 25)$ b) $(p - 2q)(p^2 + 2pq + 4q^2)$

c) $(u - v)(u + v) - (u + v)^2$ d) $(c + d)^3 - c(c + d)^2 - d(c + d)^2$

Algebraic fractions

You should have seen all these methods before when working with numerical fractions — but you need to learn them for **algebraic fractions** too.

The first rule is that if you're **adding fractions** together and they all have the same **denominator** — you can just add the **numerators**.

$$\frac{a}{x} + \frac{b}{x} + \frac{c}{x} \equiv \frac{a+b+c}{x}$$

Tip: This equals sign with 3 lines $\equiv$ means it's true for all values of a, b, c or x — this is called an **identity**.

x is called a **common denominator**. If the fractions you want to add don't have a common denominator you can 'find' one — **rewrite** the fractions so that the denominators are the same by multiplying **top** and **bottom** by the same thing.

Example 1

a) **Simplify** $\dfrac{1}{2x} - \dfrac{1}{3x} + \dfrac{1}{5x}$.

You need to rewrite these so that all the denominators are equal. What you want is something that all these denominators divide into.

30 is the lowest number that 2, 3 and 5 all go into and each denominator contains an x. So make the common denominator $30x$.

Multiply the top and bottom lines of each fraction by whatever makes the bottom line $30x$.

$$\frac{1}{2x} - \frac{1}{3x} + \frac{1}{5x} = \frac{1}{2x} \cdot \frac{15}{15} - \frac{1}{3x} \cdot \frac{10}{10} + \frac{1}{5x} \cdot \frac{6}{6}$$

$$= \frac{15}{30x} - \frac{10}{30x} + \frac{6}{30x}$$

$$= \frac{15 - 10 + 6}{30x}$$

$$= \frac{11}{30x}$$

Always check that these cancel down to give what you started with.

b) **Simplify** $\dfrac{3}{x+2} + \dfrac{5}{x-3}$.

Again, the first step is to rewrite the fractions so that they have a common denominator.

You need an expression that both $(x + 2)$ and $(x – 3)$ divide into — you can get one by multiplying the denominators together to give a common denominator of $(x + 2)(x – 3)$.

Make the denominator of each fraction into the common denominator.

$$\frac{3(x-3)}{(x+2)(x-3)} + \frac{5(x+2)}{(x+2)(x-3)}$$

Multiply the top and bottom lines of each fraction by whatever makes the bottom line the same as the common denominator.

Combine into one fraction

$$= \frac{3(x-3) + 5(x+2)}{(x+2)(x-3)}$$

All the bottom lines are the same — so you can just add the top lines.

$$= \frac{3x - 9 + 5x + 10}{(x+2)(x-3)}$$

All you need to do now is tidy up the top.

$$= \frac{8x + 1}{(x+2)(x-3)}$$

c) **Simplify** $\frac{3}{2x^2} + \frac{6}{5x}$.

Tip: Finding any old common denominator is easy — just multiply all the denominators together. But if you're careful and don't include any bits twice, you'll have a lot less simplifying to do at the end.

Finding a common denominator here is a bit more tricky. You could still multiply the two denominators together to get $10x^3$ — but this wouldn't give the simplest one.

You've got $2x^2 = 2 \times x \times x$ and $5x = 5 \times x$ and you need to find a term which both of them divide into. You must include each different factor at least once in your term — but some more than once.

The different factors are 2, 5 and x so you need at least one of each — there are two x's in the first denominator so you'll need an x^2, but you don't need another for the x in the second denominator since this is accounted for by multiplying by the x^2.

So the common denominator is $2 \times 5 \times x \times x = 10x^2$.

$$\frac{3}{2x^2} + \frac{6}{5x} = \frac{3 \times 5}{2x^2 \times 5} + \frac{6 \times 2x}{5x \times 2x}$$

Rewrite fractions with a common denominator.

$$= \frac{15}{10x^2} + \frac{12x}{10x^2}$$

$$= \frac{15 + 12x}{10x^2}$$

Add the numerators.

$$= \frac{3(5 + 4x)}{10x^2}$$

Factorise the numerator.

Chapter 1 Algebra

Algebraic fractions can sometimes be simplified by cancelling **terms** that appear in both the top and bottom lines.

You can do this in **two ways**. Use whichever you prefer — but make sure you understand the ideas behind both.

Example 2

Simplify $\dfrac{ax + ay}{az}$.

You can either...

(1) Factorise — then cancel.

Factorise the top line.

$$\frac{ax + ay}{az} = \frac{a(x + y)}{az} = \frac{\cancel{a}(x + y)}{\cancel{a}z} = \frac{x + y}{z}$$

Cancel the 'a'.

...Or

(2) Split into two fractions — then cancel.

$$\frac{ax + ay}{az} = \frac{ax}{az} + \frac{ay}{az}$$

This is just the rule from p.7 for adding fractions — but backwards.

$$= \frac{\cancel{a}x}{\cancel{a}z} + \frac{\cancel{a}y}{\cancel{a}z} = \frac{x}{z} + \frac{y}{z} = \frac{x + y}{z}$$

Exercise 1.3

Q1 Express each of these as a single fraction.

a) $\dfrac{x}{3} + \dfrac{x}{4}$ b) $\dfrac{2}{t} + \dfrac{13}{t^2}$ c) $\dfrac{1}{2p} - \dfrac{1}{5q}$

d) $\dfrac{ab}{c} + \dfrac{bc}{a} + \dfrac{ca}{b}$ e) $\dfrac{2}{mn} - \dfrac{3m}{n} + \dfrac{n^2}{m}$ f) $\dfrac{2}{ab^3} - \dfrac{9}{a^3 b}$

Q2 Express the following as single fractions in their simplest form.

a) $\dfrac{5}{y - 1} + \dfrac{3}{y - 2}$ b) $\dfrac{7}{r - 5} - \dfrac{4}{r + 3}$ c) $\dfrac{8}{p} - \dfrac{1}{p - 3}$

d) $\dfrac{w}{2(w - 2)} + \dfrac{3w}{w - 7}$ e) $\dfrac{z + 1}{z + 2} - \dfrac{z + 3}{z + 4}$ f) $\dfrac{1}{q + 1} + \dfrac{3}{q - 2}$

Q3 Simplify these expressions.

a) $\dfrac{2x + 10}{6}$ b) $\dfrac{6a - 12b - 15c}{3}$

c) $\dfrac{np^2 - 2n^2 p}{np}$ d) $\dfrac{4st + 6s^2 t + 9s^3 t}{2t}$

e) $\dfrac{10yz^3 - 40y^3 z^3 + 60y^2 z^3}{10z^2}$ f) $\dfrac{12cd - 6c^2 d + 3c^3 d^2}{12c^2 de}$

2. Laws of Indices

Learning Objectives:

- Be able to use the laws of indices to simplify expressions.

The laws of indices are just a set of simple rules for manipulating expressions involving indices (powers). They'll be used regularly in this module and others for simplifying expressions, equations and formulas.

Laws of indices

You should already know that the expression x^n just means *n* **lots** of x multiplied together. The n is called the **index** or power of x. So when you square a number, the index or power is 2.

OK, now you're ready to see the laws. Here are the first **three** you need to know:

Tip: Don't forget — index and power mean the same thing. We'll use power for the rest of the section.

> If you multiply two numbers — you **add** their powers.
> $$a^m \times a^n = a^{m+n}$$

> If you divide two numbers — you **subtract** their powers.
> $$\frac{a^m}{a^n} = a^{m-n}$$

> If you have a power to the power of something else — you **multiply** the powers together.
> $$(a^m)^n = a^{mn}$$

There are also laws for manipulating **fractional** and **negative** powers...

Tip: $\sqrt[m]{a}$ is the mth root of a.

$$a^{\frac{1}{m}} = \sqrt[m]{a}$$

$$a^{-m} = \frac{1}{a^m}$$

$$a^{\frac{m}{n}} = \sqrt[n]{a^m} = \left(\sqrt[n]{a}\right)^m$$

...and one simple law for **zero** powers, which works for any non-zero number or letter.

$$a^0 = 1$$

Now, let's see the laws in action in some worked examples.

Examples

Simplify the following:

a)   (i) a^2a (ii) $x^{-2} \cdot x^5$ (iii) $(a+b)^2(a+b)^5$ (iv) $ab^3 \cdot a^2b$

(i) $a^2a = a^{2+1} = a^3$ $\boxed{a^m \times a^n = a^{m+n}}$

(ii) $x^{-2} \cdot x^5 = x^{-2+5} = x^3$

(iii) $(a+b)^2(a+b)^5 = (a+b)^{2+5} = (a+b)^7$

(iv) $ab^3 \cdot a^2b = a^{1+2}b^{3+1} = a^3b^4$ ← Add the powers of a and b separately.

Tip: Note that $x = x^1$.

b)   (i) $(x^2)^3$ (ii) $\{(a+b)^3\}^4$ (iii) $(ab^2)^4$

(i) $(x^2)^3 = x^6$ $\boxed{(a^m)^n = a^{mn}}$

(ii) $\{(a+b)^3\}^4 = (a+b)^{12}$

(iii) $(ab^2)^4 = a^4(b^2)^4 = a^4b^8$ ← This power of 4 applies to both bits inside the brackets.

Tip: To understand part b) (iii), remember that:

$(ab^2)^4 = (ab^2)(ab^2)(ab^2)(ab^2)$

$= a \cdot a \cdot a \cdot a \cdot b^2 \cdot b^2 \cdot b^2 \cdot b^2$

$= a^4 \cdot (b^2)^4 = a^4b^8.$

c)   (i) $\dfrac{x^{\frac{3}{4}}}{x}$ (ii) $\dfrac{x^3y^2}{xy^3}$

(i) $\dfrac{x^{\frac{3}{4}}}{x} = x^{\frac{3}{4}-1} = x^{-\frac{1}{4}}$ $\boxed{\dfrac{a^m}{a^n} = a^{m-n}}$

(ii) $\dfrac{x^3y^2}{xy^3} = x^{3-1}y^{2-3} = x^2y^{-1}$ ← Subtract the powers of x and y separately.

d)   (i) $4^{\frac{1}{2}}$ (ii) $125^{\frac{1}{3}}$

(i) $4^{\frac{1}{2}} = \sqrt{4} = 2$ $\boxed{a^{\frac{1}{m}} = \sqrt[m]{a}}$

(ii) $125^{\frac{1}{3}} = \sqrt[3]{125} = 5$

e) (i) $9^{\frac{3}{2}}$ (ii) $16^{\frac{3}{4}}$

$$a^{\frac{m}{n}} = \sqrt[n]{a^m} = (\sqrt[n]{a})^m$$

(i) $9^{\frac{3}{2}} = \left(9^{\frac{1}{2}}\right)^3 = (\sqrt{9})^3 = 3^3 = 27$

(ii) $16^{\frac{3}{4}} = \left(16^{\frac{1}{4}}\right)^3 = (\sqrt[4]{16})^3 = 2^3 = 8$

It's often easier to work out the root first, then raise it to the power.

f) (i) 2^{-3} (ii) $(x + 1)^{-1}$

(i) $2^{-3} = \dfrac{1}{2^3} = \dfrac{1}{8}$ $a^{-m} = \dfrac{1}{a^m}$

(ii) $(x + 1)^{-1} = \dfrac{1}{x + 1}$

g) (i) 2^0 (ii) $(a + b)^0$

(i) $2^0 = 1$ $a^0 = 1$

(ii) $(a + b)^0 = 1$

Example

Express $\dfrac{\left(7^{\frac{1}{3}}\right)^6 \times (7^{-1})^4}{(7^{-4})^{-2}}$ **as 7^k, where k is an integer.**

This one looks really complicated but it's just a series of easy steps. Just make sure to work through it slowly and don't jump ahead.

$$\frac{\left(7^{\frac{1}{3}}\right)^6 \times (7^{-1})^4}{(7^{-4})^{-2}} = \frac{7^{\frac{6}{3}} \times 7^{-1 \times 4}}{7^{-4 \times -2}}$$

$(a^m)^n = a^{mn}$

$$= \frac{7^2 \times 7^{-4}}{7^8}$$

$$= \frac{7^{2 - 4}}{7^8}$$

$a^m \times a^n = a^{m+n}$

$$= \frac{7^{-2}}{7^8}$$

$$= 7^{-2 - 8}$$

$\dfrac{a^m}{a^n} = a^{m-n}$

$$= 7^{-10}$$

Q1 Simplify the following, leaving your answer as a power:

a) $2^3 \times 2^4$

b) 10×10^4

c) $7^2 \times 7^5 \times 7^3$

d) $p^6 \times p^{-4} \times p^5$

e) $y^{-1} \times y^{-2} \times y^7$

f) $5^{\frac{1}{2}} \times 5^3 \times 5^{-\frac{3}{2}}$

g) $6^5 \div 6^2$

h) $x^{10} \div x^9$

i) $3^4 \div 3^{-1}$

j) $\dfrac{7^{15}}{7^5}$

k) $\dfrac{6^{11}}{6}$

l) $\dfrac{r^2}{r^6}$

m) $(3^2)^3$

n) $(10^6)^{-1}$

o) $(k^{-2})^5$

p) $(t^8)^{\frac{1}{2}}$

q) $(z^4)^{-\frac{1}{8}}$

r) $(8^{-6})^{-\frac{1}{2}}$

s) $cd^2 \times c^3 d^4$

t) $\dfrac{p^5 q^4}{p^4 q}$

u) $\dfrac{c^{-1} d^{-2}}{c^2 d^4}$

v) $(ab^2)^2$

w) $(x^2 y^3 z^4)^5$

x) $\dfrac{12yz^{-\frac{1}{2}}}{4yz^{\frac{1}{2}}}$

Q2 Evaluate:

a) $4^{\frac{1}{2}} \times 4^{\frac{3}{2}}$

b) $\dfrac{2^3 \times 2}{2^5}$

c) $\dfrac{7^5 \times 7^3}{7^6}$

d) $(3^2)^5 \div (3^3)^3$

e) $\left(4^{-\frac{1}{2}}\right)^2 \times (4^{-3})^{-\frac{1}{3}}$

f) $\dfrac{(2^{\frac{1}{2}})^6 \times (2^{-2})^{-2}}{(2^{-1})^{-1}}$

g) 1^0

h) $\left(\dfrac{4}{5}\right)^0$

i) $(-5.726324)^0$

Q3 Express the following as negative or fractional powers or both:

a) $\dfrac{1}{p}$

b) $\sqrt{q}$

c) $\sqrt{r^3}$

d) $\sqrt[4]{s^5}$

e) $\dfrac{1}{\sqrt[3]{t}}$

Q4 Evaluate:

a) $9^{\frac{1}{2}}$

b) $8^{\frac{1}{3}}$

c) $4^{\frac{3}{2}}$

d) $27^{-\frac{1}{3}}$

e) $16^{-\frac{3}{4}}$

3. Surds

Learning Objectives:

- Be able to simplify expressions containing surds.
- Be able to rationalise denominators.

This section will cover how to simplify expressions containing square roots. There are laws for simplifying these expressions just like the ones for powers.

The laws of surds

Put $\sqrt{2}$ into a calculator and you'll get 1.414213562...
But square 1.414213562 and you get 1.999999999.

Tip: A rational number is a number that can be expressed as $\frac{p}{q}$ where p and q are integers and $q \neq 0$. An irrational number is just one which is not rational.

No matter how many decimal places you use, you'll never get exactly 2. This is because $\sqrt{2}$ is an **irrational number** – its decimal expansion **continues forever**.

The only way to express a number like this **exactly** is to leave it as a root. Numbers like $\sqrt{2}$ that can only be written exactly using roots are called **surds**. The number $\sqrt{3}$ is a surd because it can't be written exactly without a root — $\sqrt{9}$ is **not** a surd because it can be simplified to 3.

There are three rules you'll need to know to be able to use surds properly:

$$\sqrt{ab} = \sqrt{a}\,\sqrt{b}$$
$$\sqrt{\frac{a}{b}} = \frac{\sqrt{a}}{\sqrt{b}}$$
$$a = (\sqrt{a})^2 = \sqrt{a}\,\sqrt{a}$$

Simplifying surds usually just means making the number in the $\sqrt{}$ sign smaller or getting rid of a fraction inside the $\sqrt{}$ sign.

Examples

a) Simplify $\sqrt{12}$.

$$\sqrt{12} = \sqrt{4 \times 3} = \sqrt{4} \times \sqrt{3} = \boxed{2\sqrt{3}}$$

$$\sqrt{ab} = \sqrt{a}\,\sqrt{b}$$

b) Simplify $\sqrt{\frac{3}{16}}$.

$$\sqrt{\frac{a}{b}} = \frac{\sqrt{a}}{\sqrt{b}}$$

$$\sqrt{\frac{3}{16}} = \frac{\sqrt{3}}{\sqrt{16}} = \boxed{\frac{\sqrt{3}}{4}}$$

c) Find $(2\sqrt{5} + 3\sqrt{6})^2$.

You'll need to multiply out squared brackets here. Remember:

$$(a+b)^2 = (a+b)(a+b) = a^2 + 2ab + b^2$$

$$(2\sqrt{5} + 3\sqrt{6})^2 = (2\sqrt{5} + 3\sqrt{6})(2\sqrt{5} + 3\sqrt{6})$$

$$= (2\sqrt{5})^2 + (2 \times (2\sqrt{5}) \times (3\sqrt{6})) + (3\sqrt{6})^2$$

$$= (2^2 \times \sqrt{5}^2) + (2 \times 2 \times 3 \times \sqrt{5} \times \sqrt{6}) + (3^2 \times \sqrt{6}^2)$$

$= 4 \times 5 = 20$

$$= 20 + 12\sqrt{30} + 54$$

$= 9 \times 6 = 54$

$$= \boxed{74 + 12\sqrt{30}}$$

$= 12\sqrt{5}\sqrt{6} = 12\sqrt{30}$

Tip: Multiply surds very carefully — it's easy to make a silly mistake.

d) **Express $\sqrt{63} - \sqrt{28}$ in the form $k\sqrt{x}$ where k and x are integers.**

Try to write both numbers as 'a square number' $\times x$. Here x is 7.

$$\sqrt{63} - \sqrt{28} = \sqrt{9 \times 7} - \sqrt{4 \times 7}$$

$$= \sqrt{9}\sqrt{7} - \sqrt{4}\sqrt{7}$$

$$= 3\sqrt{7} - 2\sqrt{7}$$

$$= \boxed{\sqrt{7}}$$

The square root of a square number simplifies.

Tip: An integer is just a positive or negative whole number, including 0,

Tip: So in this case, k is just 1.

Exercise 3.1

Q1 Simplify the following surds:

a) $\sqrt{8}$ b) $\sqrt{24}$ c) $\sqrt{50}$ d) $\sqrt{63}$

e) $\sqrt{72}$ f) $\sqrt{\dfrac{5}{4}}$ g) $\sqrt{\dfrac{7}{100}}$ h) $\sqrt{\dfrac{11}{9}}$

Q2 Evaluate the following.
Give your answer as either a whole number or a surd.

a) $2\sqrt{3} \times 4\sqrt{3}$ b) $\sqrt{5} \times 3\sqrt{5}$

c) $(\sqrt{7})^2$ d) $2\sqrt{2} \times 3\sqrt{5}$

e) $(2\sqrt{11})^2$ f) $5\sqrt{8} \times 2\sqrt{2}$

g) $4\sqrt{3} \times 2\sqrt{27}$ h) $2\sqrt{6} \times 5\sqrt{24}$

i) $\dfrac{\sqrt{10}}{6} \times \dfrac{12}{\sqrt{5}}$ j) $\dfrac{\sqrt{12}}{3} \times \dfrac{2}{\sqrt{27}}$

Q3 Express the following in the form $k\sqrt{x}$, where k and x are integers and x is as small as possible.

a) $\sqrt{20} + \sqrt{5}$ b) $\sqrt{32} - \sqrt{8}$

c) $\sqrt{27} + 4\sqrt{3}$ d) $2\sqrt{8} - 3\sqrt{2}$

e) $3\sqrt{10} + \sqrt{250}$ f) $4\sqrt{27} + 2\sqrt{48} + 5\sqrt{108}$

Q3 Hint: To add two or more surds, you'll need to make sure the $\sqrt{x}$ bit is the same in each term.

Q4 Expand the following expressions.
Give your answers in the simplest form.

a) $(1 + \sqrt{2})(2 + \sqrt{2})$ 　　　　　 b) $(3 + 4\sqrt{3})(2 - \sqrt{3})$

c) $(\sqrt{11} + 2)(\sqrt{11} - 2)$ 　　　　 d) $(9 - 2\sqrt{5})(9 + 2\sqrt{5})$

e) $(\sqrt{3} + 2)^2$ 　　　　　　　　　 f) $(3\sqrt{5} - 4)^2$

Q5 Hint: You'll need to use Pythagoras here.

Q5 Triangle ABC is right-angled with angle ABC = 90°.
Side AC has length $5\sqrt{2}$ cm and side AB has length $\sqrt{2}$ cm.
Find the length of side BC in the form $k\sqrt{3}$ cm,
where k is an integer.

Rationalising the denominator

Surds are pretty complicated — they're probably the last thing you want at the bottom of a fraction. You can remove surds from the denominators of fractions by **rationalising the denominator**.

Tip: Multiplying a fraction by the same thing on the top and bottom won't change its value.

To rationalise the denominator you multiply **top and bottom** of the fraction by an **expression** that will get rid of surds in the denominator.

Examples

a) **Show that** $\dfrac{9}{\sqrt{3}} = 3\sqrt{3}$.

To get rid of the surd multiply top and bottom by $\sqrt{3}$.

$$\frac{9}{\sqrt{3}} = \frac{9 \times \sqrt{3}}{\sqrt{3} \times \sqrt{3}} = \frac{9\sqrt{3}}{3} = \boxed{3\sqrt{3}}$$

Cancelling 3 from top and bottom.

b) **Rationalise the denominator of** $\dfrac{1}{1 + \sqrt{2}}$.

If a fraction is of the form $\dfrac{1}{a + \sqrt{b}}$, multiply top and bottom by $a - \sqrt{b}$
— the denominator with the opposite sign in front of the surd.

Tip: This method works because of the difference of two squares rule:
$(a + b)(a - b) = a^2 - b^2$

If there is a square root in the brackets, it goes away when you square it.

$$\frac{1}{1 + \sqrt{2}} \times \frac{1 - \sqrt{2}}{1 - \sqrt{2}} = \frac{1 - \sqrt{2}}{(1 + \sqrt{2})(1 - \sqrt{2})}$$

$$= \frac{1 - \sqrt{2}}{1^2 + \sqrt{2} - \sqrt{2} - \sqrt{2}^2}$$

$$= \frac{1 - \sqrt{2}}{1 - 2}$$

The surds cancel each other out.

$$= \frac{1 - \sqrt{2}}{-1}$$

$$= \boxed{-1 + \sqrt{2}}$$

c) Rationalise the denominator of $\dfrac{7+\sqrt{5}}{3+\sqrt{5}}$.

$$\frac{7+\sqrt{5}}{3+\sqrt{5}} \times \frac{3-\sqrt{5}}{3-\sqrt{5}} = \frac{(7+\sqrt{5})(3-\sqrt{5})}{(3+\sqrt{5})(3-\sqrt{5})}$$

Multiply top and bottom by $3-\sqrt{5}$.

$$= \frac{(7\times 3)-7\sqrt{5}+3\sqrt{5}-(\sqrt{5})^2}{3^2+3\sqrt{5}-3\sqrt{5}-(\sqrt{5})^2}$$

The surds cancel each other out.

$$= \frac{21-4\sqrt{5}-5}{9-5}$$

Now cancel 4 from each term.

$$= \frac{16-4\sqrt{5}}{4}$$

$$= 4-\sqrt{5}$$

Exercise 3.2

Q1 Simplify the following, giving your answers in the form $p\sqrt{q}$, where p and q are integers:

a) $\dfrac{6}{\sqrt{3}}$

b) $\dfrac{21}{\sqrt{7}}$

c) $\dfrac{30}{\sqrt{5}}$

d) $\sqrt{45}+\dfrac{15}{\sqrt{5}}$

e) $\dfrac{\sqrt{54}}{3}-\dfrac{12}{\sqrt{6}}$

f) $\dfrac{\sqrt{300}}{5}+\dfrac{30}{\sqrt{12}}$

Q2 Express the following in the form $a+b\sqrt{k}$, where a, b and k are integers:

a) $\dfrac{4}{1+\sqrt{3}}$

b) $\dfrac{11}{4-\sqrt{5}}$

c) $\dfrac{8}{\sqrt{7}+3}$

d) $\dfrac{8}{-1+\sqrt{5}}$

e) $\dfrac{1}{\sqrt{26}-5}$

f) $\dfrac{18}{\sqrt{10}-4}$

Q3 Express the following in the form $p+q\sqrt{r}$, where r is an integer, and p and q are integers or fractions:

a) $\dfrac{\sqrt{2}+1}{\sqrt{2}-1}$

b) $\dfrac{\sqrt{5}+3}{\sqrt{5}-2}$

c) $\dfrac{3-\sqrt{3}}{4+\sqrt{3}}$

d) $\dfrac{3\sqrt{5}-1}{2\sqrt{5}-3}$

e) $\dfrac{\sqrt{2}+\sqrt{3}}{3\sqrt{2}-\sqrt{3}}$

f) $\dfrac{2\sqrt{7}-\sqrt{5}}{\sqrt{7}+2\sqrt{5}}$

Q4 Solve the equation $8=(\sqrt{5}-1)x$ giving your answer in the form $a+b\sqrt{5}$ where a and b are integers.

Q5 Solve the equation $5+\sqrt{7}=(3-\sqrt{7})y$ giving your answer in the form $p+q\sqrt{7}$ where p and q are integers.

Q6 A rectangle has an area of $(2+\sqrt{2})$ cm² and a width of $(3\sqrt{2}-4)$ cm. Find the length of the rectangle. Give your answer in the form $a+b\sqrt{2}$ where a and b are integers.

Review Exercise — Chapter 1

Q1 Which of these are identities (i.e. true for all variable values)?

   A $(x + b)(y - b) = xy + b(y - x) - b^2$

   B $(2y + x^2) = 10$

   C $a^2 - b^2 = (a - b)(a + b)$

   D $a^3 + b^3 = (a + b)(a^2 - ab + b^2)$

Q1 Hint: Remember, an identity is just an equation where the left hand side is identical to the right hand side, no matter what values you choose.

Q2 Remove the brackets and simplify the following expressions:

   a) $(a + b)(a - b)$ b) $(a + b)(a + b)$

   c) $35xy + 25y(5y + 7x) - 100y^2$ d) $(x + 3y + 2)(3x + y + 7)$

Q3 Take out the common factors from the following expressions:

   a) $2x^2y + axy + 2xy^2$ b) $a^2x + a^2b^2x^2$

   c) $16y + 8yx + 56x$ d) $x(x - 2) + 3(2 - x)$

Q4 Put the following expressions over a common denominator:

   a) $\frac{2x}{3} + \frac{y}{12} + \frac{x}{5}$ b) $\frac{5}{xy^2} - \frac{2}{x^2y}$ c) $\frac{1}{x} + \frac{x}{x + y} + \frac{y}{x - y}$

Q5 Simplify these expressions:

   a) $\frac{2a}{b} - \frac{a}{2b}$ b) $\frac{2p}{p + q} + \frac{2q}{p - q}$

Q6 Simplify these:

   a) $x^3 . x^5$ b) $a^7 . a^8$ c) $\frac{x^8}{x^2}$

   d) $(a^2)^4$ e) $(xy^2) . (x^3yz)$ f) $\frac{a^2b^4c^6}{a^3b^2c}$

Q7 Work out the following:

   a) $16^{\frac{1}{2}}$ b) $8^{\frac{1}{3}}$ c) $16^{\frac{3}{4}}$

   d) x^0 e) $49^{-\frac{1}{2}}$

Q8 Hint: 'Exact answers' means leave your answers as surds (and don't forget that there'll be 2 solutions to each equation).

Q8 Find exact answers to these equations:

   a) $x^2 - 5 = 0$ b) $(x + 2)^2 - 3 = 0$

Q9 Simplify:

   a) $\sqrt{28}$ b) $\sqrt{\frac{5}{36}}$ c) $\sqrt{18}$ d) $\sqrt{\frac{9}{16}}$

Q10 Show that a) $\frac{8}{\sqrt{2}} = 4\sqrt{2}$, and b) $\frac{\sqrt{2}}{2} = \frac{1}{\sqrt{2}}$

Q11 Find $(6\sqrt{3} + 2\sqrt{7})^2$

Q12 Rationalise the denominator of $\frac{2}{3 + \sqrt{7}}$

1   a)   Write down the value of $27^{\frac{1}{3}}$.

          (1 mark)

    b)   Find the value of $27^{\frac{4}{3}}$.

          (2 marks)

2   Simplify

    a) $(5\sqrt{3})^2$

          (1 mark)

    b) $(5 + \sqrt{6})(2 - \sqrt{6})$

          (2 marks)

3   Given that $10000\sqrt{10} = 10^k$, find the value of k.

          (3 marks)

4   Express $\dfrac{5 + \sqrt{5}}{3 - \sqrt{5}}$ in the form $a + b\sqrt{5}$, where a and b are integers.

          (4 marks)

5   Factorise completely
$$2x^4 - 32x^2.$$

          (3 marks)

6   Write
$$\frac{x + 5x^3}{\sqrt{x}}$$

in the form $x^m + 5x^n$, where m and n are constants.

          (2 marks)

7   Show that
$$\frac{(5 + 4\sqrt{x})^2}{2x}$$

can be written as $\dfrac{25}{2}x^{-1} + Px^{-\frac{1}{2}} + Q$, and find the value of the integers P and Q.

          (3 marks)

1. Quadratic Equations

In this section, you'll learn three methods that are used for solving quadratic equations — factorising, completing the square and the quadratic formula. These methods will also help you to sketch graphs of quadratic functions later in the chapter.

Factorising a quadratic

Quadratic equations are equations of the general form:

$$ax^2 + bx + c = 0$$

where a, b and c are constants (i.e. numbers) and $a \neq 0$.

Factorising a quadratic means putting it into two brackets called **factors** — the **solutions** to the equation can be easily worked out from these factors.

There are **two cases** that you need to know:

Factorising when $a = 1$

Fortunately, there's a step-by-step method you can follow when factorising this sort of quadratic:

Tip: All quadratics can be rearranged into this standard form.

> To factorise a quadratic with $a = 1$:
>
> - Rearrange into the standard $ax^2 + bx + c$ form.
>
> - Write down the two **brackets**:
> $$(x \qquad)(x \qquad)$$
>
> - Find two numbers that **multiply** to give 'c' and **add / subtract** to give 'b' (ignoring signs).
>
> - Put the numbers in the brackets and choose their **signs**.

This will all make more sense once you've seen a worked example...

Example 1

Solve $x^2 - 8 = 2x$ by factorising.

(1) Rearrange into standard $ax^2 + bx + c = 0$ form.

Subtract $2x$ from both sides to give...

$$x^2 - 2x - 8 = 0$$

So $a = 1$, $b = -2$, $c = -8$.

(2) Write down the two brackets with x's in:

$$x^2 - 2x - 8 = (x \qquad)(x \qquad)$$

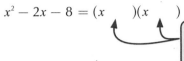

Since $a = 1$, you know that there will be an x in each bracket, which will multiply together to give x^2.

(3) Find the numbers.

Find two numbers that **multiply** together to make c but which also **add or subtract** to give b (you can ignore any minus signs for now).

1 and 8 multiply to give 8 — and add / subtract to give 9 and 7.

2 and 4 multiply to give 8 — and add / subtract to give 6 and 2.

These are the values for c and b you're after — so this is the right combination: 2 and 4.

(4) Find the signs.

So far you've got: $x^2 - 2x - 8 = (x \quad 4)(x \quad 2)$

Now all you have to do is put in the plus or minus signs.

It must be +2 and –4 because $2 \times (-4) = -8$ and $2 + (-4) = 2 - 4 = -2$

$$x^2 - 2x - 8 = (x + 2)(x - 4)$$

If c is negative, then the signs must be opposite.

Tip: If two things multiplied together give a negative answer, they must have opposite signs.

Now that you've factorised using the step by step method — you can use the factors to solve the equation.

$$(x + 2)(x - 4) = 0$$

The factors (brackets) multiply to give 0, so one of them **must** be 0.

$$\Rightarrow x + 2 = 0 \text{ or } x - 4 = 0$$

$$\Rightarrow x = -2 \text{ or } x = 4$$

Don't forget this last step. The factors aren't the answer.

Tip: If two things multiply together to give 0, one of them must be equal to 0.

Example 2

Solve $x^2 + 4x - 21 = 0$ by factorising.

- It's already in the standard form, so start by writing down the brackets:
$$x^2 + 4x - 21 = (x \quad)(x \quad)$$

- 1 and 21 multiply to give 21 — and add / subtract to give 22 and 20.
3 and 7 multiply to give 21 — and add / subtract to give 10 and 4.

These are the values you need so 3 and 7 are the right numbers:
$$x^2 + 4x - 21 = (x \quad 3)(x \quad 7)$$

- c is negative so we must need opposite signs.
The signs must be -3 and $+7$ because $7 - 3 = 4$ and $7 \times (-3) = -21$

So...
$$x^2 + 4x - 21 = (x - 3)(x + 7)$$

And solving the equation to find x...
$$(x - 3)(x + 7) = 0$$
$$\Rightarrow x = 3 \text{ or } x = -7$$

Factorising when $a \neq 1$

The basic method's the same as before — but it can be a bit more awkward.

> **To factorise a quadratic with $a \neq 1$:**
>
> - Rearrange into the standard $ax^2 + bx + c$ form.
>
> - Write down the two brackets, but instead of just having x in each, you need two things that will multiply to give ax^2:
> $$(nx \quad)(mx \quad)$$
> where n and m are two numbers that multiply to give a.
>
> - Find two numbers that multiply to give 'c' but which will give you bx when you multiply them by nx and mx, and then add / subtract them.
>
> - Put the numbers in the brackets and choose their **signs**.

Tip: In practice, this third step is a case of working through all possible cases until you get it right.

Again, a worked example will help.

Example

Factorise $3x^2 + 4x - 15$.

(1) This quadratic's already in the standard form so you don't need to rearrange it.

(2) As before, write down two brackets — but instead of just having x in each, you need two things that will multiply to give $3x^2$. It's got to be $3x$ and x here.
$$3x^2 + 4x - 15 = (3x \quad)(x \quad)$$

(3) Work out the numbers.

You need to find two numbers that multiply together to make 15 — but which will give you $4x$ when you multiply them by x and $3x$, and then add / subtract them.

$(3x \quad 1)(x \quad 15) \Rightarrow x$ and $45x$
which then add or subtract to give $46x$ and $44x$.

$(3x \quad 15)(x \quad 1) \Rightarrow 15x$ and $3x$
which then add or subtract to give $18x$ and $12x$.

$(3x \quad 3)(x \quad 5) \Rightarrow 3x$ and $15x$
which then add or subtract to give $18x$ and $12x$.

$(3x \quad 5)(x \quad 3) \Rightarrow 5x$ and $9x$
which then add or subtract to give $14x$ and $\boxed{4x.}$

This is the value you're after — so this is the right combination.

Tip: It's a good idea to write out the brackets for each possible number combination — it makes it easier to see if you've got the right numbers.

(4) Add the signs.

You know the brackets must be like these...
$(3x \quad 5)(x \quad 3) = 3x^2 + 4x - 15$

'c' is negative — that means the signs in the brackets are opposite. The numbers must be -5 and $+3$ since $9x - 5x = 4x$ and $-5 \times 3 = -15$.

So,...

$$(3x - 5)(x + 3) = 3x^2 + 4x - 15$$

Tip: You've only got two choices for the signs of the numbers, -5 and 3 or 5 and -3. If you're unsure which it is, just multiply each case out to see which is right.

Exercise 1.1

Q1 Factorise the following expressions.
a) $x^2 - 6x + 5$
b) $x^2 - 3x - 18$
c) $x^2 + 22x + 121$
d) $x^2 - 12x$
e) $y^2 - 13y + 42$
f) $x^2 + 51x + 144$
g) $x^2 - 121$
h) $x^2 + 2\sqrt{3}x + 3$

Q1 Hint: If b or c is zero, use the factorising methods from Chapter 1.

Q2 Solve the following equations.
a) $x^2 - 2x - 8 = 0$
b) $2x^2 + 2x - 40 = 0$
c) $p^2 + 21p + 38 = 0$
d) $x^2 - 15x + 54 = 0$
e) $x^2 + 18x = -65$
f) $x^2 - x = 42$
g) $x^2 + 1100x + 100\,000 = 0$
h) $3x^2 - 3x - 6 = 0$

Q2 Hint: Look out for questions where the equation can be simplified before factorising — for example by dividing through by a number.

Q3 Factorise the following expressions.
a) $4x^2 - 4x - 3$
b) $2x^2 + 23x + 11$
c) $7x^2 - 19x - 6$
d) $-x^2 - 5x + 36$
e) $2x^2 - 2$
f) $3x^2 - 3$

Q4 Solve the following equations.
a) $-5x^2 - 22x + 15 = 0$
b) $32x^2 + 60x + 13 = 0$
c) $5a^2 + 12a = 9$
d) $8x^2 + 22x + 15 = 0$

Q5 Solve $(x - 1)(x - 2) = 37 - x$.

Q6 $f(x) = -x^2 + 7x + 30$. Find the x coordinates of the point or points at which the graph of $f(x)$ meets the x-axis.

Q6 Hint: The graph of $f(x)$ meets the x-axis when $f(x) = 0$.

Q7 Factorise $x^2 + 6xy + 8y^2$.

The quadratic formula

You should now be comfortable with solving quadratics by factorising. But there are two important points to bear in mind:

- The expression **won't** always factorise.
- Sometimes factorising is so messy that it's **easier** to just use other methods.

So if the question doesn't tell you to factorise, **don't assume** it will factorise.

Example

Solve $6x^2 + 87x - 144 = 0$.

This will actually factorise, but there are 2 possible bracket forms to try:

$$(6x \quad)(x \quad) \quad \text{or} \quad (3x \quad)(2x \quad)$$

And for each of these, there are 8 possible ways of making 144 to try.

If you tried to factorise this example, you'd be going all day.

Luckily, there's a formula which will work out the **solutions** of a quadratic equation, even when you can't factorise — it's known as **the quadratic formula**.

If $ax^2 + bx + c = 0$ then:

$$x = \frac{-b \pm \sqrt{b^2 - 4ac}}{2a}$$

The quadratic formula will solve **any** quadratic equation — no matter what.

Example 1

**Solve the quadratic equation $3x^2 - 4x = 8$,
leaving your answer in surd form.**

The mention of surds in the answer suggests that the quadratic will
be too hard to factorise, so we'll use the quadratic formula instead.

- Get the equation in the standard $ax^2 + bx + c = 0$ form.

$$3x^2 - 4x = 8$$

So... $3x^2 - 4x - 8 = 0$

> **Tip:** If the question asks you to give your answer in surd form or as a decimal, that's a big hint to use the quadratic formula instead of trying to factorise.

- Write down the coefficients a, b and c
  — making sure you don't forget minus signs.

$$3x^2 - 4x - 8 = 0$$

$a = 3$ $b = -4$ $c = -8$

> **Tip:** If any of the **coefficients** (i.e. if a, b or c) in your quadratic equation are **negative**, be especially careful.

- Very carefully, plug these numbers into the formula.
  It's best to write down each stage as you do it.

$$x = \frac{-b \pm \sqrt{b^2 - 4ac}}{2a}$$

$$x = \frac{-(-4) \pm \sqrt{(-4)^2 - 4 \times 3 \times (-8)}}{2 \times 3}$$

$$x = \frac{4 \pm \sqrt{16 + 96}}{6}$$

These minus signs multiply together to get a plus.

> **Tip:** There are a couple of minus signs in the formula which can catch you out if you're not paying attention.

Simplify your answer as much as possible, using the rules of surds.

$$x = \frac{4 \pm \sqrt{112}}{6}$$

$$x = \frac{4 \pm \sqrt{16}\sqrt{7}}{6}$$

$$x = \frac{2 \pm 2\sqrt{7}}{3}$$

The $\pm$ sign means that you actually have two different expressions
for x, which you get by replacing the $\pm$ with $+$ and $-$.
Doing this gives you the two solutions to the quadratic equation.

$$x = \frac{2 + 2\sqrt{7}}{3} \quad \text{or} \quad x = \frac{2 - 2\sqrt{7}}{3}$$

Example 2

Solve the quadratic equation $2x^2 = 4x + 3$, leaving your answer in the form $p \pm q\sqrt{r}$ where p, q and r are whole numbers or fractions.

Rearranging $2x^2 = 4x + 3$ you get $2x^2 - 4x - 3 = 0$ and so $a = 2$, $b = -4$ and $c = -3$

So plugging these values into the quadratic formula, you get:

$$x = \frac{-b \pm \sqrt{b^2 - 4ac}}{2a}$$

$$x = \frac{-(-4) \pm \sqrt{(-4)^2 - 4 \times 2 \times (-3)}}{2 \times 2}$$

$$x = \frac{4 \pm \sqrt{16 + 24}}{4} = \frac{4 \pm \sqrt{40}}{4} = \frac{4 \pm 2\sqrt{10}}{4} = \frac{2 \pm \sqrt{10}}{2}$$

$$= \frac{2}{2} \pm \frac{1}{2}\sqrt{10} = \boxed{1 \pm \frac{1}{2}\sqrt{10}}$$

Exercise 1.2

Q1   Solve the following equations using the quadratic formula, giving your answers in surd form where necessary.

    a) $x^2 - 4x = -2$ b) $x^2 - 2x - 44 = 0$

    c) $x^2 - 14x + 42 = 0$ d) $4x^2 + 4x - 1 = 0$

    e) $x^2 - \frac{5}{6}x + \frac{1}{6} = 0$ f) $x^2 - x - \frac{35}{2} = 0$

Q2   a)   Multiply out $(x - 2 + \sqrt{5})(x - 2 - \sqrt{5})$.

       b)   Solve the equation $x^2 - 4x - 1 = 0$ using the quadratic formula.

       c)   How does your answer to b) relate to the expression given in a)?

Q3   The roots of the equation $x^2 + 8x + 13 = 0$ can be written in the form $x = A \pm \sqrt{B}$ where A and B are integers. Find A and B.

Q4   Solve the following equations, giving your answers in surd form where necessary.

    a) $x^2 + x + \frac{1}{4} = 0$ b) $25x^2 - 30x + 7 = 0$

    c) $60x - 5 = -100x^2 - 3$ d) $2x(x - 4) = 7 - 3x$

Completing the square

You could be asked to **solve** a quadratic equation by **completing the square** so you need to know this method just as well as the others. And what's more — it gives you loads of **useful information** about the quadratic.

> Completing the square just means writing a quadratic expression $ax^2 + bx + c$ in the form $a(x + \textbf{something})^2 + d$.
>
> - Basically, the '**square**' is this bit:
> $$a(x + \text{something})^2$$
> The 'something' is chosen so that it will produce the correct x^2 and x terms when the square is multiplied out.
>
> - But this square won't always give the right constant term — so you need to '**complete**' it by adding a number to the square to make it the **same** as the original quadratic:
> $$a(x + \text{something})^2 + d$$

The method can seem complicated at first, but is actually very simple when you get it. As always, working through examples is the best way to learn it.

When $a = 1$

We'll start with the slightly easier case of $a = 1$...

Example 1

Rewrite $x^2 + 6x + 3$ by completing the square.

First, write down a square of the form $(x + \text{something})^2$. Choose it so that when you multiply it out you get the correct x^2 and x terms.

$$(x + 3)^2$$

> This number is just half the coefficient of x i.e. $\frac{b}{2}$.

Now complete the square:

$$(x + 3)^2 - 6$$

> This square multiplies out to give $x^2 + 6x + 9$ but we need the constant term to be $+3$...

> ...so subtract 6 from the square to match the original quadratic.

So...

$$x^2 + 6x + 3 = (x + 3)^2 - 6$$

Check that your answer multiplies out to give what you started with.

$$(x + 3)^2 - 6 = x^2 + 3x + 3x + 9 - 6 = x^2 + 6x + 3 \checkmark$$

Example 2

Rewrite $x^2 - 5x - 1$ by completing the square.

Again, start by writing down the square:

This example has a negative coefficient of x
— so make sure you have a minus sign in the brackets.

$$\left(x - \tfrac{5}{2}\right)^2$$

Now complete the square.... ← Remember, this is just $\tfrac{b}{2}$.

$$\left(x - \tfrac{5}{2}\right)^2 - \tfrac{25}{4} - 1$$

The square multiplies out to give $x^2 - 5x + \tfrac{25}{4}$ but we need the constant term to be –1.

...so subtract the $\tfrac{25}{4}$ and then 'add' –1.

Tip: You can always find the number that completes the square by subtracting off the number term you get from the bracket and adding on the number term from the original quadratic.

$$x^2 - 5x - 1 = \left(x - \tfrac{5}{2}\right)^2 - \tfrac{29}{4}$$ ← Simplify the number.

Check your answer...

$$\left(x - \tfrac{5}{2}\right)^2 - \tfrac{29}{4} = x^2 - \tfrac{5}{2}x - \tfrac{5}{2}x + \tfrac{25}{4} - \tfrac{29}{4} = x^2 - 5x - 1 \checkmark$$

When $a \neq 1$

It's a little more complicated in cases where a is not 1. You have to put a outside of the squared bracket, and allow for this when choosing the number to go inside the bracket — basically by dividing by a.

Example 3

Rewrite $2x^2 + 3x - 5$ by completing the square.

Start by writing the square —
$a = 2$ so it will be of the form $2(x + \text{something})^2$:

$$2\left(x + \tfrac{3}{4}\right)^2$$

When a is not 1, this number will always be the coefficient of x divided by $2a$, i.e. $\tfrac{b}{2a}$.

Now complete the square:

$$2\left(x + \tfrac{3}{4}\right)^2 - \tfrac{9}{8} - 5$$

The square multiplies out to give $2x^2 + 3x + \tfrac{9}{8}$, but we need the constant term to be –5...

...so subtract the $\tfrac{9}{8}$ and then 'add on' –5.

So...

$$2x^2 + 3x - 5 = 2\left(x + \frac{3}{4}\right)^2 - \frac{49}{8}$$ ← Simplify the number.

Check your answer...

$$2\left(x + \frac{3}{4}\right)^2 - \frac{49}{8} = 2\left(x^2 + \frac{3}{2}x + \frac{9}{16}\right) - \frac{49}{8}$$
$$= 2x^2 + 3x + \frac{9}{8} - \frac{49}{8} = 2x^2 + 3x - 5 \checkmark$$

Tip: If the constant terms are fractions, don't forget to put them over a common denominator before you try to add / subtract them.

Example 4

Rewrite $3 - 4x - x^2$ by completing the square.

Again, start by writing the square. Here $a = -1$:

$$-(x + 2)^2$$

This number is just $\frac{b}{2a}$ again.

Now complete the square:

$$-(x + 2)^2 + 7$$

The square multiplies out to give $-x^2 - 4x - 4$ but we want the constant to be $+3$...

...so add 7 to the square to make it match the original quadratic.

So...

$$3 - 4x - x^2 = -(x + 2)^2 + 7$$

Check your answer...

$$-(x + 2)^2 + 7 = -(x^2 + 4x + 4) + 7 = -x^2 - 4x - 4 + 7$$
$$= -x^2 - 4x + 3 \quad (= 3 - 4x - x^2) \checkmark$$

Tip: If it helps, rewrite the expression in the standard form $ax^2 + bx + c$.

Once you've completed the square, a quadratic equation becomes very easy to **solve**:

- Take the **constant term** to the other side of the equals sign.
- Square root both sides — don't forget the **negative** square root.
- **Rearrange** to find the solutions.

Example 5

Solve $3 - 4x - x^2 = 0$ by completing the square.

From Example 4, you can write $3 - 4x - x^2$ as $-(x + 2)^2 + 7$ by completing the square.

So now all you need to do is set this equal to zero and rearrange.

$$-(x + 2)^2 + 7 = 0$$

$$-(x + 2)^2 = -7 \quad \longleftarrow \boxed{\text{Take the constant to the other side.}}$$

$$(x + 2)^2 = 7 \quad \boxed{\begin{array}{l}\text{Take a square root —}\\ \text{don't forget the } \pm \text{ sign.}\end{array}}$$

$$x + 2 = \pm\sqrt{7}$$

$$\boxed{x = -2 \pm \sqrt{7}} \quad \longleftarrow \boxed{\text{Subtract 2 from both sides.}}$$

So $x = -2 + \sqrt{7}$ or $x = -2 - \sqrt{7}$

Tip: When you take the square root of something, you need to put a $\pm$ sign in front of the $\sqrt{}$ sign.

Exercise 1.3

Q1 Solve the following equations, leaving your answer in surd form where appropriate:

a) $(x + 4)^2 = 25$

b) $(5x - 3)^2 = 21$

Q1 Hint: In these questions you don't need to complete the square — they'll just give you practice at the 'solving' bit.

Q2 Rewrite the following expressions in the form $p(x + q)^2 + r$:

a) $x^2 + 6x + 8$ b) $x^2 + 8x - 10$

c) $x^2 - 3x - 10$ d) $x^2 - 20x + 15$

e) $x^2 - 2mx + n$ f) $3x^2 - 12x + 7$

Q3 Solve the following equations by completing the square:

a) $x^2 - 6x - 16 = 0$ b) $p^2 - 10p = 200$

c) $x^2 + 2x + k = 0$ d) $9x^2 + 18x = 16$

e) $x^2 + 4x - 8 = 0$ f) $2x^2 - 12x + 9 = 0$

g) $2x^2 - 12x - 54 = 0$ h) $5x^2 - 3x + \frac{2}{5} = 0$

Q4 By completing the square, show that the roots of $ax^2 + bx + c = 0$ are found at $x = \dfrac{-b \pm \sqrt{b^2 - 4ac}}{2a}$.

2. Quadratic Functions and Roots

The roots of a quadratic function f(x) are just the solutions to the equation f(x) = 0. But you don't actually need to solve the equation to find out how many roots there are.

The roots of a quadratic function

Quadratic functions are just functions of the form $f(x) = ax^2 + bx + c$. Their graphs all have the same **general shape**, no matter what the values of a, b and c are — they are either '**u**'-shaped or '**n**'-shaped:

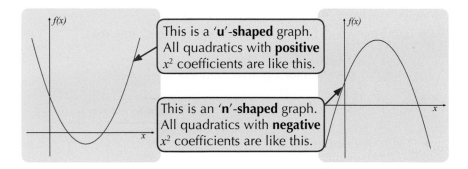

This is a '**u**'-shaped graph. All quadratics with **positive** x^2 coefficients are like this.

This is an '**n**'-shaped graph. All quadratics with **negative** x^2 coefficients are like this.

The **roots** of a quadratic function are the values of x where the function $f(x)$ is equal to **zero** — i.e. where the graph **crosses the x-axis**. They are the same as the **solutions** to the quadratic equation $f(x) = 0$. The functions shown above each have 2 roots because their graphs cross the x-axis twice.

A quadratic function may have **0**, **1** or **2 roots**. You'll see two methods for finding out which it is — **completing the square** and using the **discriminant**.

Using the completed square

If you've already **completed the square**, you can easily work out the number of roots by examining the completed square. The function will look like this:

$$f(x) = p(x + q)^2 + r$$

The key to this method is remembering that anything squared is ≥ 0.

So, let's assume for now that p is positive:

- Since p is positive, the graph will be u-shaped and have a minimum.
- The smallest value that $f(x)$ can take will occur when the bracket is 0 (since the square is ≥ 0). At that point $f(x)$ is just r, and x must be $-q$.
- So the minimum is $(-q , r)$.

Now the **value of r** tells us the number of roots...

- If $r < 0$, the minimum is below the x-axis, so the graph must cross the axis twice — meaning there are **two roots**.
- If $r > 0$, the graph is always above the x-axis — so there are **no roots**.
- If $r = 0$, the minimum point is on the x-axis, so there's **one root**.

So that covers cases where p is positive, i.e. u-shaped graphs.

Tip: Just picture what the graph looks like — remember, it's u-shaped. The number of times the graph crosses the x-axis depends on whether the minimum is above, below or on the axis.

Next, we'll see what happens when p is negative:

$$f(x) = p(x + q)^2 + r$$

- Since p is negative, the graph will be n-shaped and have a maximum.
- And also because p is negative, the highest value of $p(x + q)^2$ will be when the bracket is 0. At that point $f(x)$ is just r, and x is $-q$.
- So the maximum is $(-q, r)$.

Look at the **value of r** to work out the number of roots...

- If $r < 0$, the graph is always below the x-axis — so there are **no roots**.
- If $r > 0$, the maximum is above the x-axis, so the graph must cross the axis twice, meaning there are **two roots**.
- If $r = 0$, the maximum point is on the x-axis, so there's **one root**.

Let's see what this all means for a few real functions.

Tip: The coordinates of the maximum are actually just the same as those we found for the minimum: $(-q, r)$.

Two real roots

$y = x^2 - 6x + 8$

- The completed square is $(x - 3)^2 - 1$.
- The minimum is $(3, -1)$ which is below the x-axis.
- So there are two roots ($x = 2$ and $x = 4$).

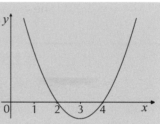

Tip: You'll see how to draw graphs of quadratic functions later in the chapter.

One real root

$y = x^2 - 6x + 9$

- The completed square is $(x - 3)^2$.
- The minimum is $(3, 0)$, so the graph just touches the x-axis.
- $x = 3$ is the only root.

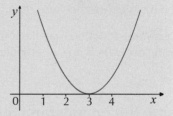

Tip: When you're factorising a quadratic equation, if both factors come out the same, in this case $(x - 3)(x - 3)$, the function has one root. We call this one **repeated** root.

No roots

$y = x^2 - 6x + 10$

- The completed square is $(x - 3)^2 + 1$.
- The minimum is $(3, 1)$ which is above the x-axis.
- So the graph never touches the x-axis, and there are no roots.

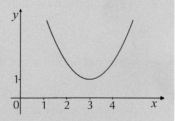

All the different cases we've covered can actually be summarised in these three simple rules:

> For a quadratic function of the form $f(x) = p(x + q)^2 + r$:
> - If p and r have **different signs**, the function has **two** real roots.
> - If **$r = 0$** then the function has **one** real root.
> - If p and r have the **same sign**, the function has **no** real roots.

Example

How many roots does the quadratic function $f(x) = x^2 + 4x + 7$ have?

Completing the square, you can rewrite the function as
$f(x) = (x + 2)^2 + 3$ so $p = 1$ and $r = 3$ are of the same sign
and so the function has no real roots.

You can see why this works using the following argument:

$$f(x) = (x + 2)^2 + 3 \longleftarrow \text{This number's positive.}$$

The smallest this bit
can be is zero (at $x = -2$).

$(x + 2)^2$ is never less than zero
so $f(x)$ is never less than three.

This means that:

a) $f(x)$ can never be negative.
b) The graph of $f(x)$ never crosses the x-axis — so there are no real roots.

Exercise 2.1

Q1   How many real roots does each quadratic function have?

a)
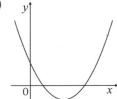

b)
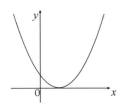

c)
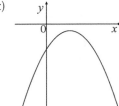

d)
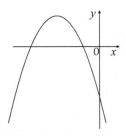

Q2   Express $f(x) = x^2 + 6x + 10$ in the form $f(x) = (x + q)^2 + r$,
where q and r are positive or negative constants.
Using your answer, state whether $f(x)$ has any real roots.

Q2 Hint: Complete the square.

Q3   The function $f(x) = -x^2 + 7x - 6$ can be expressed in the form
$$f(x) = -\left(x + \frac{7}{2}\right)^2 + \frac{25}{4}$$
Does this function have any real roots? Explain your answer.

Using the discriminant

Remember the **quadratic formula** for solving an equation of the form $ax^2 + bx + c = 0$:

$$x = \frac{-b \pm \sqrt{b^2 - 4ac}}{2a}$$

The $b^2 - 4ac$ bit is called the **discriminant**.

- If the discriminant is **positive**, the formula will give you **two** different values for x — when you **add** and **subtract** the $\sqrt{b^2 - 4ac}$ bit.

- If it's **zero**, you'll only get **one** value for x, since adding and subtracting zero gets the same value.

- If it's **negative**, you don't get any (real) values for x because you can't take the square root of a negative number.

Tip: In some areas of maths, you can actually take the square root of negative numbers and get 'imaginary' or 'complex' numbers. That's why we say no 'real' roots.

To picture what this means, recall the examples from p.32:

Two roots	One root	No roots
$b^2 - 4ac > 0$	$b^2 - 4ac = 0$	$b^2 - 4ac < 0$

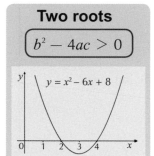

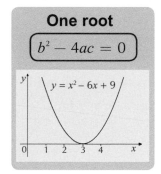

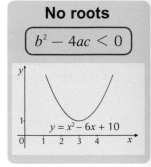

When working out the **discriminant**, the first thing you have to do is to work out what a, b and c are. Make sure you get them the right way round — it's easy to get mixed up if the quadratic's in a different order.

Example 1

Find the discriminant of $15 - x - 2x^2$.
How many real roots does the function $f(x) = 15 - x - 2x^2$ have?

- First, identify a, b and c:

    $a = -2$, $b = -1$ and $c = 15$ (NOT $a = 15$, $b = -1$ and $c = -2$).

- Then put these values into the formula for the discriminant:

    $b^2 - 4ac = (-1)^2 - (4 \times -2 \times 15) = 1 + 120 = \boxed{121}$

- The discriminant is > 0, so $15 - x - 2x^2$ has $\boxed{\text{two distinct real roots.}}$

You may need to work with a quadratic where one or more of a, b and c are given in terms of an **unknown**. This means that you'll end up with an equation or inequality for the discriminant in terms of the unknown — you might have to solve it to find the **value** or **range of values** of the unknown.

Example 2

Find the range of values of k for which the function $f(x) = 3x^2 + 2x + k$:
   a) has 2 distinct roots,   b) has 1 root,   c) has no real roots.

- First, decide what a, b and c are: $a = 3, b = 2, c = k$

- Then work out what the discriminant is: $b^2 - 4ac = 2^2 - 4 \times 3 \times k$
$$= 4 - 12k$$

a) Two distinct roots means:
$\boxed{b^2 - 4ac > 0}$ $\Rightarrow 4 - 12k > 0$
$\Rightarrow 4 > 12k$
$\Rightarrow$ $k < \dfrac{1}{3}$

b) One root means:
$\boxed{b^2 - 4ac = 0}$ $\Rightarrow 4 - 12k = 0$
$\Rightarrow 4 = 12k$
$\Rightarrow$ $k = \dfrac{1}{3}$

The working is exactly the same in all three cases. The only difference is the equality / inequality symbol.

c) No roots means:
$\boxed{b^2 - 4ac < 0}$ $\Rightarrow 4 - 12k < 0$
$\Rightarrow 4 < 12k$
$\Rightarrow$ $k > \dfrac{1}{3}$

Tip: The discriminant often comes up in exam questions — but sometimes they'll be sneaky and not actually tell you that's what you have to find.
Any question that mentions **roots** of a quadratic will probably mean that you need to find the **discriminant**.

Example 3

The equation $x^2 + kx + 9 = 0$ has two distinct roots. Find k.

- First, decide what a, b and c are: $a = 1, b = k, c = 9$

- Then work out what the discriminant is: $b^2 - 4ac = k^2 - 4 \times 1 \times 9$
$$= k^2 - 36$$

- Two distinct roots means
$\boxed{b^2 - 4ac > 0}$ $\Rightarrow k^2 - 36 > 0$
$\Rightarrow k^2 > 36$
$\Rightarrow k^2 > 36 \Rightarrow k > 6 \text{ or } k < -6$

Tip: You'll learn more about quadratic inequalities in Chapter 3 — but here you just need to notice that if $k^2 > 36$, then k must either be bigger than 6 or less than −6.

Q1 Find the discriminants of the following equations.

a) $x^2 + 8x + 15 = 0$

b) $x^2 + 2\sqrt{3}x + 3 = 0$

c) $(2x + 1)(5x - 3) = 0$

d) $-3x^2 - \frac{11}{5}x - \frac{2}{5} = 0$

e) $9x^2 + 20x = 0$

f) $\frac{19}{16}x^2 - 4 = 0$

Q1 Hint: Make sure the equation is written in the form $ax^2 + bx + c = 0$ before trying to calculate the discriminant.

Q2 The discriminant of the equation $15x^2 + bx = 2$ is 169, where b is a positive number. Find all possible values of b.

Q3 The equation $0 = ax^2 + 7x + \frac{1}{4}$ has one real root. Find a.

Q4 Determine the number of real roots of the following equations, without solving them:

a) $13x^2 + 8x + 2 = 0$

b) $\frac{x^2}{3} + \frac{5}{2}x + 3 = 0$

Q5 Find the range of values of p for which $x^2 - 12x + 27 + p = 0$ has two distinct real roots.

Q6 Find the range of values of q for which $10x^2 - 10x + \frac{q}{2} = 0$ has two distinct real roots

Q7 The equation $2x^2 + (10p + 1)x + 5 = 0$ has no real roots. Show that p satisfies:

$$p(5p + 1) < \frac{39}{20}$$

Q8 Find the range of values of k for which $-2x^2 - 2x + k = 0$ has:

a) two distinct roots,

b) one real root,

c) no roots

Q9 The equation $x^2 + (k + 5)x + \frac{k^2}{4} = 0$, where k is a constant, has no real roots.

a) Show that k satisfies $10k + 25 < 0$

b) Find the range of possible values of k.

Q10 a) Find the discriminant of $(k - \frac{6}{5})x^2 + \sqrt{k}x + \frac{5}{4}$.

b) For what values of k would the equation $(k - \frac{6}{5})x^2 + \sqrt{k}x + \frac{5}{4} = 0$ have:

(i) one real root?

(ii) no real roots?

(iii) two distinct real roots?

3. Quadratic Graphs

Using the methods you've learnt for finding roots of quadratic functions, you'll be able to draw the graph of any quadratic function at all.

Sketching a quadratic graph

There are two pieces of information you **always need** to know about a quadratic function before you can sketch it.

- The **shape** — u-shaped or n-shaped.
- The coordinates of the **points of intersection** with the x- and y-axes.

Sometimes, there will be two **different** graphs which have the same points of intersection and shape — in this case you'll need to work out the location of the **vertex point** (maximum or minimum) to decide which graph is right.

Tip: The **vertex** of a quadratic graph is just the point where the graph changes direction. It is either a maximum point or a minimum point depending on the shape of the graph.

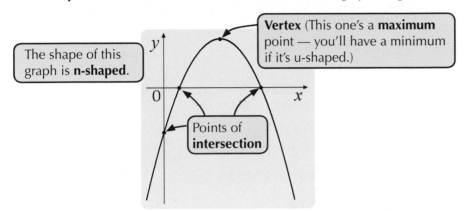

The shape of this graph is **n-shaped**.

Vertex (This one's a **maximum** point — you'll have a minimum if it's u-shaped.)

Points of **intersection**

Shape

The first thing you need to decide is the **shape** of the graph — look at the coefficient of the x^2 term.

- If the coefficient of x^2 is **positive** — the graph will be **u-shaped**.
- If the coefficient of x^2 is **negative** — the graph will be **n-shaped**.

Intercepts

The next bit of information you need is where the graph **intersects the axes** — set x or y equal to zero and work out the other coordinate.

If you're sketching the function $y = ax^2 + bx + c$:

- To find the **y-intercept** — let $x = 0$ and calculate the value of y.
- To find the **x-intercepts** — let $y = 0$ and solve the equation $0 = ax^2 + bx + c$ to find the value or values of x.

Tip: Use one of the methods of solving quadratics from earlier in the chapter to work out the x-intercepts — they're just the solutions of the equation.

Don't forget the x-intercepts correspond to the roots of the quadratic function — bear in mind that there may be only **one** root, or **no** roots.

Example 1

Draw the graph of the quadratic function f(x) = x^2 – 4x + 3, including any points of intersection with the axes.

- The coefficient of x^2 is positive...

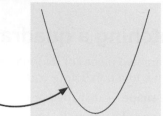

$$f(x) = x^2 - 4x + 3$$

...so the graph's [u-shaped.]

- Let $x = 0$ in the function to find the y-intercept.
$$f(0) = (0)^2 - 4(0) + 3 = 3$$

[So the y-intercept is at 3.]

- Solve f(x) = 0 to find the x-intercepts
This equation will factorise:

$$x^2 - 4x + 3 = 0$$
$$\Rightarrow (x - 3)(x - 1) = 0$$
$$\Rightarrow x - 3 = 0 \text{ or } x - 1 = 0$$
$$\Rightarrow x = 3 \text{ or } x = 1$$

[So the x-intercepts are at 1 and 3.]

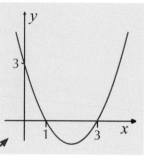

- Put all this information together to draw the graph.

Vertex points

You'll sometimes need to find the minimum or maximum of the graph — which one it is depends on whether your graph is u-shaped or n-shaped.

One way to find the vertex is to **complete the square** and then interpret this. We actually did this back on pages 31-32 when finding the number of roots of a quadratic. Have a look back at that page to remind yourself of the method. But here's the key result you need...

Tip: This comes from the fact that a square is always positive and so can never be less than 0.

A function of the form **$y = p(x + q)^2 + r$** has a vertex at **($-q$, r)**.
If $p > 0$, the graph is u-shaped, so the vertex is a minimum.
If $p < 0$, the graph is n-shaped, so the vertex is a maximum.

Example 2

Find the vertex of $f(x) = 3x^2 - 6x - 7$, stating whether it is a maximum or minimum.

As it's a quadratic function and the coefficient of x^2 is positive, it's a **u-shaped** graph so it has a minimum.

Completing the square gives $f(x) = 3x^2 - 6x - 7 = 3(x-1)^2 - 10$.

This is a square — it can never be negative. The smallest it can be is 0.

When the squared bit is zero, $f(x)$ reaches its minimum value. So find the value of x that makes the squared bit zero.

$f(x) = 3(x-1)^2 - 10$ ——— This bracket is 0 when $x = 1$...

$f(1) = 3(1-1)^2 - 10$

$f(1) = 3(0)^2 - 10 = -10$ ◄—— ...so the minimum is -10.

The vertex is $(1, -10)$.

Tip: $f(1)$ means using $x = 1$ in the function

Find where the graph of $y = f(x)$ crosses the axes and hence sketch the graph.

$f(x)$ crosses the y-axis when $x = 0$ which gives $y = -7$

$f(x)$ crosses the x-axis when $f(x) = 0$ so...

$$3x^2 - 6x - 7 = 0$$
$$\Rightarrow 3(x-1)^2 - 10 = 0 \quad \longleftarrow \text{ Complete the square.}$$
$$\Rightarrow (x-1)^2 = \frac{10}{3} \quad \longleftarrow \text{Solve it to find where } f(x) \text{ crosses the } x\text{-axis.}$$
$$\Rightarrow x - 1 = \pm\sqrt{\frac{10}{3}}$$
$$\Rightarrow x = 1 \pm \sqrt{\frac{10}{3}}$$

So $f(x)$ crosses the x-axis when... $x = 1 + \sqrt{\frac{10}{3}}$ or $x = 1 - \sqrt{\frac{10}{3}}$

Now use this information to sketch the graph...

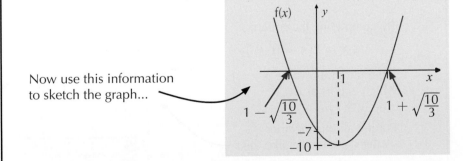

If a function has **no real roots**, the shape and the axis intercepts won't be **enough** to draw the graph. In these cases you'll **have** to find the coordinates of the **vertex point**, even if the question doesn't ask you to.

Example 3

Sketch the graph of the function $y = 2x^2 - 4x + 3$, showing any intersection points with the axes.

- The coefficient of x^2 here is positive...

$$y = 2x^2 - 4x + 3$$

...so the graph's u-shaped.

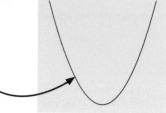

- Now find the places where the graph crosses the axes (both the y-axis and the x-axis).

  (i) Put $x = 0$ to find where it meets the y-axis.

  $$y = 2x^2 - 4x + 3$$

  $$y = (2 \times 0^2) - (4 \times 0) + 3$$

  so $\boxed{y = 3}$ is where it crosses the y-axis.

  (ii) Solve $y = 0$ to find where it meets the x-axis (or show that it doesn't).

  Let $2x^2 - 4x + 3 = 0$

  $b^2 - 4ac = -8 < 0$

  So it has $\boxed{\text{no solutions,}}$ and doesn't cross the x-axis.

Tip: You could use the quadratic formula to try to solve the equation:

$$x = \frac{-b \pm \sqrt{b^2 - 4ac}}{2a}$$

But if you did you'd quickly realise that there will be no solutions.

- Now the information we have so far isn't enough to say exactly what the graph will look like — it could be either of these...

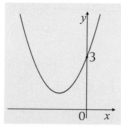
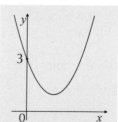

  ...so we need to find the minimum to tell us which it is.

  By completing the square...

  $$y = 2(x - 1)^2 + 1$$

  ...the minimum value is $y = 1$, which occurs at $x = 1$.

  Putting all this together — the sketch looks like this:

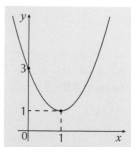

So we've seen a couple of examples of finding the vertex by completing the square. But if you've already worked out the roots, and found that there are **one** or **two** real roots, you can work out the vertex more easily like this:

If the function has **two distinct roots** — use symmetry of quadratic graphs

- The graph of a quadratic function is **symmetrical**, so the x-coordinate of the vertex is **halfway** between the roots of the function
- Work out the x-value halfway between the two roots and put it into the function to find the corresponding y-value of the vertex.

If the function has **one root** — the vertex is at the root

- If a function has one root, then its graph just **touches** the x-axis at the root — this point will always be the vertex.

Example 4

Sketch a graph of the function $y = 8 - 2x - x^2$ showing all intersection points with the axes and the vertex point.

- The coefficient of x^2 is negative so the graph is n-shaped...
- Now find the places where the graph crosses the axes.

    (i) Putting $x = 0$ gives $y = 8$ as the y-intercept.

    (ii) Putting $y = 0$ gives: $8 - 2x - x^2 = 0$
    $$\Rightarrow (2 - x)(4 + x) = 0$$
    $$\Rightarrow x = 2 \text{ and } x = -4 \text{ as the } x\text{-intercepts}$$

- Now find the vertex.

    The graph is n-shaped so it has a maximum.

    The two distinct roots of the function are known, so you can work out the maximum by finding the x-value halfway between the two roots.

    The maximum point is at $x = -1$ ◄———— Halfway between 2 and –4

    $x = -1$ gives $y = 8 - (2 \times -1) - (-1)^2 = 9$

    So the graph has a   maximum at the point $(-1, 9)$.

    Putting all this together — the sketch looks like this:

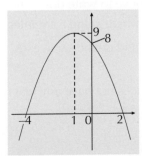

Tip: If you find this factorisation confusing, rewrite the equation as $x^2 + 2x - 8 = 0$ and you'll get the factorisation $(x + 4)(x - 2) = 0$ which will give you the same answers.

Tip: You could still find the vertex by completing the square, but this method is easier when you've already found the roots.

Q1 Sketch the following graphs on the same set of axes, indicating the x-intercepts of each.

a) $y = x^2 - 1$

b) $y = x^2 - 9$

Q2 a) Factorise the expression $f(x) = x^2 - 10x + 9$.

b) Use your answer to a) to sketch the graph of $f(x)$, showing the points where it crosses both axes.

c) Sketch the graph of $-f(x)$ on the same axes.

Q3 For each of the following quadratic functions:

(i)   Describe its shape.

(ii)   Find the value of the y-intercept

(iii) Find the number of real roots.

(iv)   Find the values of x at which the graph intersects the x-axis — if it does.

(v)   Find the coordinates of the vertex.

(vi)   Sketch the graph of the function, marking on all the information you've found.

a) $y = -x^2 + 2x + 1$ b) $y = x^2 - 7x + 15$ c) $y = 2x^2 + 4x - 9$

Q4 The graph below shows the quadratic function $f(x)$.

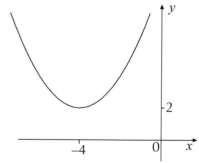

a) Use the sketch above to write down the function $f(x)$ in the form $f(x) = (x + q)^2 + r$ where q and r are integers.

b) Copy the sketch, and on the same axes, sketch the function $g(x) = (x + 4)^2$.

c) Which function does not have any real roots, $f(x)$ or $g(x)$?

Q5 a) Complete the square of the expression $x^2 - 6x + 5$.

b) Use part a) to solve the equation $x^2 - 6x + 5 = 0$

c) Draw a graph of $y = x^2 - 6x + 5$ showing any intersections with the axes and marking the vertex.

Q6 Sketch the following graphs, showing any intersections with the axes:

a) $y = x^2 - 2x + 1$ b) $y = x^2 + x - 1$

c) $y = x^2 - 8x + 18$ d) $y = -x^2 + 3$

Q7 a) What are the roots of the quadratic function shown in the graph below?

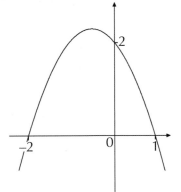

b) The quadratic can be written in the form $y = -x^2 + px + q$ where p and q are integers. Use your answer to part a) to find p and q.

Q7b) Hint: If you know the roots, you can find the factors by working backwards. This will be covered in detail in C2 when you do the Factor Theorem.

4. Factorising Cubics

Learning Objectives:

- Be able to use factorisation to solve cubic equations in which each term contains an x.

Some cubic equations can be solved using factorisation just like quadratics can. Factorising cubics will also help you to draw their graphs later in the module.

Solving cubics by factorising

Factorising a **cubic** means exactly what it meant with a quadratic — putting **brackets** in. For now, you'll only need to be able to factorise cubics that have an x in **every term**.

To factorise a cubic of the form $ax^3 + bx^2 + cx$, just **take out** x as your first factor as follows:

$$ax^3 + bx^2 + cx = x(ax^2 + bx + c)$$

Now you can just factorise the **quadratic** inside the brackets to get the other factors using the methods learnt earlier in the chapter. Once you've factorised, you can solve a cubic equation just as you would with a quadratic.

Example 1

Factorise and solve the following cubic equations.

a) $x^3 - 2x^2 - 24x = 0$

Start by taking out a factor of x...

$$x^3 - 2x^2 - 24x = x(x^2 - 2x - 24)$$

This quadratic will factorise.

$$= x(x\quad)(x\quad)$$

$$= x(x\quad 6)(x\quad 4)$$

$$= x(x - 6)(x + 4)$$

Put in the x's, work out the numbers then choose the signs.

$$\Rightarrow x(x - 6)(x + 4) = 0$$

So either $x = 0$, $x - 6 = 0$ or $x + 4 = 0$

$$\Rightarrow \boxed{x = 0,\ x = 6 \text{ or } x = -4}$$

b) $-x^3 - 2x^2 + 3x = 0$

If the x^3 coefficient is negative, take out a factor of $-x$...

...but don't forget these signs change.

$$-x^3 - 2x^2 + 3x = -x(x^2 + 2x - 3)$$

$$= -x(x\quad)(x\quad)$$

$$= -x(x\quad 3)(x\quad 1)$$

$$= -x(x + 3)(x - 1)$$

Factorise the quadratic in the brackets using the normal method.

$$\Rightarrow -x(x + 3)(x - 1) = 0$$

So either $x = 0$, $x + 3 = 0$ or $x - 1 = 0$

$$\Rightarrow \boxed{x = 0,\ x = -3 \text{ or } x = 1}$$

Tip: Cubic equations have one, two or three solutions (usually three). So unlike quadratics, they always have at least one real solution.

Example 2

Solve the cubic equation $-4x^3 - 4x^2 + x = 0$

The first thing you need to do is factorise.

The x^3 coefficient is negative, so take out a factor of $-x$ again...

$$-4x^3 - 4x^2 + x = 0$$

$$-x(4x^2 + 4x - 1) = 0$$

Now $-x(4x^2 + 4x - 1) = 0$ so either $x = 0$ or $4x^2 + 4x - 1 = 0$. $x = 0$ is one solution and solving the quadratic equation will give the other two.

This quadratic $4x^2 + 4x - 1$ won't factorise so use the quadratic formula.

$$
\begin{aligned}
x &= \frac{-b \pm \sqrt{b^2 - 4ac}}{2a} \\
&= \frac{-4 \pm \sqrt{4^2 - 4 \times 4 \times (-1)}}{2 \times 4} \\
&= \frac{-4 \pm \sqrt{32}}{8} \\
&= \frac{-4 \pm 4\sqrt{2}}{8} \\
&= -\frac{1}{2} \pm \frac{1}{2}\sqrt{2}
\end{aligned}
$$

So the solutions are $x = 0$, $x = -\frac{1}{2} + \frac{1}{2}\sqrt{2}$ and $x = -\frac{1}{2} - \frac{1}{2}\sqrt{2}$.

Exercise 4.1

Q1 Factorise the following cubic expressions:

a) $x^3 + 5x^2 + 6x$ b) $x^3 + 6x^2 - 7x$

c) $x^3 - 18x^2 + 81x$ d) $x^3 + 7x^2 + 10x$

e) $-x^3 + 4x^2 - 3x$ f) $2x^3 + 15x^2 + 25x$

g) $x^3 - 49x$ h) $x^3 - \frac{9}{4}x$

Q2 Solve the following cubic equations:

a) $-x^3 + 2x^2 + 24x = 0$ b) $x^3 - \frac{7}{9}x^2 + \frac{10}{81}x = 0$

c) $2x^3 + 9x^2 + 4x = 0$ d) $3x^3 - 3x^2 + 4x = 0$

e) $x^2(4x + 3) = x$ f) $2x^3 + 8x^2 = -3x$

Q2 Hint: Some of the quadratics may not factorise — use the quadratic formula to get the remaining solutions.

Review Exercise — Chapter 2

Q1 Factorise the following expressions:

a) $x^2 + 2x + 1$ b) $x^2 - 13x + 30$ c) $x^2 - 4$

d) $3 + 2x - x^2$ e) $2x^2 - 7x - 4$ f) $5x^2 + 7x - 6$

Q2 Solve the following equations:

a) $x^2 - 3x + 2 = 0$ b) $x^2 + x - 12 = 0$ c) $2 + x - x^2 = 0$

d) $x^2 + x - 16 = x$ e) $3x^2 - 15x - 14 = 4x$ f) $4x^2 - 1 = 0$

g) $6x^2 - 11x + 9 = 2x^2 - x + 3$

Q3 Rewrite these quadratics by completing the square. Then state their maximum or minimum value and the value of x where this occurs. Also, say if and where their graphs cross the x-axis.

a) $x^2 - 4x - 3$ b) $3 - 3x - x^2$

c) $2x^2 - 4x + 11$ d) $4x^2 - 28x + 48$

Q4 How many roots do these quadratic equations have?
Sketch the graph of each quadratic function.

a) $x^2 - 2x - 3 = 0$ b) $x^2 - 6x + 9 = 0$ c) $2x^2 + 4x + 3 = 0$

Q5 Solve these quadratic equations, leaving your answers in surd form where necessary.

a) $3x^2 - 7x + 3 = 0$ b) $2x^2 - 6x - 2 = 0$ c) $x^2 + 4x + 6 = 12$

Q6 If the quadratic equation $x^2 + kx + 4 = 0$ has two roots, what are the possible values of k?

Q7 a) Find the coordinates of the points of intersection of the graphs of $y = f(x)$ and $y = g(x)$, where $f(x) = 5x^3 - 13x^2 + 6x$ and $g(x) = -5x^3 + 7x^2 + 6x$.

b) Using your answer to part a) or otherwise, express $f(x) = 5x^3 - 13x^2 + 6x$ as the product of three factors.

> **Q7 Hint:** The points where the graphs intersect are found by setting the functions equal to each other and solving to find x.

Q8 a) Show that the x-coordinates of the points where the curves $y = x(x - 6)^2$ and $y = -x(2x - 31)$ intersect are given by the solutions to the equation $x^3 - 10x^2 + 5x = 0$.

b) Find the x-coordinates of the points where the two curves meet. Where appropriate, express your answers in surd form.

1   The equation $x^2 + 2kx + 4k = 0$, where k is a non-zero integer, has equal roots.

Find the value of k.

(4 marks)

2   The equation $px^2 + (2p + 3)x + p = 0$ has 2 distinct real solutions for x (p is a constant).

Find the range of possible values for p.

(4 marks)

3   Given that
$$5x^2 + nx + 14 \equiv m(x + 2)^2 + p \, ,$$

find the values of the integers m, n and p.

(3 marks)

4   a)   Rewrite $x^2 - 12x + 15$ in the form $(x - a)^2 + b$, for integers a and b.

(2 marks)

b)   (i)   Find the minimum value of $x^2 - 12x + 15$.

(1 mark)

(ii)   State the value of x at which this minimum occurs.

(1 mark)

5   a)   Use the quadratic formula to solve the equation $x^2 - 14x + 25 = 0$.
         Leave your answer in simplified surd form.

(3 marks)

    b)   Sketch the curve of $y = x^2 - 14x + 25$, giving the coordinates
         of the points where the curve crosses the x- and y-axis.

(3 marks)

    c)   Hence solve the inequality $x^2 - 14x + 25 \leq 0$.

(1 mark)

6   a)   (i)   Express $10x - x^2 - 27$ in the form $-(m - x)^2 + n$,
               where m and n are integers.

(2 marks)

         (ii) Hence show that $10x - x^2 - 27$ is always negative.

(1 mark)

    b)   (i)   State the coordinates of the maximum point
               of the curve $y = 10x - x^2 - 27$.

(2 marks)

         (ii) Sketch the curve, showing where the curve crosses the y-axis.

(2 marks)

1. Inequalities

Solving an inequality is very similar to solving an equation. But when multiplying or dividing both sides of an inequality, you've got to make sure that you keep the inequality sign pointing the right way.

Learning Objectives:

- Be able to solve linear inequalities, e.g. $ax + b > cx + d$.
- Be able to solve quadratic inequalities, e.g. $ax^2 + bx + c \geq 0$.

Linear inequalities

Solving where the inequality sign doesn't change direction

Solve inequalities like you'd solve equations — whatever you do to one side, you have to do to the other.

- If you **add** or **subtract** something from both sides of an inequality, the inequality sign **doesn't** change direction.
- Multiplying or dividing both sides of an inequality by a **positive** number **doesn't** affect the direction of the inequality sign.

Example 1

Find the set of values for x which satisfy:

a) $x - 3 < -1 + 2x$

$\Rightarrow x - 3 + 1 < -1 + 2x + 1$ ◄── Adding 1 to both sides leaves the inequality sign pointing in the same direction.

$\Rightarrow \quad x - 2 < 2x$

$\Rightarrow x - 2 - x < 2x - x$ ◄── Subtracting x from both sides doesn't affect the direction of the inequality sign.

$\Rightarrow \boxed{-2 < x}$ And this is the same as... $\boxed{x > -2}$

b) $8x + 2 \geq 2x + 17$

$\Rightarrow 8x + 2 - 2 \geq 2x + 17 - 2$ ◄── Subtracting 2...

$\Rightarrow \quad\quad 8x \geq 2x + 15$

$\Rightarrow \quad 8x - 2x \geq 2x + 15 - 2x$ ◄── ...and then $2x$, from both sides...

$\Rightarrow \quad\quad 6x \geq 15$

$\Rightarrow \quad\quad \dfrac{6x}{6} \geq \dfrac{15}{6}$ ◄── ...and dividing both sides by 6...

$\Rightarrow \boxed{x \geq \dfrac{5}{2}}$ ◄── ...leaves the inequality sign pointing in the same direction.

Tip: Solve an inequality just like you would an equation, by getting x (or whatever letter you're looking for) on its own.

Solving where the inequality sign does change direction

When solving inequalities, multiplying or dividing by **negative** numbers **changes** the direction of the inequality sign.

Example 2

Find the set of values of x for which $4 - 3x \leq 16$.

$\Rightarrow 4 - 3x - 4 \leq 16 - 4$ ⟵——— Subtract 4 from both sides.

$\Rightarrow \qquad -3x \leq 12$

$\Rightarrow \qquad \dfrac{-3x}{-3} \geq \dfrac{12}{-3}$ ⟵——— Then divide both sides by –3 — but change the direction of the inequality sign.

$\Rightarrow \boxed{x \geq -4}$

Tip: The reason for the sign changing direction is because it's just the same as swapping everything from one side to the other:

$$-3x \leq 12$$
$$\Rightarrow -12 \leq 3x$$
$$\Rightarrow -4 \leq x$$
$$\Rightarrow \quad x \geq -4$$

Example 3

Find the set of values of x for which $\dfrac{2 - 4x}{3} > \dfrac{5 - 3x}{4}$.

$\Rightarrow \quad 4(2 - 4x) > 3(5 - 3x)$ ⟵——— Multiply both sides by 12 to remove the fractions.

$\Rightarrow \quad 8 - 16x > 15 - 9x$ ⟵——— Multiply out the brackets.

$\Rightarrow \qquad -16x > 7 - 9x$ ⟵——— Subtract 8 from both sides.

$\Rightarrow \qquad -7x > 7$ ⟵——— Add $9x$ to both sides.

$\Rightarrow \quad \boxed{x < -1}$ ⟵——— Then divide both sides by –7 and change the direction of the inequality sign.

Finding the solution to two inequalities

You may be given two inequalities and be asked to find a solution which satisfies **both** of them.

Example 4

Find the set of values for x which satisfy both the inequalities $x - 5 < -3 + 2x$ and $2x > 4x - 6$.

- Solve both inequalities separately.

$x - 5 < -3 + 2x$	$2x > 4x - 6$
$\Rightarrow x - 2 < 2x$	$\Rightarrow 2x + 6 > 4x$
$\Rightarrow \boxed{-2 < x}$	$\Rightarrow \qquad 6 > 2x$
	$\Rightarrow \qquad \boxed{3 > x}$

Tip: You can write these solutions as $x > -2$ and $x < 3$ if you prefer.

- Show both solutions on a number line.
- Each line has an open circle at the end to show that this number isn't equal to x.

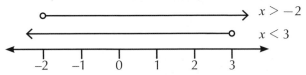

- Look where the two lines overlap to find the set of values that satisfy **both** inequalities.
- They overlap between –2 and 3, so:

$$-2 < x < 3$$

Tip: Solutions with a ≤ or ≥ sign end with a dark circle (●→) to show that number is a possible value of x.

Tip: It might seem a faff, but it's always a good idea to use a number line to check where your solutions overlap.

Exercise 1.1

Q1 Find the set of values for x which satisfy:
   a) $2x - 1 < x + 4$
   b) $4 - 3x \geq 10 - 5x$
   c) $5x + 7 > 3x + 1$
   d) $3 - 2x \leq 5x - 4$
   e) $9 - x \geq 7x + 5$

Q2 Find the set of values for x which satisfy:
   a) $2(x + 3) > 3(x + 2)$
   b) $5(1 + 3x) \leq 7$

Q2 Hint: Don't be a hero — multiply out the brackets first.

Q3 Find the set of values for x which satisfy:
   a) $\dfrac{6 - 5x}{2} < \dfrac{4 - 8x}{3}$
   b) $\dfrac{3x - 1}{4} \geq 2x$
   c) $\dfrac{x - 2}{2} - \dfrac{2x + 3}{3} < 7$

Q4 Find the set of values for x which satisfy:
   a) $-5 < 2x - 3 < 15$
   b) $-5 \leq 4 - 3x < 19$

Q4 Hint: Whatever you do to one part of the inequality, you have to do to all the other parts too.

Q5 Solve the following inequalities, and represent the solutions on a number line:
   a) $2x \geq 3 - x$
   b) $5x - 1 < 3x + 5$
   c) $2x + 1 \geq 3x + 2$
   d) $3x - 1 \leq 5x - 7$
   e) $9 - x \leq 3 - 4x$
   f) $\dfrac{2(x - 3)}{3} + 1 < \dfrac{2x - 1}{2}$

Q5 Hint: Look at the inequality sign to decide the direction of your arrow and whether the line should end with an open or black circle.

Q6 a) Find the set of values of x for which $7 \leq 3x - 2 < 16$.
   b) Show your solution to part a) on a number line.

Q7 Find the set of values for x which satisfy **both** $4 - 2x < 10$ and $3x - 1 < x + 7$. Draw the solutions to both inequalities on a number line to help you.

Q8 Find the values of x which satisfy both inequalities:

a) $2x \geq 3x - 5$ and $3x - 2 \geq x - 6$

b) $5x + 1 \leq 11$ and $2x - 3 < 5x - 6$

c) $2x - 1 \leq 3x - 5$ and $5x - 6 > x + 22$

d) $3x + 5 < x + 1$ and $6x - 1 \geq 3x + 5$

Quadratic inequalities

When solving inequalities, it's important that you **don't divide** or **multiply** by **variables** (anything you don't know the value of, e.g. x or y).

- The variable might be **negative** — so the inequality sign may end up pointing in the wrong direction.
- The variable could be equal to **zero** — you can't divide something by zero.

Example 1

$36x < 6x^2$

- Start by dividing by 6.
- Dividing by 6 is okay because 6 is definitely positive.

$$\Rightarrow 6x < x^2$$

- It's tempting to divide both sides by x now — but x could be negative (or zero).
- So instead take $6x$ from both sides.

$$\Rightarrow \boxed{0 < x^2 - 6x} \quad \text{Which is...} \quad \boxed{x^2 - 6x > 0}$$

Method for solving quadratic inequalities

The best way to solve a quadratic inequality is to do the following:

- Rewrite the inequality with zero on one side.
- Sketch the graph of the quadratic function.
- Use the graph to find the solution.

Example 2

Find the values of x which satisfy $-x^2 + 2x + 4 \geq 1$.

- First rewrite the inequality with zero on one side.

$$-x^2 + 2x + 3 \geq 0$$

Tip: See pages 20-23 if you need a refresher on how to factorise a quadratic.

- Then you need to draw the graph of $y = -x^2 + 2x + 3$.
- So find where it crosses the x-axis (i.e. where $y = 0$), by factorising to find the roots:

$$-x^2 + 2x + 3 = 0 \Rightarrow x^2 - 2x - 3 = 0$$

$$\Rightarrow (x + 1)(x - 3) = 0$$

$$\Rightarrow \boxed{x = -1 \quad \text{or} \quad x = 3}$$

- And the coefficient of x^2 is negative, so the graph is n-shaped. So it looks like this:

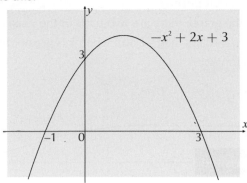

Tip: See pages 37-41 for more on drawing graphs of quadratic functions.

- Now you're trying to solve the inequality $-x^2 + 2x + 3 \geq 0$, so you're interested in when the graph is positive or zero, i.e. when it's above the x-axis.
- From the graph, this is when x is between -1 and 3 (including those points).
- So the solution is: $-1 \leq x \leq 3$

Tip: Look at the inequality sign to tell you which bit of the graph you want — it'll either be the range(s) of x where the graph is below the x-axis or the range(s) where it's above.

Tip: Here you're looking for when it's positive **or** zero because the inequality sign in the quadratic equation tells us it's "greater than or equal to" zero.

Example 3

Find the values of x which satisfy $2x^2 + 2x - 5 > 3x - 2$.

- First rewrite the inequality with zero on one side.
$$2x^2 - x - 3 > 0$$

- Then draw the graph of $y = 2x^2 - x - 3$
- So factorise the quadratic equation to find where it crosses the x-axis:

$$2x^2 - x - 3 = 0$$
$$\Rightarrow (2x - 3)(x + 1) = 0$$
$$\Rightarrow x = \tfrac{3}{2} \text{ or } x = -1$$

- And the coefficient of x^2 is positive, so the graph is u-shaped. And it looks like this:

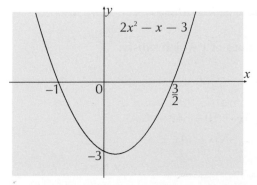

- Now you're trying to solve $2x^2 - x - 3 > 0$, so you need to say when the graph is positive.
- Looking at the graph, there are two parts of the x-axis where this is true — when x is less than -1 and when x is greater than $\frac{3}{2}$.
- So the solution is:

$$x < -1 \text{ or } x > \tfrac{3}{2}$$

Example 1 revisited

- On page 52 you had to solve $\mathbf{36x < 6x^2}$.

$$36x < 6x^2$$
$$\Rightarrow 6x < x^2$$
$$\Rightarrow 0 < x^2 - 6x$$

- So draw the graph of $y = x^2 - 6x = x(x - 6)$:

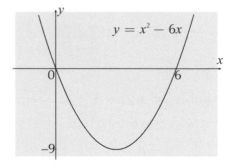

$$y = x^2 - 6x$$

- You're looking for when it is positive.
- And this is positive when:

$$x < 0 \quad \text{or} \quad x > 6$$

You may be asked to find the set of values for x which satisfy **both** a quadratic inequality and a linear equality. To do this, you just work out the solution of each inequality separately and then use a **graph** to help you find the solution that satisfies both.

Example 4

Find the set of values of x which satisfy:

a) $5x - 10 > 4x - 7$

- Solve in the usual way.

$$\Rightarrow 5x - 10 > 4x - 7$$
$$\Rightarrow \quad 5x > 4x + 3$$
$$\Rightarrow \quad \boxed{x > 3}$$

b) $2x^2 - 11x + 5 < 0$

- You've already got zero on one side, so just factorise the quadratic to find where the graph crosses the x-axis:

$$2x^2 - 11x + 5 = 0$$
$$\Rightarrow (2x - 1)(x - 5) = 0$$
$$\Rightarrow \boxed{x = \tfrac{1}{2} \text{ or } x = 5}$$

- The coefficient of x^2 is positive, so the graph is u-shaped. And looks like this:

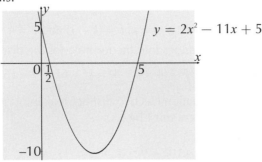

- You're interested in when this is negative, i.e. when it's below the x-axis.
- From the graph, this is when x is between $\frac{1}{2}$ and 5.
- So $2x^2 - 11x + 5 < 0$ when:

$$\boxed{\tfrac{1}{2} < x < 5}$$

> **Tip:** You're looking for when it is negative as the inequality sign tells us it is less than zero.

c) both $5x - 10 > 4x - 7$ **and** $2x^2 - 11x + 5 < 0$

- You already know the solutions to both inequalities — and the graph above shows the solution to the quadratic inequality.
- So add the line $x = 3$ to your graph.
- You're now interested in when the curve is negative, **and** when the x values are greater than 3.

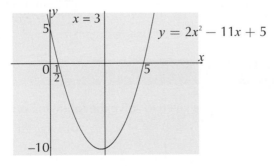

- So both inequalities are satisfied when:

$$\boxed{3 < x < 5}$$

Solving a quadratic inequality to find k

Tip: The discriminant is just the $b^2 - 4ac$ part of the quadratic formula — see page 34 for more.

On page 35 we covered questions where the quadratic contained an **unknown constant** (k), and by using the formula for the discriminant we ended up with linear inequalities in terms of the unknown. We'll now take a look at a similar example that results in a **quadratic inequality**.

Example 5

The equation $kx^2 + (k + 3)x + 4 = 0$ has two distinct real solutions. Show that $k^2 - 10k + 9 > 0$, and find the set of values of k which satisfy this inequality.

Tip: This question doesn't mention finding the discriminant — but that's what you've got to do first, to get that quadratic inequality in terms of k.

- Identify a, b and c: $a = k$, $b = (k + 3)$ and $c = 4$
- Then put these values into the formula for the discriminant:

$$b^2 - 4ac = (k + 3)^2 - (4 \times k \times 4) = k^2 + 6k + 9 - 16k = k^2 - 10k + 9$$

- The original equation has two distinct real solutions, so the discriminant must be > 0.
- So:

$$k^2 - 10k + 9 > 0.$$

- Now, to find the set of values for k, you have to factorise the quadratic:

$$k^2 - 10k + 9 = (k - 1)(k - 9)$$

- So, the graph of the quadratic will cross the horizontal axis at $k = 1$ and $k = 9$ and it's u-shaped.
- Sketching the graph, you can see that the quadratic is > 0 when:

$$k < 1 \quad \text{or when} \quad k > 9$$

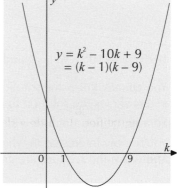

$y = k^2 - 10k + 9$
$= (k - 1)(k - 9)$

Exercise 1.2

Q1   Use the graphs given to solve the following quadratic inequalities:

a) $x^2 + 2x - 3 < 0$

b) $4x - x^2 < 0$

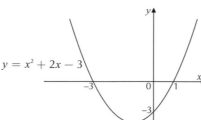

$y = x^2 + 2x - 3$

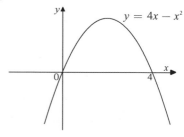

$y = 4x - x^2$

c) $2x^2 \geq 5 - 9x$

$y = 2x^2 + 9x - 5$

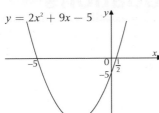

d) $x^2 - 2x - 5 > 0$

$y = x^2 - 2x - 5$

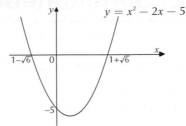

Q2 Use the graphs given to help you solve the following quadratic inequalities:

Q2 Hint: Here, you're given the graphs but you'll have to calculate where the x-intercepts are yourself.

a) $x^2 \leq 4$

$y = x^2 - 4$

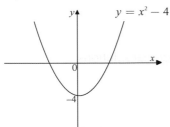

b) $13x < 3x^2 + 4$

$y = -3x^2 + 13x - 4$

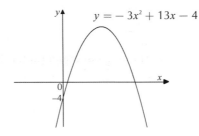

c) $x^2 + 4 < 6x$

$y = x^2 - 6x + 4$

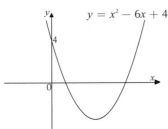

Q3 Find the ranges of values of x which satisfy the following quadratic inequalities. Include a sketch of the graph for each answer.

a) $x^2 + 5x - 6 \geq 0$ b) $x^2 - 3x + 2 < 0$
c) $6 - 5x > 6x^2$ d) $x^2 - 5x + 24 \leq 5x + 3$
e) $36 - 4x^2 \leq 0$ f) $x^2 - 6x + 3 > 0$
g) $x^2 - x + 3 > 0$ h) $6 \geq 5x^2 + 13x$

Q4 The sides of a rectangle are $(x - 9)$ m and $(x - 6)$ m respectively. Find the values of x for which the area of the rectangle is greater than 28 m².

Q5 By using the discriminant, find the set of values of k for which $x^2 - 6x + k = 0$ has two distinct real solutions.

Q6 Find the set of values for k which gives the equation $x^2 - kx + k = 0$ no real roots.

Q7 Find the values of x which satisfy both $4(3 - x) \geq 13 - 5x$ and $7x + 6 \geq 3x^2$.

2. Simultaneous Equations

Learning Objectives:

- Be able to solve two linear simultaneous equations using elimination or substitution.
- Be able to solve simultaneous equations where one is linear and one is quadratic using substitution.

Solving simultaneous equations just means finding the answers to two equations at the same time — i.e. finding values for x and y for which both equations are true.

Simultaneous equations — both linear

Solving by elimination

Simultaneous equations are just a pair of equations containing two unknown quantities, usually x and y.

This is how simultaneous equations are often shown:

$$3x + 5y = -4$$
$$-2x + 3y = 9$$

But they'll look different sometimes, maybe like this:

$$4 + 5y = -3x$$
$$-2x = 9 - 3y$$

Tip: You can also solve two linear simultaneous equations by substitution — see pages 60-63.

You can solve two linear simultaneous equations by **elimination**. Before you can use the method, you need to **rearrange** them as '$ax + by = c$'.

$$4 + 5y = -3x \qquad\qquad 3x + 5y = -4$$
$$-2x = 9 - 3y \longrightarrow -2x + 3y = 9$$

The elimination method involves **four** steps:

1) **Match the coefficients**
   Multiply the equations by numbers that will make either the x's or the y's **match** in the two equations. (Ignoring minus signs.)

2) **Eliminate to find one variable**
   If the coefficients are the **same** sign, you'll need to **subtract** one equation from the other. If the coefficients are **different** signs, you need to **add** the equations.

3) **Find the other variable (that you eliminated)**
   When you've found one variable, put its value into one of the **original equations** so you can find the **other** variable.

4) **Check your answer**
   By putting these values into the **other original equation**.

Example

Solve the simultaneous equations $3x + 5y = -4$ and $-2x + 3y = 9$

- Number your equations 1 and 2.

$$① \quad 3x + 5y = -4$$
$$② \quad -2x + 3y = 9$$

Tip: It's a good idea to label them as equation ① and equation ② — so you know which one you're working with.

- Match the coefficients:
  To get the x's to match, you need to multiply the
  first equation by 2 and the second by 3:

  ①×2 $6x + 10y = -8$ ——③   Number these
  ②×3 $-6x + 9y = 27$ ——④   new equations.

Tip: Go for the lowest common multiple (LCM), e.g. LCM of 2 and 3 is 6.

- Eliminate to find one variable:
  Add the new equations together to eliminate the x's.

  ③+④ $19y = 19$
  $$y = 1$$

- Find the variable you eliminated:
  So $y = 1$. Now stick that value for y into one of the equations to find x:

  $y = 1$ in ① $\Rightarrow 3x + 5 = -4$
  $$3x = -9$$
  $$x = -3$$

- So the solution is $x = -3, y = 1$.

- Check your answer:
  Putting these values into the other equation

  ② $-2x + 3y = 9$ ◄——   If these two numbers are the
  $x = -3$ same, then the values you've
  $y = 1$ got for the variables are right.
  $\Rightarrow -2 \times (-3) + 3 \times 1 = 6 + 3 = 9$

Tip: You should always check your answer to make sure you've worked out x and y correctly. Then pat yourself on the back if you have. You deserve it.

If you drew the **graph** of each equation you'd get two straight lines

- The point where these two lines **intersect** gives the **solution** to the two simultaneous equations.
- For the last example, the graph of the two lines $3x + 5y = -4$ and $-2x + 3y = 9$ would look like this:

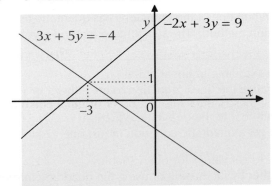

Tip: See Chapter 4 for more on how to draw straight lines graphs.

- And the point where the two lines intersect is $(-3, 1)$ — which is the same as the answer worked out above.
- However, **not all** simultaneous equations have solutions that work in both equations — for example, no values of x and y satisfy both $2x + 3y = 5$ and $4x + 6y = 7$. This would be obvious if you **sketched the graphs** — the lines are **parallel** so they never intersect.

Tip: In an exam, if they ask you to find the coordinates of the point of intersection, you should find them using one of the algebraic methods rather than using a graph.

Q1 Solve the following simultaneous equations:

a) $2x - 3y = 3$
$x + 3y = 6$

b) $3x + 2y = 7$
$7x - y = -12$

Q1 Hint: Don't forget to rearrange the equations so they're in the form $ax + by = c$. It makes life much easier.

c) $4x + 3y = -4$
$6x - 4y = 11$

d) $7x - 6y = 4$
$11x + 9y = -6$

e) $6x + 2y - 8 = 0$
$4x + 3 = -3y$

f) $2x + 18y - 21 = 0$
$-14y = 3x + 14$

g) $2x + 16y = 10$
$64y - 5 + 3x = 0$

Q2 Hint: Although this question is phrased differently to Q1, it's still asking you to do the same thing — but remember, not all simultaneous equations have solutions (see previous page).

Q2 Find the point of intersection of each pair of straight lines.

a) $y = 2x - 3$
$y = \frac{1}{2}x + 3$

b) $y = -\frac{2}{3}x + 7$
$y = \frac{1}{2}x + \frac{21}{2}$

c) $x + 2y + 5 = 0$
$3x - 5y - 7 = 0$

d) $2x - 3y = 7$
$5x - \frac{15}{2}y = 9$

e) $8x = -3y + 10$
$9y = 3 - 6x$

f) $7x - 5y = 15$
$2x - 9 = 3y$

Simultaneous equations —
if one is quadratic

Solving by substitution

Elimination is great for simple equations, but it won't always work. Sometimes one of the equations has not just x's and y's in it — but bits with x^2 and y^2 as well. When one of the equations has quadratic terms, you can **only** use the **substitution** method. The substitution method involves **four** steps:

1) Isolate variable in linear equation
Rearrange the linear equation to get either x or y on its own.

2) Substitute into the quadratic equation
— to get a quadratic equation in just one variable.

3) Solve to get values for one variable
— either by factorising or using the quadratic formula.

4) Stick these values in the linear equation
— to find corresponding values for the other variable.

Tip: Always check your answer at the end too, by putting the values back into the original equations.

Example 1

Solve the simultaneous equations $-x + 2y = 5$ and $x^2 + y^2 = 25$.

- Start by labelling the two equations. Here the linear equation is labelled ①, and the equation with quadratic terms is labelled ②.

$$-x + 2y = 5 \quad \text{——①}$$
$$x^2 + y^2 = 25 \quad \text{——②}$$

Tip: The linear equation is the one with only x's and y's in. The quadratic is the one with x^2 or y^2 terms.

- Rearrange the linear equation so that either x or y is on its own on one side of the equals sign.

$$① \ -x + 2y = 5$$
$$\Rightarrow x = 2y - 5$$

- Substitute this expression into the quadratic...

$$\text{Sub into } ②: \quad x^2 + y^2 = 25$$
$$\Rightarrow (2y - 5)^2 + y^2 = 25$$

- ...and then rearrange this into the form $ax^2 + bx + c = 0$, so you can solve it — either by factorising or using the quadratic formula.

$$\Rightarrow (4y^2 - 20y + 25) + y^2 = 25$$
$$\Rightarrow 5y^2 - 20y = 0$$
$$\Rightarrow 5y(y - 4) = 0$$
$$\Rightarrow y = 0 \ \text{ or } \ y = 4$$

- Finally put both these values back into the linear equation to find corresponding values for x:

When $y = 0$:

$$-x + 2y = 5 \quad ①$$
$$\Rightarrow x = -5$$

When $y = 4$:

$$-x + 2y = 5 \quad ①$$
$$\Rightarrow -x + 8 = 5$$
$$\Rightarrow \quad x = 3$$

- So solving these simultaneous equations has actually produced a **pair** of solutions:

$$x = -5, y = 0 \quad \text{and} \quad x = 3, y = 4$$

Tip: You'll often, but not always, get a pair of solutions if one of the equations is quadratic.

- Now, **check your answers** by putting each set of values back into the original equations.

$$x = -5, y = 0: -(-5) + 2 \times 0 = 5 \ \checkmark$$
$$(-5)^2 + 0^2 = 25 \ \checkmark$$

$$x = 3, y = 4: -(3) + 2 \times 4 = 5 \ \checkmark$$
$$3^2 + 4^2 = 25 \ \checkmark$$

Tip: Don't worry too much about circles — you don't need to know about them till C2.

- The equation $x^2 + y^2 = 25$ is actually a circle about the origin with radius 5 and the linear equation is just a standard straight line.

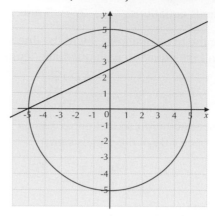

- So by solving the simultaneous equations you're actually finding the two points where the line passes through the circle — the points $(-5, 0)$ and $(3, 4)$.

Tip: The solutions to simultaneous equations are just the points where their graphs meet. If there are 2 solutions, the graphs will cross in 2 places. If there are no solutions, the graphs will never meet.

Example 2

Find any points of intersection of the following graphs:

a) $y = x^2 - 4x + 5$ and $y = 2x - 4$

- Label the two equations:

$$y = x^2 - 4x + 5 \quad ——①$$
$$y = 2x - 4 \quad ——②$$

- Substitute ② in ①:

$$2x - 4 = x^2 - 4x + 5$$

- Rearrange and solve:

$$x^2 - 6x + 9 = 0$$
$$(x - 3)^2 = 0$$
$$\boxed{x = 3} \longleftarrow \text{Double root — i.e. you only get 1 solution from the quadratic equation.}$$

- In Equation ② this gives:

$$y = 2 \times 3 - 4$$
$$\boxed{y = 2}$$

- So there's one solution: $\boxed{x = 3, y = 2}$

- Since the equations have only one solution, the two graphs only meet at one point — $(3, 2)$.

- The straight line is actually a tangent to the curve.

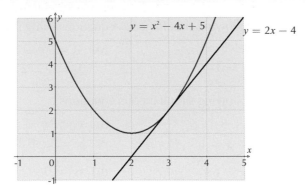

b) $y = x^2 - 4x + 5$ and $y = 2x - 5$

- Label the two equations:

$$y = x^2 - 4x + 5 \quad \text{——①}$$
$$y = 2x - 5 \quad \text{——②}$$

- Substitute ② in ① :

$$2x - 5 = x^2 - 4x + 5$$

- Rearrange and try to solve with the quadratic formula:

$$x^2 - 6x + 10 = 0$$
$$b^2 - 4ac = (-6)^2 - 4 \times 1 \times 10$$
$$= 36 - 40 = -4$$

- $b^2 - 4ac < 0$, so the quadratic has no real roots.

> So the simultaneous equations have no solutions.

- This means the graphs never meet:

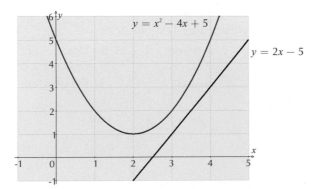

> **Observation:** How sad.

Q1   Solve the following simultaneous equations using substitution:

a) $y = 4x + 3$
    $2y - 3x = 1$

b) $5x + 2y = 16$
    $2y - x - 4 = 0$

Q2   Solve the following simultaneous equations:

a) $y = 2x + 5$
    $y = x^2 - x + 1$

b) $y = 2x^2 - 3$
    $y = 3x + 2$

c) $2x^2 - xy = 6$
    $y - 3x + 7 = 0$

d) $xy = 6$
    $2y - x + 4 = 0$

e) $y = x^2 - 2x - 3$
    $y + x + 8 = 0$

f) $y = 2x^2 - 3x + 5$
    $5x - y = 3$

g) $2x^2 + 3y^2 = 77$
    $x + 3y = 14$

Q3   Find the points of intersection of the following curves and straight lines:

a) $y = \frac{1}{2}x^2 + 4x - 8$
    $y = \frac{3}{2}x + 4$

b) $y = 2x^2 + x - 6$
    $5x - y + 10 = 0$

c) $x^2 + y^2 = 50$
    $x + 2y = 5$

d) $2x^2 - y + 3x + 1 = 0$
    $y - x - 5 = 0$

Q4 Hint: Here, you don't even need to draw a graph, just describe what your answer to part a) means.

Q4   a) Solve the simultaneous equations $x^2 + y^2 = 10$ and $x - 3y + 10 = 0$.

b) Say what your answer to part a) means geometrically.

Q5   Without drawing the graphs, determine whether the following curves and lines intersect at one or two points, or do not intersect at all:

a) $y = x^2 + 6x - 7$ and $y = 2x - 3$
b) $3x^2 + 4y^2 = 7$ and $3x + 4y = 7$
c) $xy + 2x - y = 8$ and $x + y = 1$

Review Exercise — Chapter 3

Q1 Solve:

a) $7x - 4 > 2x - 42$

b) $12y - 3 \leq 4y + 4$

c) $9y - 4 \geq 17y + 2$

d) $x + 6 < 5x - 4$

e) $4x - 2 > x - 14$

f) $7 - x \leq 4 - 2x$

Q2 Find the set of values for x that satisfy the following inequalities:

a) $3x^2 - 5x - 2 \leq 0$

b) $x^2 + 2x + 7 > 4x + 9$

c) $3x^2 + 7x + 4 \geq 2(x^2 + x - 1)$

d) $x^2 + 3x - 1 \geq x + 2$

e) $2x^2 > x + 1$

f) $3x^2 - 12 < x^2 - 2x$

> **Q2 Hint:** Watch that you use the right kind of inequality sign in your answers.

Q3 Solve these sets of simultaneous equations:

a) $3x - 4y = 7$ and $-2x + 7y = -22$

b) $2x - 3y = \frac{11}{12}$ and $x + y = -\frac{7}{12}$

Q4 Find where the following lines meet:

a) $y = 3x - 4$ and $y = 7x - 5$

b) $y = 13 - 2x$ and $7x - y - 23 = 0$

c) $2x - 3y + 4 = 0$ and $x - 2y + 1 = 0$

Q5 Find where possible the solutions to these sets of simultaneous equations. Interpret your answers geometrically.

a) $y = x^2 - 7x + 4$
    $2x - y - 10 = 0$

b) $y = 30 - 6x + 2x^2$
    $y = 2(x + 11)$

> **Q5 Hint:** The "where possible" bit of this question is a bit of a clue.

c) $2x^2 + 2y^2 - 3 = 0$
    $y = x + 4$

Q6 Without drawing the graphs, decide whether the curve $y = x^2 - 2x - 3$ and line $y = 3x + 11$ intersect at one or two points, or do not intersect at all.

1   Find the set of values of x that satisfy the following inequalities:

   a) $3x + 2 \leq x + 6$,

                                (2 marks)

   b) $20 - x - x^2 > 0$,

                                  (4 marks)

   c) $3x + 2 \leq x + 6$ and $20 - x - x^2 > 0$.

                                  (1 mark)

2   Solve the inequalities:

   a) $3 \leq 2p + 5 \leq 15$,

                                  (3 marks)

   b) $q^2 - 9 > 0$.

                                  (4 marks)

3   a)   Factorise $3x^2 - 13x - 10$.

                                  (1 mark)

   b)   Hence, or otherwise, solve $3x^2 - 13x - 10 \leq 0$.

                                  (3 marks)

4   Solve the simultaneous equations:

   a) $2x + 3y = 5$
        $5x + 4y = 2$,

                                  (3 marks)

   b) $y = -5x + 6$
        $7x + 2y - 6 = 0$.

                                  (4 marks)

5   a)   Eliminate x from the following equations:
$$x^2 + y^2 = 13$$
$$x - 5y + 13 = 0$$
     to show that:
$$y^2 - 5y + 6 = 0$$

                                  (3 marks)

   b)   Hence, or otherwise, solve the simultaneous equations:
$$x^2 + y^2 = 13$$
$$x - 5y + 13 = 0$$

                                  (4 marks)

6   Find the coordinates of any points of intersection for the following curve and line:
$$x^2 + 2y^2 = 36, \quad x + y = 6$$

(6 marks)

7   The curve C has equation $y = -x^2 + 3$ and the line l has equation $y = -2x + 4$.

a)   Find the coordinates of the point (or points) of intersection of C and l.

(4 marks)

b)   Sketch the graphs of C and l on the same axes, clearly
      showing where the graphs intersect the x- and y- axes.

(5 marks)

8   The line l has equation $y = 2x - 3$ and the curve C has equation $y = (x + 2)(x - 4)$.

a)   Sketch the line l and the curve C on the same axes, showing the coordinates
      of the x- and y- intercepts.

(5 marks)

b)   Show that the x-coordinates of the points of intersection of l and C satisfy the
      equation $x^2 - 4x - 5 = 0$.

(2 marks)

c)   Hence, or otherwise, find the points of intersection of l and C.

(4 marks)

1. The Equation of a Straight Line

Learning Objectives:

- Be able to find the equation of a straight line passing through two given points, or though one point with a certain gradient.

- Write straight line equations in any of the three forms:
$y - y_1 = m(x - x_1)$,
$y = mx + c$ and
$ax + by + c = 0$.

Any straight line can be described by an equation made up of an x term, y term and constant term (though one of these may actually be zero). There are three standard ways of arranging straight line equations that you need to learn.

$$y - y_1 = m(x - x_1)$$

This is the first form you need to know.

$$y - y_1 = m(x - x_1)$$

m is the **gradient**

x_1 and y_1 are the **coordinates** of one of the points on the line.

If you're told **two points** that a straight line passes through, this is probably the easiest one to use. You do need to be a little careful using the formula, so here's a method to follow:

1) **LABEL** the points (x_1, y_1) and (x_2, y_2).

2) **GRADIENT** — find this using $m = \dfrac{y_2 - y_1}{x_2 - x_1}$.

3) **WRITE DOWN THE EQUATION** $y - y_1 = m(x - x_1)$.

4) **SUBSTITUTE** in your values for m, x_1 and y_1.

Tip: Remember that the gradient just means the steepness of the line, and in its simplest form is just $m = \dfrac{\text{change in } y}{\text{change in } x}$ for two points.

Tip: Make sure you subtract the same way round on the top and bottom of the fraction.

In other words, **don't** do this: $\dfrac{y_2 - y_1}{x_1 - x_2}$

Tip: This would work fine if you used x_2 and y_2 instead. The equation would look different, but still represent the line.

Example

Find the equation of the line that passes through the points (–3, 10) and (1, 4), and write it in the form $y - y_1 = m(x - x_1)$.

- Label the points.

$$\text{Point 1} \longrightarrow (x_1, y_1) = (-3, 10)$$
$$\text{Point 2} \longrightarrow (x_2, y_2) = (1, 4)$$

- Find the gradient of the line using $m = \dfrac{y_2 - y_1}{x_2 - x_1}$.

$$m = \frac{4 - 10}{1 - (-3)} = \frac{-6}{4} = -\frac{3}{2}$$

- Write down the equation of the line.

$$y - y_1 = m(x - x_1)$$

- Now just substitute in the values for m, x_1 and y_1.

$$x_1 = -3, \; y_1 = 10, \; m = -\tfrac{3}{2} \longrightarrow y - 10 = -\tfrac{3}{2}(x - (-3))$$

$$y - 10 = -\tfrac{3}{2}(x + 3)$$

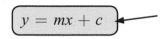

$y = mx + c$

This form for the straight line equation is probably the most popular — it's certainly the easiest form to make sense of.

$$y = mx + c$$

m is the **gradient** of the line
c is the **y-intercept** (where it crosses the y-axis).

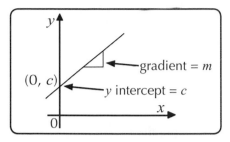

When in $y = mx + c$ form, you can simply read off the values of m and c — and together these give you a fairly good idea of what the graph will look like.

Tip: This diagram shows a straight line with positive values for m and c. A negative value for m would make the graph slope downwards.

As well as being easy to interpret, it's fairly easy to find the equation of a line in $y = mx + c$ form. Here are a couple of examples — you're given different information in each case.

Examples

A straight line has a gradient of –2 and passes through the point (3, 1). Find the equation of the line.

- To find c, sub in the values of m, x and y given in the question.

$$y = mx + c$$
$$1 = (-2 \times 3) + c$$
$$7 = c$$

- Then put your values of m and c into the equation $y = mx + c$.

$$y = -2x + 7$$

Tip: It's a good idea to put the x- and y-values of your given point into your final equation to check it's right.

Find the equation of the straight line that passes through the points (–18, 16) and (10, 2).

- Start by finding m.

$$m = \frac{2 - 16}{10 - (-18)} = \frac{-14}{28} = -\frac{1}{2}$$

- Write down the equation with $m = -\frac{1}{2}$.

$$y = -\frac{1}{2}x + c$$

- Using one of the given points, substitute in values for x and y — this will find c.

$$x = 10, y = 2 \text{ gives: } \quad 2 = -\frac{1}{2}(10) + c$$
$$c = 7$$

- So the equation is:

$$y = -\frac{1}{2}x + 7$$

Tip: This method is very similar to that on the previous page — find the gradient, then put in the x and y values of one of the points...

Q1 Give the gradient and y-intercept of the following straight lines:

a) $y = -4x + 11$ b) $y = 4 - x$ c) $y = 1.7x - 2.3$

Q2 Give equations for the following straight lines in the form $y = mx + c$:

a) gradient -3, y-intercept $(0, 2)$

b) gradient 5, y-intercept $(0, -3)$

c) gradient $\frac{1}{2}$, y-intercept $(0, 6)$

d) gradient 0.8, y-intercept $(0, 1.2)$

Q3 Use the information in the diagrams to the find the equation of each straight line in the form $y = mx + c$.

a)

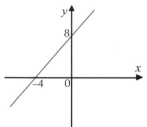

b)

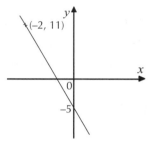

c)

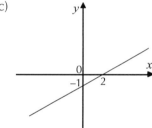

Q4 Find the equations of the lines that pass through the following pairs of points. Give each answer in these forms:

(i) $y - y_1 = m(x - x_1)$ (ii) $y = mx + c$.

a) $(4, 1), (0, -3)$ b) $(12, -3), (14, 1)$

c) $(5, 7), (-2, 5)$ d) $(-3, 6), (4, -2)$

Q5 Find the equation of the straight line which passes through the point $(-4, -3)$ and has a gradient of $\frac{1}{4}$. Give your answer in the form $y = mx + c$.

Q6 A straight line has gradient 3 and passes through the point $(2, -7)$. State which of the following coordinates are points on the line.

a) $(1, -10)$ b) $(-2, -7)$

c) $(5, 2)$ d) $(0.5, 2.5)$

e) $(7, 8)$ f) $(0, -12)$

$ax + by + c = 0$

This the last form you need to know for straight line equations.

$$\boxed{ax + by + c = 0}$$ Where a, b and c are **integers**.

Note that this form doesn't involve m. As a result, it's not as easy to work with. So if you're asked to give an equation in this form, it's often easiest just to find it in one of the previous two forms, then rearrange it at the end.

One important thing to remember when using this form is that a, b and c are integers, so you must get rid of any fractions.

Example 1

Find the gradient and y-intercept of the line $5x + 2y - 10 = 0$.

- The easiest way to answer this question is to rearrange the equation into the form $y = mx + c$.

$$5x + 2y - 10 = 0$$
$$\Rightarrow 2y = -5x + 10$$
$$\Rightarrow y = -\frac{5}{2}x + 5$$

- Now compare the equation with $y = mx + c$.
- So for the line $5x + 2y - 10 = 0$:

$$\text{gradient} = -\frac{5}{2} \text{ and the } y\text{-intercept is } (0, 5)$$

Example 2

Find the equation of the line that passes through the point $(2, -15)$ and has gradient $-\frac{3}{2}$, giving your answer in the form $ax + by + c = 0$, where a, b and c are integers.

- Start by finding the equation in one of the easier forms. We'll use $y - y_1 = m(x - x_1)$ this time, but $y = mx + c$ would be just as easy...

$$m = -\frac{3}{2} \text{ gives: } y - y_1 = -\frac{3}{2}(x - x_1)$$

- Now sub in $x_1 = 2$ and $y_1 = -15$:

$$y + 15 = -\frac{3}{2}(x - 2)$$

- Now you can start rearranging into $ax + by + c = 0$ form:

$$y + \frac{3}{2}x + 15 - 3 = 0$$

$$y + \frac{3}{2}x + 12 = 0$$

$$\Rightarrow 3x + 2y + 24 = 0$$

Tip: If you end up with an equation like $\frac{3}{2}x - \frac{4}{3}y + 6 = 0$, where you've got a 2 and a 3 on the bottom of the fractions — multiply everything by the lowest common multiple of 2 and 3, i.e. 6.

Q1 Write the following equations in the form $ax + by + c = 0$, where a, b and c are integers.

a) $y = 5x + 2$

b) $3y = -\frac{1}{2}x + 3$

c) $2(x - 1) = 4y - 1$

d) $7x - 3 = 2y + 6$

e) $\frac{1}{2}(4x + 3) = 3(y - 2)$

f) $3(y - 4) = 4(x - 3)$

Q2 Hint: You'll need to convert to a different form so that you can interpret the equations.

Q2 Find the gradient and y-intercept of the following lines:

a) $6x - 2y + 3 = 0$

b) $-9x + 3y - 12 = 0$

c) $-x - 4y - 2 = 0$

d) $7x + 8y + 11 = 0$

Q3 Find the equation of the line that passes through the following points. Write your answer in the form $ax + by + c = 0$, where a, b and c are integers.

a) $(5, 2)$, $(3, 4)$

b) $(9, -1)$, $(7, 2)$

c) $(-6, 1)$, $(4, 0)$

d) $(-12, 3)$, $(5, 7)$

Q4 Hint: Again, it's easiest to find the equation in a different form, then convert it at the end.

Q4 Find the equation of the lines below in the form $ax + by + c = 0$, where a, b and c are integers.

a)

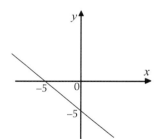

b)

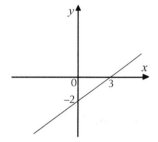

2. Parallel and Perpendicular Lines

You can work out the equation of a line, if 1) it is parallel or perpendicular to a line you already know the equation of, and 2) if you know a point that the line passes through. The first thing you need to do is find the gradient of the line.

Parallel lines

Parallel lines have **equal gradient** — that's what makes them parallel. So when finding the equation of a line parallel to a line with a given equation, you know the gradient will be the same for both.

Example 1

Find the line parallel to $y = \frac{3}{4}x - \frac{7}{4}$ that:

a) has a y-intercept of (0, 4)

- Parallel lines have the same gradient, so the gradient of the line you want is also $\frac{3}{4}$.

- You then need to find c — this is just the y-intercept which we already know is at 4.

- So putting m and c into the equation $y = mx + c$ gives: $\boxed{y = \frac{3}{4}x + 4}$

b) passes through the point (3, –1).

- The gradient is $\frac{3}{4}$. So the new equation will be: $\boxed{y = \frac{3}{4}x + c}$

- You then need to find c. We know that the line passes through point (3, –1) , so stick $x = 3$ and $y = -1$ into the equation to find c:

$$-1 = \frac{3}{4}(3) + c \quad \Rightarrow \quad c = -\frac{13}{4}$$

- So the equation of the line is: $\boxed{y = \frac{3}{4}x - \frac{13}{4}}$

Example 2

Find the line parallel to $2x - 8y + 11 = 0$ that passes through the point (3, –1). Give your equation in the form $ax + by + c = 0$, where a, b and c are integers.

- First, put the given line in a more useful form, i.e. $y = mx + c$...

$$2x - 8y + 11 = 0$$
$$-8y = -2x - 11$$
$$y = \frac{1}{4}x + \frac{11}{8}$$

- The gradient of the given line is $\frac{1}{4}$, so that's also the gradient of the parallel line you want.

$$y = \frac{1}{4}x + c$$

$x = 3$ and $y = -1 \longrightarrow$ $\quad -1 = \frac{1}{4}(3) + c \quad \Rightarrow \quad c = -\frac{7}{4}$

So $y = \frac{1}{4}x - \frac{7}{4}$ which rearranges to $\boxed{x - 4y - 7 = 0}$

You may be asked whether two lines are parallel or not. To work this out you need to **compare** their gradients. This is easiest when both equations are in the **same form** — so one or both equations may need **rearranging**.

Example 3

Line l_1 is given by the equation $y = \frac{1}{2}x + 6$ and line l_2 is given by the equation $3x + 6y - 1 = 0$. Find out whether the lines are parallel.

- To compare the gradients you want both lines in the form $y = mx + c$. So rearrange line l_2 into this form:

$$3x + 6y - 1 = 0$$
$$\Rightarrow 6y = -3x + 1$$
$$\Rightarrow y = -\frac{3}{6}x + \frac{1}{6}$$
$$\Rightarrow y = -\frac{1}{2}x + \frac{1}{6}$$

> **Tip:** Rearranging the equations into the form $y = mx + c$, rather than $ax + by + c = 0$, makes it a hundred million times* easier to compare the gradients. *Approximately.

- Then compare the two equations:

$$y = \frac{1}{2}x + 6 \quad \longleftarrow \text{ Line } l_1$$
$$y = -\frac{1}{2}x + \frac{1}{6} \quad \longleftarrow \text{ Line } l_2$$

- You are only concerned about the gradient so look at the bit before the x. Here line l_1 has a gradient of $\frac{1}{2}$ and line l_2 has a gradient of $-\frac{1}{2}$.
- So:

The lines l_1 and l_2 are NOT parallel.

Exercise 2.1

Q1 State which of the following straight lines are parallel to $y = -3x - 1$.

a) $2y = -6x + 2$ b) $y - 3x - 1 = 0$

c) $6y + 18x = 7$ d) $\frac{1}{3}(y + 1) = x$

e) $-9y - 2 = 27x$ f) $4y = 12x$

Q2 Find the equations of the parallel lines shown in blue.
Write them in the form $ax + by + c = 0$, where a, b and c are integers.

a) $y = 4x - 1$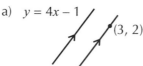

b) $(-4, -5)$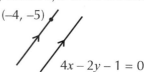

$4x - 2y - 1 = 0$

Q3 State whether the following pairs of lines are parallel.

a) $y = 2x + 1$ b) $2x - 3y + 1 = 0$ c) $-5x + 4y + 3 = 0$

$\quad\; y + \frac{1}{2}x = 1$ $y = \frac{2}{3}x + 2$ $8y = 10x$

Q4 Line A passes through the point (4, 3) and is parallel to the line $2x - 4y + 3 = 0$. Find the equation of line A in the form:

a) $y = mx + c$,   b) $ax + by + c = 0$.

Perpendicular lines

Finding the equations of **perpendicular** lines (or '**normals**') is just as easy as finding the equations of parallel lines — you just need to know one key fact:

> The gradients of perpendicular lines **multiply to give –1**.

Which means:

> Gradient of the perpendicular line =
> **–1 ÷ the gradient of the other one**.

Tip: Remember, 'perpendicular' just means 'at right angles'.

Tip: So if a line has a gradient of m, a line perpendicular to it will have a gradient of $-\frac{1}{m}$.

Example 1

Find the equation of the line perpendicular to $y = \frac{1}{3}x - 1$ that passes through (–2, 4).

- Use the gradient rule:

  Gradient of perpendicular line $= -1 \div$ gradient of the other one

  $$= -1 \div \frac{1}{3} = -3$$

  So: $\boxed{y = -3x + c}$

Tip: Remember, to divide by a fraction, turn it upside down and then multiply by it.

- To find c, put the coordinates (–2, 4) into the equation

  $$4 = (-3) \times (-2) + c$$
  $$\Rightarrow c = 4 - 6 = -2$$

- So the equation of the line is: $\boxed{y = -3x - 2}$

Example 2

Find the equation of the line perpendicular to $7x - 3y + 5 = 0$ that passes through the point (–3, –11).

- Start by converting the equation into a more useful form:

  $$7x - 3y + 5 = 0$$
  $$-3y = -7x - 5$$
  $$y = \frac{7}{3}x + \frac{5}{3} \quad \longleftarrow \quad \text{So the gradient is } \tfrac{7}{3}.$$

- Now use the gradient rule:

  Gradient of perpendicular line $= -1 \div \frac{7}{3} = -\frac{3}{7}$

  So we have: $\boxed{y = -\frac{3}{7}x + c}$

- Substitute in the coordinates (–3, –11) to find c:

  $$-11 = -\frac{3}{7}(-3) + c$$
  $$c = -11 - \frac{9}{7} = -\frac{86}{7}$$

- So the perpendicular line has equation:

  $$y = -\frac{3}{7}x - \frac{86}{7} \Rightarrow \boxed{3x + 7y + 86 = 0}$$

You can use the fact that the gradients of perpendicular lines **multiply** to **–1** to work out whether two lines are perpendicular.

Example 3

Show that the line $2x + 5y + 3 = 0$ is perpendicular to $y = \frac{5}{2}x + 5$.

- To work out if they are perpendicular, first find the gradient of both lines.
- Rearrange $2x + 5y + 3 = 0$ into the form $y = mx + c$ to find its gradient:

$$2x + 5y + 3 = 0$$
$$\Rightarrow 5y = -2x - 3$$
$$\Rightarrow y = -\frac{2}{5}x - \frac{3}{5}$$

- So the gradient of this line is $-\frac{2}{5}$.

- Comparing $y = \frac{5}{2}x + 5$ to $y = mx + c$, its gradient is $\frac{5}{2}$.

- The two lines are perpendicular if the gradients of the two lines **multiply** together to make **–1**.

$$-\frac{2}{5} \times \frac{5}{2} = -1$$

> The two lines are perpendicular.

Example 4

The points A (2, 5) and B (6, 0) lie on the line l_1. The line l_2 is perpendicular to l_1 and passes through point A.

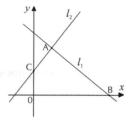

a) Find an equation for l_2 in the form $ax + by + c = 0$, where a, b and c are integers.

- To find the equation of l_2 we need to find its gradient. We know two points on the line l_1, so work out its gradient first.

$$(x_1, y_1) = (2, 5), (x_2, y_2) = (6, 0)$$

$$m = \frac{0 - 5}{6 - 2} = -\frac{5}{4}$$

- The gradient of a perpendicular line is: $-1 \div$ the other one. So the gradient of l_2 is:

$$m = -1 \div -\frac{5}{4}$$

$$\Rightarrow m = \frac{4}{5}$$

- So l_2 is: $y = \frac{4}{5}x + c$

- To find c, put the coordinates for point A (2, 5) into $y = \frac{4}{5}x + c$.

$$5 = \frac{4}{5} \times 2 + c$$

$$\Rightarrow c = \frac{17}{5}$$

- So the equation of the l_2 is:

$$y = \frac{4}{5}x + \frac{17}{5} \Rightarrow \boxed{4x - 5y + 17 = 0}$$

b) Find the coordinates of point C.

- At C, $x = 0$. So put $x = 0$ into the equation $y = \frac{4}{5}x + \frac{17}{5}$:

$$\Rightarrow y = \frac{4}{5} \times 0 + \frac{17}{5} = \frac{17}{5}$$

So the coordinates of point C are $(0, \frac{17}{5})$.

Tip: This is actually the value of c you just found.

Exercise 2.2

Q1 Find the equations of the dotted lines.
Give your answers in the form $y = mx + c$

a)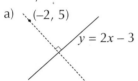
(–2, 5)
$y = 2x - 3$

b)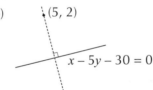
(5, 2)
$x - 5y - 30 = 0$

Q2 Find the equations of the lines which are perpendicular to each of the following lines and pass through the points given. Give your answers in the form $ax + by + c = 0$, where a, b, and c are integers.

a) $y = \frac{1}{4}x - 1$ (–1, 2)

b) $2x + 3y - 1 = 0$ (–3, –1)

c) $5x - 10y + 1 = 0$ (6, –5)

d) $y = \frac{3}{2}x + 2$ (2, 1)

Q3 Work out which of the following pairs of lines are perpendicular.

a) $y = \frac{4}{3}x - 2$ and $3x + 4y - 1 = 0$

b) $y = \frac{3}{2}x - 1$ and $3x + 2y - 3 = 0$

c) $4x - y + 3 = 0$ and $2x + 8y + 1 = 0$

Q4 Triangle ABC has vertices at A(0, 2), B(4, 3) and C(5, –1).
a) Find the equations of the lines AB, BC and AC in the form $y = mx + c$.
b) What type of triangle is ABC? Explain why.

Q5 Line A passes through the point (a, b) and is perpendicular to the line $3x - 2y = 6$. Find an equation of line A in terms of a and b.

3. Curve Sketching

Learning Objectives:

- Be able to sketch graphs of simple cubic functions and the reciprocal function $y = \frac{k}{x}$.
- Be able to interpret graphs of simple cubic functions.
- Be able to use the intersection points of graphs to solve equations.
- Know what the term asymptote means.

Being able to sketch the graph of a curve is an important skill at A-Level. It can help you get your head round tricky questions. Usually, you only need a rough sketch of a graph — so just knowing the basic shapes of these graphs will do.

Cubic functions and higher positive powers

Cubic functions have an x^3 term in them — as the highest power of x. They can be written $y = ax^3 + bx^2 + cx + d$ (for $a \neq 0$).

The graphs of cubic functions all have a characteristic 'wiggle'. This happens when the curve changes direction — from bending clockwise to bending anti-clockwise, or vice versa.

Here are the graphs for the two simplest cubic functions.

Tip: The graphs of $y = x^3$ and $y = -x^3$ briefly 'flatten out' at the point where the curve starts bending the other way.

Other cubics have an actual dip in the graph (see examples on next page).

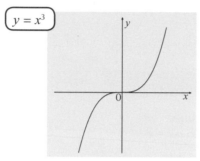

- A **positive** coefficient of x^3 gives a '**bottom-left** to **top-right**' shape.

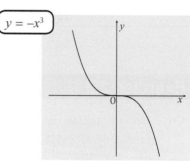

- A **negative** coefficient of x^3 gives a '**top-left** to **bottom-right**' shape.

In general, for any graph in the form $y = kx^n$, where $n > 0$:

Tip: As well as learning the shapes of the graphs, it's a good idea to try out lots of values in the function to check it does what you expect.

Trying very large positive and negative numbers helps to check what happens at the extremes.

- If n is POSITIVE and EVEN — you get a u-shape or an n-shape.
- And if k is NEGATIVE — the graph goes below the axis.

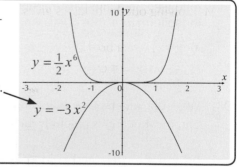

- If n is POSITIVE and ODD — you get a 'corner-to-corner' shape.
- And if k is NEGATIVE — you get a 'top-left to bottom-right' shape.

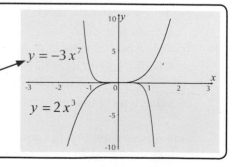

As well as knowing the shapes, you may need to sketch some simple cubics. The key is finding where the graphs **cross the axes**, particularly the x-axis.

Example

Sketch the graphs of the following cubic functions.

a) $f(x) = x(x-1)(2x+1)$

- If you multiplied out the brackets, you'd get $2x^3 - x^2 - x$. But it's just the $2x^3$ term we're interested in for deciding the rough shape.

- So as n is positive and odd and k is positive — the graph will have a **bottom-left** to **top-right** shape.

- Now we need to find where the graph crosses the x-axis, i.e. where the function is zero. The cubic is actually given in factorised form here, so we can simply read off the solutions.

$$x(x-1)(2x+1) = 0 \implies \boxed{x = 0, 1 \text{ or } -\frac{1}{2}}$$

- So the curve crosses the x-axis **three times** and will look like this:

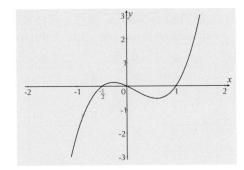

Tip: For all cubics, it's the x^3 term that gives the **overall cubic** shape, i.e. corner-to-corner with a 'wiggle'.

The other terms just affect how much it bends and where.

Tip: This graph has a much more pronounced wiggle than $y = x^3$ creating an actual dip in the graph. The dip makes the graph cross the x-axis 3 times, creating the 3 roots.

b) $g(x) = (x-3)^2(x+1)$

- Multiplying out the brackets gives $x^3 - 5x^2 + 3x + 9$.
- Here n is positive and odd, and k is positive — so the graph will have a bottom-left to top-right shape.
- Now find where it crosses both axes:
- $x = 0$ gives $y = (-3)^2 = 9$, so the y-intercept is $(0, 9)$.
- For the x-intercepts, find where $g(x) = 0$. Again, the function is helpfully factorised...

$$(x-3)^2(x+1) = 0 \implies \boxed{x = 3, \text{ or } -1}$$

- So the graph only crosses the axis **twice** and looks like this:

Tip: Again you don't actually need to multiply out the whole function — you only need to know what the x^3 term will be.

The cubic has a 'double root' at $x = 3$ — the result of this is that the graph **just touches** the x-axis there but doesn't go through.

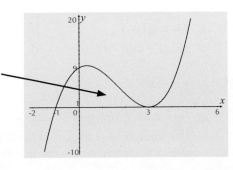

c) $h(x) = (2-x)^3$

- Expanding the brackets gives $h(x) = 8 - 12x + 6x^2 - x^3$.
- Here n is positive and odd and k is negative — so the graph will have a top-left to bottom-right shape.
- $x = 0$ gives a y-intercept of 8.
- The function is zero **only once**, at $x = 2$ — this is a **triple root**.
- The graph looks like this:

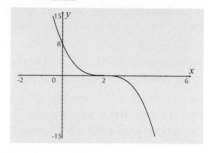

Tip: This graph is actually just the graph of $y = -x^3$ shifted 2 to the right. Graph transformations like this are covered a little later in the chapter.

Exercise 3.1

Q1 The diagram shows four graphs A, B, C and D.
State which graph would represent each of the following functions.

a) $y = -1.5x^4$ b) $y = 0.5x^3$ c) $y = 2x^6$ d) $y = -3x^3$

A
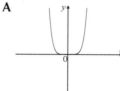

B
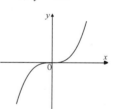

C
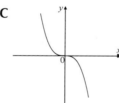

D

Hint: If you're not sure exactly what the graph will do, stick some values for x into the function, especially around the roots.

For Questions 2-4, sketch the graphs of the functions showing clearly where they meet the coordinate axes.

Q2   a) $y = x(x + 2)(x - 3)$ b) $y = (x + 1)(2x - 1)(x - 3)$
      c) $y = x(x + 1)(2 - x)$ d) $y = 3x(4 - x)(1 - 2x)$

Q3   a) $y = x^2(2x - 5)$ b) $y = x(5 - x)^2$
      c) $y = (1 - x)(2 - x)^2$ d) $y = -3x(2x - 7)^2$

Q4   a) $y = -5x^2(3x - 2)$ b) $y = (7 - x)(9 - 2x)(3 - x)$ c) $y = (4 + x)^3$

Q5   a) Factorise completely $x^3 - 7x^2 + 12x$.
      b) Use your answer to part a) to sketch the graph of $y = x^3 - 7x^2 + 12x$, showing clearly where the graph meets the coordinate axes.

Q6 Sketch the graphs of these functions, showing clearly where the graph meets the coordinate axes.

a) $y = x^3 - 16x$ b) $y = 2x^3 - 12x^2 + 18x$

Q7 a) Use graph paper to draw the graphs of $y = x(x^2 + 3)$ and $y = 5 - 3x$ on the same axes for $-0.5 \leq x \leq 1.5$.

b) Show that any solutions of $x^3 + 6x - 5 = 0$ are given by the x-coordinates of the points of intersection of $y = x(x^2 + 3)$ and $y = 5 - 3x$.

c) Use the graphs from part a) to estimate the solution to $x^3 + 6x - 5 = 0$. Note — there is only one real solution.

Q8 Sketch the graphs of the following cubics:

a) $y = x(x^2 - 3x + 12)$
b) $y = (2 - 3x)(4x^2 + 5x + 4)$
c) $y = x(2x^2 - 5x + 5)$

> **Q8 Hint:** Work out if the quadratic factor has real roots — if it doesn't, the graph will only cross the x-axis once.

The reciprocal function and other negative powers

Reciprocal functions are those of the form $y = \frac{k}{x}$, where k is a constant.

The graph of a reciprocal function always has **asymptotes**.

> An **asymptote** of a curve is a **line** which the curve gets infinitely close to, but **never** touches.

You need to be able to sketch the graphs of reciprocal functions. Here are some examples:

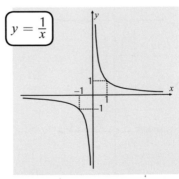

$y = \frac{1}{x}$

- The graphs never crosses the x- or y-axes, as you can't divide by zero.
- So the y-axis is a vertical asymptote ($x = 0$) and the x-axis is a horizontal asymptote ($y = 0$).

> **Tip:** Normally, to find where the graph crosses the x- and y-axes, you'd set $y = 0$ and $x = 0$, respectively. Doing that here means you'd end up with a zero as the denominator.

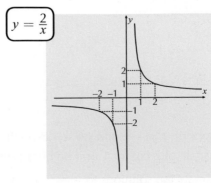

$y = \frac{2}{x}$

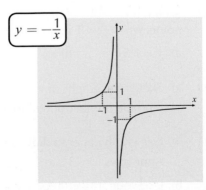

$y = -\frac{1}{x}$

> **Tip:** As always with curve sketching, it's a good idea to pop in some real values of x to see what happens.
>
> For these graphs, try very small positive and negative numbers, e.g. 0.001 and –0.001, and very large positive and negative numbers, e.g. 10000 and –10000.

In general, for any graph in the form $y = \dfrac{k}{x^n}$ $(n > 0)$:

- **If n is EVEN** —
  you get a graph with two bits next to each other.
- **AND If k is NEGATIVE** —
  the graph is below the x-axis.

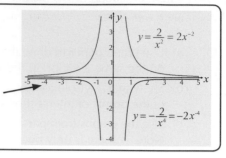

Tip: All these graphs have asymptotes of $x = 0$ and $y = 0$.

- **If n is ODD** —
  you get a graph with two bits opposite each other.
- **AND If k is NEGATIVE** —
  it's in the top-left and the bottom-right quadrants.

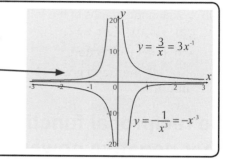

Exercise 3.2

Q1 The diagram shows four graphs A, B, C and D.
State which graph would represent each of the following functions:

a) $y = x^{-2}$ b) $y = -3x^{-3}$ c) $y = -\dfrac{3}{x^4}$ d) $y = 2x^{-5}$

Q1 Hint: You could work this out easily by popping in a positive and negative value of x into each function and seeing what you get.

A
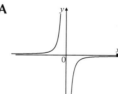

B
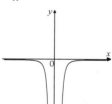

C
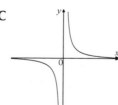

D
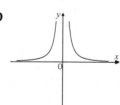

Q2 Sketch the graphs of the following reciprocal functions, showing the points where $x = 1$ and $x = -1$:

a) $y = 1.5x^{-5}$ b) $y = 7x^{-2}$ c) $y = -\dfrac{6}{x}$ d) $y = -1.2x^{-4}$

Q3 a) Sketch the graphs of $y = 3x^{-2}$ and $y = -x^3 - 2x^2$ on the same axes.
   b) Find the number of real roots of $3x^{-2} = -x^3 - 2x^2$.

Q4 a) Use graph paper to draw the graphs of $y = -\dfrac{2}{x}$ and $y = 4 - x^2$ on the same axes for $-3 \le x \le 3$. Use a scale of 2 cm for 1 unit on both axes.
   b) Use your answer to part a) to estimate the solutions to $-\dfrac{2}{x} = 4 - x^2$.

4. Transformations

If you have a function f(x), you can transform its graph in three different ways — by translating it, stretching it or reflecting it.

Translations

Translating the graph of a function means moving it either horizontally or vertically. The shape of the graph itself doesn't change, it just moves. There are two types of translation:

$y = f(x) + a$

Adding a number to the **whole function** translates the graph in the **y-direction**.

- If $a > 0$, the graph goes **upwards**.
- If $a < 0$, the graph goes **downwards**.

$y = f(x + a)$

Writing '$x + a$' instead of 'x' means the graph moves **sideways** ("translated in the **x-direction**").

- If $a > 0$, the graph goes to the **left**.
- If $a < 0$, the graph goes to the **right**.

Learning Objectives:

- Know the effect of the transformations $y = f(x) + a$, $y = f(x + a)$, $y = af(x)$, $y = f(ax)$.
- Apply any of these transformations to quadratic, cubic and reciprocal functions.
- Given the graph of a function f(x), sketch the graph resulting from any of the above transformations.

Tip: Function notation is used a lot in this section — don't get confused, it's quite simple.
E.g. if $f(x) = 3x^2$ then...
$f(5)$ means $3(5)^2 = 75$
$f(x - 2)$ means $3(x - 2)^2$
$af(x)$ means $a \times 3x^2$

Example 1

Shown below is the graph of $y = f(x)$, where $f(x) = x(x + 2)(x - 2)$.

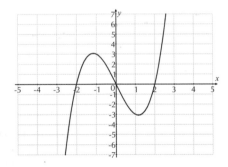

a) Sketch the graph $y = f(x) + 2$.

- Here 2 has been added to the **whole function**, i.e. $a = 2$.
- So the graph will be translated 2 units in the y-direction, i.e. shifted upwards by 2.

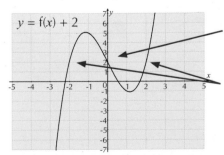

$y = f(x) + 2$

The point (0, 0) on f(x) has become the point (0, 2).

The other roots of f(x), (−2, 0) and (2, 0), have become (−2, 2) and (2, 2).

Tip: The equation of the transformed function is:
$y = x(x + 2)(x - 2) + 2$,
$= x^3 - 4x + 2$.

But you don't need to know this to sketch the transformed function.

Tip: When sketching a transformed graph, you need to show what happens to its **key points**, e.g. where it crosses the axes, max / min points, etc.

Exactly how much info to give will depend on the question.

b) Sketch the graph $y = f(x) - 4$.

- Here -4 has been added to the whole function, so $a = -4$
- The graph will move '-4' units in the y-direction, i.e. down 4.

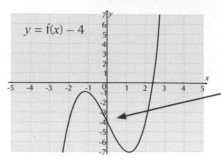

$y = f(x) - 4$

The point $(0, 0)$ on $f(x)$ has become the point $(0, -4)$.

c) Sketch the graph $y = f(x + 2)$.

- It's of the form $y = f(x + a)$ so it's translation in the x-direction.
- $a = 2$ — so as a is positive, it's a translation to the **left**, and it's by 2 units.

Tip: If you wanted to know the equation of the new curve, replace the x's in the original equation with $x + 2$:

Original equation is:
$f(x) = x(x - 2)(x + 2)$

So...
$f(x + 2) = (x + 2)(x)(x + 4)$
$\qquad = x(x + 2)(x + 4)$

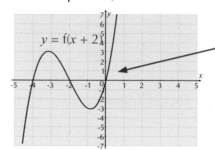

$y = f(x + 2)$

The x-coordinate of every point becomes 2 less.

E.g. the three roots of $f(x)$, $(-2, 0)$, $(0, 0)$ and $(0, 2)$ are now $(-4, 0)$, $(-2, 0)$ and $(0, 0)$.

d) Sketch the graph $y = f(x - 1)$.

- Again, it's of the form $y = f(x + a)$ so it's a translation in the x-direction.
- $a = -1$ which is negative, so it's a translation to the **right** by 1 unit.

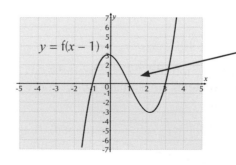

$y = f(x - 1)$

1 is added to the x-coordinate of every point.

E.g. $(-2, 0)$ becomes $(-1, 0)$.

Example 2

Given that $f(x) = \frac{1}{x}$:

a) Sketch the graph of $y = f(x) + 2$ and state the equations of the asymptotes.

- First, sketch the graph
  of $f(x) = \frac{1}{x}$:

$y = f(x) = \frac{1}{x}$

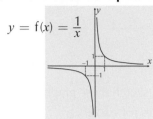

> **Tip:** See pages 81-82
> for more on sketching
> reciprocal functions.

- The graph $y = f(x) + 2$ is
  a translation of the graph
  upwards by 2.

$y = f(x) + 2$

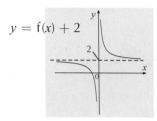

- For $f(x) = \frac{1}{x}$, the horizontal asymptote is $y = 0$ and the vertical
  asymptote is $x = 0$. So for $y = f(x) + 2$, the horizontal asymptote becomes
  $y = 2$ (as it has moved up 2) but the vertical asymptote is still $x = 0$.

> **Tip:** The vertical
> asymptote is the same
> for both as the graph has
> only moved upwards.

**b) Find the coordinates of the point where $y = f(x) + 2$
crosses a coordinate axis.**

- From the sketch we can see that the graph doesn't cross
  the y-axis, but it does cross the x-axis once, so set $y = 0$:

$$0 = \frac{1}{x} + 2 \quad \Rightarrow -2 = \frac{1}{x} \quad \Rightarrow x = -\frac{1}{2}$$

- So the graph crosses the x-axis, at $\left(-\frac{1}{2}, 0\right)$

Exercise 4.1

Q1 The diagram shows the graph of $y = f(x)$. The curve has a
maximum at (2, 4) and meets the x-axis at (0, 0) and (5, 0).

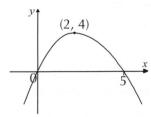

a) Sketch the graph of $y = f(x) + 2$, labelling the coordinates
of the maximum and where the curve meets the y-axis.

b) Sketch the graph of $y = f(x + 2)$ labelling the points
where the curve meets the x-axis and the maximum.

Q2 The diagram below shows the graph of $y = g(x)$ and two other graphs. Which graph represents $y = g(x - 1)$?

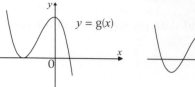 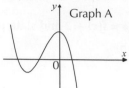 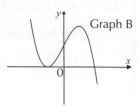

Q3 If $g(x) = -\dfrac{2}{x}$ sketch these graphs and write down the equations of the asymptotes for each.

    a) $y = g(x)$ b) $y = g(x + 3)$ c) $y = g(x) + 3$

Q4 Given that $y = x^2(x - 4)$, describe how would you translate the graph to give the graph of $y = (x - 2)^2(x - 6)$.

Q5 Explain how the graph of $y = x^3 + 3x + 7$ can be translated to give the graph of $y = x^3 + 3x + 2$.

Q6 The graph of $y = x^2 - 3x + 7$ is translated 1 unit left.
Write down the equation of the new graph.
Give your answer in as simple a form as possible.

Q7 The diagram shows the graph of $y = f(x)$.

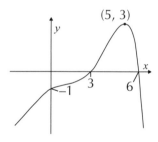

The graph has a maximum at (5, 3), crosses the x-axis at (3, 0) and (6, 0) and crosses the y-axis at (0, −1).

    a) Sketch the graph of $y = f(x) - 2$.

    b) Label the coordinates of the maximum and the point where the graph meets the y-axis.

Q8   a) Sketch the graph of $y = (x - 1)(2x - 3)(4 - x)$ and label the points where the graph meets the coordinate axes.

    b) The graph in part a) is translated 2 units in the positive x-direction. Give the equation of the translated graph in its simplest form.

    c) On separate axes sketch the graph of the equation from part b), labelling all the points where the graph meets the x-axis.

Stretches and reflections

The graph of a function can be stretched, squashed or reflected by **multiplying** the whole function or the x's in the function by a number. The result you get depends on what you multiply and whether the number is positive or negative.

> **$y = a\mathrm{f}(x)$**
>
> Multiplying the **whole function** by a, stretches the graph **vertically** by a scale factor of a.
>
> - If $a > 1$ or $a < -1$ (i.e. $|a| > 1$), the graph is **stretched**.
> - If $-1 < a < 1$ (i.e. $|a| < 1$), the graph is **squashed**.
> - If a is **negative**, the graph is **also reflected** about the x-axis.
>
> For every point on the graph, the x-coordinate stays the same and the y-coordinate is multiplied by a.

Tip: Remember that all these stretches or squashes are in the **vertical** direction. (i.e. parallel to the y-axis).

Example 1

The diagram shows the graph of a function f(x).

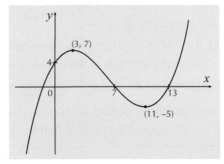

Tip: There are 5 key points marked on the graph that you'll need to keep track of: (0, 4), (3, 7), (7, 0), (11, –5) and (13, 0)

a) **Sketch the graph $y = \frac{1}{3}\mathrm{f}(x)$.**

- The graph above will be stretched vertically by a scale factor of $\frac{1}{3}$.
- As $\frac{1}{3}$ is less than 1, the 'stretch' will actually be a squash.
- The diagram gives a number of key points on the graph — you need to show where each of these points has moved to on the transformed graph:

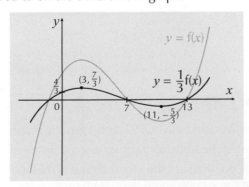

Tip: When finding the new points, remember the x-coordinates don't change, so just multiply the y-coordinates by a.

Tip: The graph still crosses the x-axis at the same points as the original graph — this is true for all $y = a\mathrm{f}(x)$ transformations.

b) Sketch the graph $y = -2f(x)$.

- Here the **whole function** has been multiplied by –2.
- So the graph will be stretched vertically by a factor of 2, but also reflected in the x-axis because of the minus sign.
- Again, you need to show what has happened to each key point.

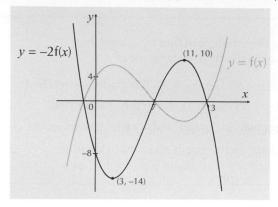

So that's vertical stretches covered. Next up are horizontal stretches:

$y = f(ax)$

Writing 'ax' instead of 'x' stretches the graph **horizontally** by a scale factor of $\frac{1}{a}$.

- If $a > 1$ or $a < -1$ (i.e. $|a| > 1$) the graph is **squashed**.
- If $-1 < a < 1$ (i.e. $|a| < 1$) the graph is **stretched**.
- **Negative** values of a **reflect** the basic shape in the y-axis.

For these transformations, the y-coordinate of each point stays the same and the x-coordinate is multiplied by $\frac{1}{a}$.

Tip: Notice that a being bigger or smaller than 1 has the **opposite effect** for horizontal stretches compared to vertical stretches.

Example 2

The diagram below shows the graph of $y = f(x)$ again.

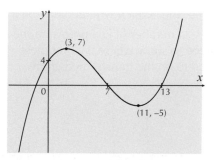

a) Sketch the graph $y = f(\frac{1}{2}x)$.

- $\frac{1}{2}$ is positive and between –1 and 1, so the graph will be stretched horizontally by a scale factor of 2.
- For each point given, the x-coordinate is multiplied by 2 but the y-coordinate doesn't change.

- The graph looks like this. (This time, the y-intercept doesn't change, but the two x-intercepts do.)

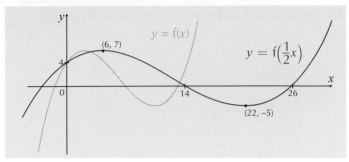

b) **Sketch the graph $y = f(-3x)$.**

- The transformation has the form $y = f(ax)$, so it's a horizontal stretch.
- $a = -3$, so the graph will be 'stretched' by a scale factor of $\frac{1}{3}$, i.e. squashed...
- ... and also **reflected** in the y-axis since a is negative.
- Find the new position of key points by multiplying their x–coordinate by $-\frac{1}{3}$ (and leaving the y-coordinate the same.)
- So the graph looks like this:

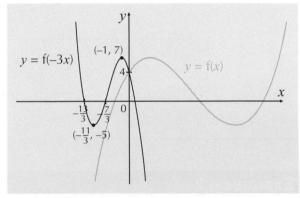

Tip: As always, label any key points, e.g. (3, 7) has become (–1, 7), and (11, –5) has become $(-\frac{11}{3}, -5)$.

Example 3

Below is the graph of a function $g(x)$.

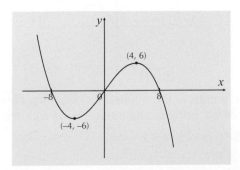

Tip: The key points to keep track of this time are: (–8, 0), (–4, –6), (0, 0), (4, 6) and (8, 0).

a) **Sketch the graph of $y = -2g(x)$**

- It's of the form $ag(x)$, so the graph will be stretched **vertically** by a scale factor of 2, but also reflected about the x-axis:

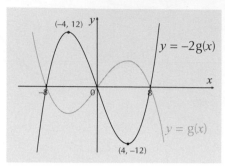

b) **Sketch the graph of $y = g(-2x)$**

- It's of the form $g(ax)$, so this time the graph will be stretched horizontally by a scale factor of $\frac{1}{2}$, and also reflected about the y-axis:

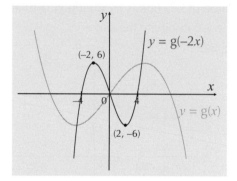

Exercise 4.2

Q1 The diagram shows the graph of $y = g(x)$. The graph has a minimum at $(-2, -3)$, a maximum at $(2, 3)$ and crosses the x-axis at $(0, 0)$, $(-4, 0)$ and $(4, 0)$.

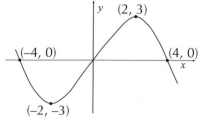

Sketch the graphs of these functions, labelling clearly the coordinates of any maxima, minima and intersections with the axes:

a) $y = 2g(x)$ b) $y = g(2x)$ c) $y = -2g(x)$ d) $y = g(-2x)$

Q2 The diagram shows the graph of f(x) and Graph A of a function that is a transformation of f(x).

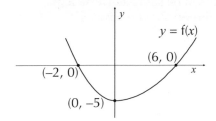 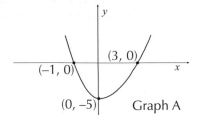

Which of these equations gives the transformed graph?
a) $y = 2f(x)$ b) $y = f(2x)$ c) $y = f(0.5x)$ d) $y = 0.5f(x)$

Q3 The diagram shows the graph of f(x) and Graph A of a function that is a transformation of f(x).

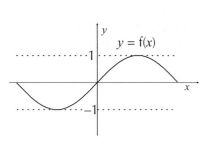 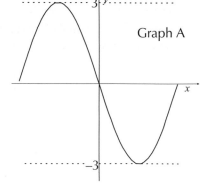

Q3 Hint: There are actually two transformations that could give Graph A, but only one of them is listed.

Which of these equations could give the transformed graph?
a) $y = 3f(x)$ b) $y = -3f(x)$ c) $y = f(-3x)$ d) $y = f(3x)$

Q4 Given that $f(x) = x^3 - x$, sketch the graphs of the following functions:
a) $y = f(x) + 2$ b) $y = f(x - 2)$ c) $y = f(-2x)$ d) $y = -2f(x)$

Q5 Describe clearly the transformation that is required to take the graph of $y = x^3 + 2x + 4$ to the graph of $y = 3x^3 + 6x + 12$.

Q6 Describe clearly the transformation that is required to take the graph of $y = x^2 + x + 4$ to the graph of $y = 4x^2 - 2x + 4$.

Q6 Hint: The terms which contain x's are different to the original, but the constant term is not.

Q7 a) Sketch the graph of $f(x) = x^2 - 6x - 7$ showing clearly the coordinates of any turning points and where the curve meets the coordinate axes.

b) Write down the equation of the graph obtained by stretching the graph of f(x) vertically with a scale factor of −2.

c) Sketch the graph with equation you found in part b) showing clearly the coordinates of any turning points and where the curve meets the coordinate axes.

Q7 a) Hint: Complete the square.

Review Exercise — Chapter 4

Q1 Find the equations of the straight lines that pass through the points
a) $(2, -1)$ and $(-4, -19)$,
b) $\left(0, -\frac{1}{3}\right)$ and $\left(5, \frac{2}{3}\right)$.

Write each of them in the forms:
  (i) $y - y_1 = m(x - x_1)$,
  (ii) $y = mx + c$,
  (iii) $ax + by + c = 0$, where a, b and c are integers.

Q2 a) The line l_1 has equation $y = \frac{3}{2}x - \frac{2}{3}$. Find the equation of the line parallel to l_1, passing through the point with coordinates $(4, 2)$.

b) The line l_2 passes through the point $(6, 1)$ and is perpendicular to $2x - y - 7 = 0$. What is the equation of l_2?

Q3 The coordinates of points R and S are $(1, 9)$ and $(10, 3)$ respectively. Find the equation of the line perpendicular to RS, passing through the point $(1, 9)$.

Q4 Draw rough sketches of the following curves:
a) $y = -2x^4$,
b) $y = \frac{7}{x^2}$,
c) $y = -5x^3$,
d) $y = -\frac{2}{x^5}$.

Q5 Sketch these cubic graphs:
a) $y = (x - 4)^3$,
b) $y = (3 - x)(x + 2)^2$,
c) $y = (1 - x)(x^2 - 6x + 8)$,
d) $y = (x - 1)(x - 2)(x - 3)$.

Q6 Use the graph of f(x) below to sketch these transformed graphs:

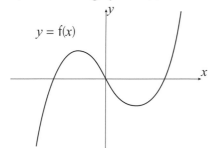

a) $y = $ f(ax), where (i) $a > 1$,
                              (ii) $0 < a < 1$,
b) $y = a$f(x), where (i) $a > 1$,
                              (ii) $0 < a < 1$,
c) (i) $y = $ f$(x+a)$, (ii) $y = $ f$(x-a)$, where $a > 0$,
d) (i) $y = $ f$(x)+a$, (ii) $y = $ f$(x)-a$, where $a > 0$.

Q7 The diagram shows the graph of $y = $ f(x).
The curve has a maximum at $(2, 4)$ and meets the x-axis at $(0, 0)$ and $(5, 0)$.

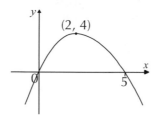

Sketch the graphs of these functions, labelling clearly the coordinates of any maxima or minima and where the curve meets the coordinate axes.
a) $y = $ f$(-x)$
b) $y = -$f(x)
c) $y = 2$f(x)
d) $y = $ f$(2x)$

1   The line PQ has equation $4x + 3y = 15$.

   a)   Find the gradient of PQ.

   (2 marks)

   b)   The point R lies on PQ and has coordinates $(3, 1)$. Find the equation of the
         line which passes through the point R and is perpendicular to PQ, giving your
         answer in the form $y = mx + c$.

   (3 marks)

2   The curve C has the equation
$$y = (2x + 1)(x - 2)^2.$$

   Sketch C, clearly showing the points where the curve meets the x- and y-axes.

   (4 marks)

3

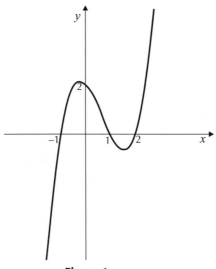

Figure 1

   Figure 1 shows a sketch of the function $y = f(x)$. The function crosses the x-axis
   at $(-1, 0)$, $(1, 0)$ and $(2, 0)$, and crosses the y-axis at $(0, 2)$.

   On separate diagrams, sketch the following:

   a) $y = f\left(\frac{1}{2}x\right)$.

   (3 marks)

   b) $y = f(x - 4)$.

   (2 marks)

   On each diagram, label any known points of intersection with the x- or y-axes.

4   a)   Sketch the curve $y = f(x)$, where $f(x) = x^2 - 4$, showing clearly the points
         of intersection with the x- and y-axes.

                                                                              (2 marks)

    b)   Describe fully the transformation that transforms the
         curve $y = f(x)$ to the curve $y = -2f(x)$.

                                                                              (2 marks)

    c)   The curve $y = f(x)$ is translated vertically two units upwards.
         State the equation of the curve after it has been transformed, in term of $f(x)$.
                                                                              (1 mark)

5   The line l passes through the point $S\,(7, -3)$ and has gradient -2.

    a)   Find an equation of l, giving your answer in the form $y = mx + c$.
                                                                              (3 marks)

    b)   The point T has coordinates $(5, 1)$. Show that T lies on l.
                                                                              (1 mark)

6

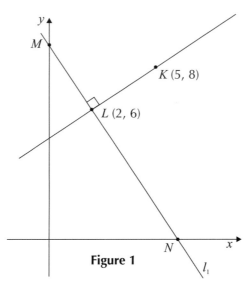

Figure 1

The points L and K have coordinates $(2, 6)$ and $(5, 8)$ respectively. The line l_1 passes
through the point L and is perpendicular to the line LK, as shown in **Figure 1**.

    a)   Find an equation for l_1 in the form $ax + by + c = 0$,
         where a, b, and c are integers.
                                                                              (4 marks)

    The line l_1 intersects the y-axis at the point M and the x-axis at the point N.

    b)   Find the coordinates of M.
                                                                              (2 marks)

    c)   Find the coordinates of N.
                                                                              (2 marks)

1. Sequences

A sequence is a list of numbers that follow a certain pattern — e.g. 2, 4, 6, 8..., –5, 2, –5, 2, –5, ... or 1, 4, 9, 16...   There are two main ways of describing sequences — from an nth term formula and from a recurrence relation.

Learning Objectives:

- Be able to use an nth term formula to generate terms in a sequence, or find the position of a term with a given value.
- Be able to write recurrence relations and use them to generate sequences.

n^{th} term

The idea behind the nth term is that you can use a formula to generate any term in a sequence from its position, n, in the sequence.

Example 1

A sequence has the nth term $4n + 1$.

a) **Find the 10th term in the sequence.**

Just substitute 10 for n in the nth term expression: $4(10) + 1 = 41$

The 10th term is **41**.

b) **A term in the sequence is 33. Find the position of this term.**

- The position of the term is n where $4n + 1 = 33$.
- So $n = (33 - 1) \div 4 = 8$

33 is the **8th** term of the sequence.

Tip: This sequence is an example of the 'common difference' type — the first few terms are 5, 9, 13, 17, ..., which have a common difference of 4. These are actually known as arithmetic sequences — there's more about them on p.100-101.

Example 2

A sequence has the nth term $n^2 - 2$.

a) **Find the first 3 terms in the sequence.**

Just substitute $n = 1, 2, 3$ in the nth term expression:
$(1)^2 - 2 = -1$
$(2)^2 - 2 = 2$
$(3)^2 - 2 = 7$

So the first 3 terms in the sequence are **–1, 2, 7**.

b) **Is 35 a term in the sequence?**

For questions like this, you need form and solve an equation in n and see if you get a whole number:

$$n^2 - 2 = 35 \implies n^2 = 37 \implies n = \sqrt{37}$$

$\sqrt{37}$ is not an integer, so 35 is **not** in the sequence.

Tip: If your value for n had been an integer, then that number would have been a term in the sequence. E.g. 34 is in the sequence, because solving $n^2 - 2 = 34$ gives $n = 6$, so 34 is the 6th term in the sequence.

Q1   A sequence has n^{th} term $3n - 5$. Find the 20th term.

Q2   Find the 4th term of the sequence with n^{th} term $n(n + 2)$.

Q3   Find the first 5 terms of the sequence with n^{th} term $(n - 1)(n + 1)$.

Q4   The kth term of a sequence is 29.
      The nth term of this sequence is $4n - 3$. Find the value of k.

Q5   A sequence has n^{th} term $= an^2 + b$, where a and b are constants.
      If the 2nd term is 15, and the 5th term is 99, find a and b.

Q6   A sequence starts 9, 20, 37... . Its nth term $= en^2 + fn + g$, where e, f
      and g are constants. Find the values of e, f and g.

Q7   The nth term of the sequence is given by $(n - 1)^2$. A term in the
      sequence is 49. Find the position of this term.

Q8   How many terms of the sequence with n^{th} term $15 - 2n$ are positive?

Q8 Hint: Start by using the nth term formula to find the first few terms of the sequence — you'll soon see what the question is getting at.

Recurrence relations

Before we get going with this section, there's some **notation** to learn:

a_k just means the kth **term** of the sequence
— so a_4 is the 4th term, and a_{k+1} is the term after a_k.

You've just seen how you can define a sequence by using a general formula for the nth term. Well, a **recurrence relation** is another way to describe a sequence. Don't be put off by the fancy name — recurrence relations are pretty easy really. The key thing to remember is:

Tip: The notation using subscripts is used to identify sequences all the time, so you need to get used to it. Any letter can be used, e.g.
$x_n = (n - 1)(n + 1)$.
It just avoids having to repeat "with n^{th} term...".

> **Recurrence relations tell you how to work out**
> **a term in a sequence from the previous term.**

So, using the new notation, what this is saying is that a recurrence relation describes how to work out a_{k+1} from a_k.

E.g. if each term in the sequence is **2 more** than the previous term:

$$a_{k+1} = a_k + 2$$

So, if $k = 5$, this says that $a_6 = a_5 + 2$, that is, the 6th term is equal to the 5th term + 2.

This recurrence relation will be true for loads of sequences, e.g. 1, 3, 5, 7..., and 4, 6, 8, 10... So to describe a **particular sequence** you also have to give one term. E.g. the sequence 1, 3, 5, 7... is described by:

Tip: $a_{k+1} = a_k + 2$, $a_2 = 3$ also describes the sequence 1, 3, 5, 7,...

$$a_{k+1} = a_k + 2, \quad a_1 = 1$$

a_1 stands for the 1st term.

Example 1

Find the recurrence relation of the sequence 5, 8, 11, 14, 17, …

- Each term in this sequence equals the one before it, plus 3.
- The recurrence relation is written like this:

$$a_{k+1} = a_k + 3$$

- **BUT**, as you saw on the previous page $a_{k+1} = a_k + 3$ on its own isn't enough to describe 5, 8, 11, 14, 17, … For example, the sequence 87, 90, 93, 96, 99, … also has each term being 3 more than the one before.
- The description needs to be more specific, so you've got to give **one term** in the sequence, as well as the recurrence relation.
- Putting all of this together gives 5, 8, 11, 14, 17, … as:

$$a_{k+1} = a_k + 3, \ a_1 = 5$$

Tip: You almost always give the first value, a_1.

Example 2

A sequence is given by the recurrence relation $a_{k+1} = a_k - 4$, $a_1 = 20$. Find the first five terms of this sequence.

- You're given the first term (a_1) — it's 20.
- Now you need to find the second term (a_2).
  If $a_1 = a_k$, then $a_2 = a_{k+1}$.

  $a_{k+1} = a_k - 4$
  $a_2 = 20 - 4$
  $a_2 = 16$ ⟵ ———— This is 4 less than the first term.

- Repeat this to find the third, fourth and fifth terms.

  $a_3 = a_2 - 4$
  $a_3 = 16 - 4$
  $a_3 = 12$

  $a_4 = a_3 - 4$
  $a_4 = 12 - 4$
  $a_4 = 8$

  $a_5 = a_4 - 4$
  $a_5 = 8 - 4$
  $a_5 = 4$

Tip: When you've got the hang of recurrence relations, you'll be able to see straight away that $a_{k+1} = a_k - 4$ just means the sequence decreases by 4 each time.

The first five terms of the sequence are **20, 16, 12, 8, 4**.

Example 3

A sequence is generated by the recurrence relation:
$$u_{n+1} = 3u_n + k, \quad u_1 = 2.$$

a) Find u_3 in terms of k.

You're given the first term, u_1, so use this to generate the second term, u_2, in terms of k, then use the second term to generate the third term, u_3.

$$u_{n+1} = 3u_n + k$$
$$u_2 = 3u_1 + k$$
$$u_2 = 3(2) + k \longleftarrow \text{Substitute in the value for } u_1.$$
$$u_2 = 6 + k$$

$$u_3 = 3u_2 + k \qquad \text{Substitute in the expression}$$
$$u_3 = 3(6 + k) + k \longleftarrow \text{for } u_2 \text{ that you found above.}$$
$$\boxed{u_3 = 18 + 4k}$$

Tip: This is the downside of recurrence relations — you have to go through each term to work out the one you're after. It'd take ages to find, say, the 100th term.

b) Given that $u_4 = 28$, find k.

- Form an expression for u_4 using the recurrence relation:
$$u_4 = 3u_3 + k$$
$$u_4 = 3(18 + 4k) + k \longleftarrow \text{Substitute in the expression for } u_3 \text{ from part a).}$$
$$u_4 = 54 + 13k$$

- The question tells you that $u_4 = 28$, so form an equation and solve to find k.
$$28 = 54 + 13k$$
$$13k = -26$$
$$\boxed{k = -2}$$

The next example's a bit harder, as there's an n^2 in there. But the method works in exactly the same way — you just end up with a slightly more complicated formula for the recurrence relation.

Example 4

A sequence has the general term $x_n = n^2$.
Write down a recurrence relation which generates the sequence.

- Start by finding the first few terms of the sequence (i.e. $n = 1, 2, 3, 4...$)
$$x_1 = 1^2 = \mathbf{1} \qquad x_2 = 2^2 = \mathbf{4} \qquad x_3 = 3^2 = \mathbf{9} \qquad x_4 = 4^2 = \mathbf{16}$$
So the first four terms are: 1, 4, 9, 16

- You're now at the same point as you were at the start of Example 1. You use the same method to form the recurrence relation, but it's a little trickier as n in the general term is squared.

- Look at the difference between each term:

$$\begin{array}{cccc} k = & 1 & 2 & 3 & 4 \\ x_k = & 1 & 4 & 9 & 16 \end{array}$$

$+3 \qquad +5 \qquad +7$
$(2 \times 1) + 1 \quad (2 \times 2) + 1 \quad (2 \times 3) + 1$

- To get from term x_k to the next term, x_{k+1}, you take the **value of term** x_k, and add $2k + 1$ to it. E.g. 3rd term $= 2^{nd}$ term $+ 2(2) + 1$. So the recurrence relation is:

$$x_{k+1} = x_k + 2k + 1$$

- To generate the sequence you need to give **one term** in the sequence, and there's no reason not to stick to convention and use the first term:

$$x_{k+1} = x_k + 2k + 1, \ x_1 = 1 \longleftarrow$$ Try substituting in different k values to check your recurrence relation does generate the sequence.

Tip: It's sometimes helpful to draw some little diagrams where n^2 is involved. E.g. these diagrams let you see that it's $2k + 1$ added each time.

1st ● 2nd ● ●
● ●

3rd ● ● ●
● ● ●
● ● ●

4th ● ● ● ●
● ● ● ●
● ● ● ●
● ● ● ●

Exercise 1.2

Q1 A sequence is defined for $n \geq 1$ by $u_{n+1} = 3u_n$ and $u_1 = 10$. Find the first 5 terms of the sequence.

Q2 Find the first 4 terms of the sequence in which $u_1 = 2$ and $u_{n+1} = u_n^2$ for $n \geq 1$.

Q3 Write down a recurrence relation which produces the sequence $3, 6, 12, 24, 48, \ldots$

Q4 a) Write down a recurrence relation which produces the sequence $12, 16, 20, 24, 28, \ldots$
b) The sequence is finite and ends at 100. Find the number of terms.

Q4b Hint: Most of the sequences you'll see are infinite — they go on forever. But you can have finite sequences which stop after a certain number of terms.

Q5 Find a recurrence relation which generates the sequence $7, 4, 7, 4, 7, \ldots$

Q6 In a sequence $u_1 = 4$ and $u_{n+1} = 3u_n - 1$ for $n \geq 1$. Find the value of k if $u_k = 95$.

Q5 Hint: You need to find an operation that goes back and forth between 4 and 7. There are two possible answers — think about one of these number facts: $7 + 4 = 11$ or $7 \times 4 = 28$.

Q7 In a sequence $x_1 = 9$ and $x_{n+1} = (x_n + 1) \div 2$ for $n \geq 1$. Find the value of r if $x_r = \frac{5}{4}$.

Q8 Find the first 5 terms of the sequence in which $u_1 = 7$ and $u_{n+1} = u_n + n$ for $n \geq 1$.

Q9 In a sequence $u_1 = 6$, $u_2 = 7$ and $u_3 = 8.5$. If the recurrence relation is of the form $u_{n+1} = au_n + b$, find the values of the constants a and b.

Q9 Hint: Form all the equations you can from the information, and then solve them.

Q10 A sequence is generated by $u_1 = 8$ and $u_{n+1} = \frac{1}{2}u_n$ for $n \geq 1$. Find the first 5 terms and a formula for u_n in terms of n.

Arithmetic sequences

Tip: Arithmetic sequences are often referred to as arithmetic progressions — it's exactly the same thing.

Right, you've got basic sequences tucked under your belt — now it's time to look at a particular type of sequence in greater detail.

When the terms of a sequence progress by **adding** a **fixed amount** each time, this is called an **arithmetic** sequence.

Here are some examples of arithmetic sequences:

5, 7, 9, 11... (add 2 each time); 20, 17, 14, 11... (add –3 each time).

The formula for the nth term of an arithmetic sequence is:

$$a + (n - 1)d$$

where:

a is the **first term** of the sequence.
d is the amount you add each time — the **common difference**.
n is the **position** of any term in the sequence.

This box shows you how the formula is derived:

Tip: Each term is made up of the previous one, plus d. It's a sort of recurrence relation.

Term	n		
1st	1	a	
2nd	2	$(a) + d$	
3rd	3	$(a + d) + d$	$= a + 2d$
4th	4	$(a + 2d) + d$	$= a + 3d$
.	.	.	.
.	.	.	.
n^{th}	n		$a + (n - 1)d$

Which is the formula to find the nth term.

Example 1

Find the 20th term of the arithmetic sequence 2, 5, 8, 11, ... and find the formula for the nth term.

- The nth term of a sequence is $a + (n - 1)d$.
- For this sequence, $a = 2$ and $d = 3$.
- Plug the numbers into the nth term formula:

$$20^{th} \text{ term} = 2 + (19 \times 3)$$
$$= 59$$

So the 20th term = **59**

- The general term is the nth term, i.e. $a + (n - 1)d$. Just substitute in the a and d values and simplify:

$$n^{th} \text{ term} = 2 + (n - 1)3$$
$$= 3n - 1$$

The nth term = **$3n - 1$**

Tip: You should always check your nth term formula is correct by sticking in some values for n and seeing if it produces the terms of the sequence.

- Finally, check the formula works with a couple of values of n:
$n = 1$ gives $3(1) - 1 = 2$ ✓
$n = 2$ gives $3(2) - 1 = 5$ ✓

Example 2

Find the nth term of the sequence –213, –198, –183, –168, ...

- The **first term**, a, is –213.
- Each term is 15 more than the one before it. So d is 15.
- Now just put these values into the formula:

$$\begin{aligned} n^{th} \text{ term} &= a + (n-1)d \\ &= -213 + 15(n-1) \\ &= \boxed{15n - 228} \end{aligned}$$

- Check it works:
  $n = 1$ gives $15(1) - 228 = -213$ ✓
  $n = 2$ gives $15(2) - 228 = -198$ ✓

You only actually need to know **two terms** of an arithmetic sequence (and their positions) — then you can work out any other term.

Example 3

The 2nd term of an arithmetic sequence is 21, and the 9th term is –7.
Find the 23rd term of this sequence.

- Set up an equation for each of the known terms:

$$2^{nd} \text{ term} = 21, \quad \text{so} \quad \begin{aligned} a + (2-1)d &= 21 \\ a + d &= 21 \end{aligned}$$

$$9^{th} \text{ term} = -7, \quad \text{so} \quad \begin{aligned} a + (9-1)d &= -7 \\ a + 8d &= -7 \end{aligned}$$

- You've now got two **simultaneous equations**
  — so solve them to find a and d:

$$a + d = 21 \qquad —①$$
$$a + 8d = -7 \qquad —②$$
$$①-②: \ -7d = 28 \ \Rightarrow \ \boxed{d = -4}$$
$$①: \ a + d = 21 \ \Rightarrow \ a - 4 = 21 \ \Rightarrow \ \boxed{a = 25}$$

Tip: The common difference and the first term have also been found along the way here (questions sometimes ask you to find these).

- Write the nth term formula...

$$\begin{aligned} n^{th} \text{ term} &= a + (n-1)d \\ &= 25 + (n-1) \times -4 \\ &= -4n + 29 \end{aligned}$$

- ... and use it to find
  the 23rd term ($n = 23$): $\quad 23^{rd} \text{ term} = -4 \times 23 + 29$

$$\boxed{23^{rd} \text{ term} = -63}$$

Q1 An arithmetic progression has first term 7 and common difference 5. Find its 10th term.

Q2 Find the nth term for each of the following sequences:
   a) 6, 9, 12, 15, ...
   b) 4, 9, 14, 19, ...
   c) 12, 8, 4, 0, ...
   d) 1.5, 3.5, 5.5, 7.5 ...

Q3-4 Hint: Sequence questions are often set in real-life contexts. But the maths behind them is just the same.

Q3 Morag starts a new job. In the first week she is paid £60, but this rises by £3 per week, so she earns £63 in the second week and £66 in the third week. How much does she earn in her 12th week?

Q4 Mario opens a sandwich shop. On the first day he sells 40 sandwiches. As people hear about the shop, sales increase and on the second day he sells 45 sandwiches. Daily sales rise in an arithmetic sequence. On which day will he sell 80 sandwiches?

Q5 In an arithmetic sequence, the fourth term is 19 and the tenth term is 43. Find the first term and common difference.

Q6 In an arithmetic progression, $u_7 = 8$ and $u_{11} = 10$. Find u_3.

Q7 In an arithmetic sequence, $u_3 = 15$ and $u_7 = 27$. Find the value of k if $u_k = 66$.

Q8 A retro cassette-walkman product is launched into the market. In the first month after launch, the product takes £300 000 of revenue. It takes £270 000 in the second month and £240 000 in the third. If this pattern continues, when would you expect monthly sales to fall below £50 000?

2. Series

Series and sequences are very similar and quite easy to confuse. Remember that a sequence is a just list of terms that follow a pattern. You'll often want to add these terms together — when you do this, it becomes a series.

Arithmetic series

Here is an arithmetic sequence. It's an infinite sequence — it goes on forever.

$$5, 8, 11, 14, 17, 20, ...$$

Now suppose you wanted to find the sum of the first 5 terms of this sequence. You'd write this by replacing the commas with '+' signs like this:

$$5 + 8 + 11 + 14 + 17$$

This is now an **arithmetic series**. It's a finite series with 5 terms. And if you actually added up the numbers you'd find that the **sum** for this series is 55.

So sequences become series when you add up their terms to find sums.

Sum of the first *n* terms

It would very quickly stop being fun if you had to find the sum of a 100 term series manually. Instead, you can use one of these **two formulas**.

S_n represents the **sum of the first *n* terms**

$$S_n = \frac{n}{2}[2a + (n-1)d]$$

For this formula, you just need to plug in the usual values of **a**, **d** and **n**

and $$S_n = n \times \frac{(a+l)}{2}$$

Here, *l* represents the **last term**. This formula is a bit easier to use if you know the value of the last term.

Learning Objectives:

- Be able to use the nth term formula to solve arithmetic series problems.
- Be able to find the sum of the first *n* terms of an arithmetic series.
- Use sigma (Σ) notation to refer to the sum of a series.
- Be able to find the sum of the first *n* natural numbers.

Tip: You can work out *a*, *d* and the *n*th term for a series, just as you would for a sequence. So in the 5-term series above, $a = 5$, $d = 3$ and *n*th term = $3n + 2$ (for $1 \leq n \leq 5$). Also, because the series is finite, you can state its last term, which is 17.

There's a nice little proof for these formulas which you need to know:

For any series, you can express S_n as:
$$S_n = a + (a + d) + (a + 2d) + ... + (a + (n-3)d) + (a + (n-2)d) + (a + (n-1)d)$$

Now, if you reverse the order of the terms you can write it as:
$$S_n = (a + (n-1)d) + (a + (n-2)d) + (a + (n-3)d) + ... + (a + 2d) + (a + d) + a$$

Adding the two expressions for S_n gives:
$$2S_n = (2a + (n-1)d) + (2a + (n-1)d) + (2a + (n-1)d) + ... + (2a + (n-1)d$$

So we've now got the term "$2a + (n-1)d$" repeated *n* times, which is:

$$2S_n = n \times (2a + (n-1)d) \implies S_n = \frac{n}{2}[2a + (n-1)d]$$

So we've derived the first formula. Now to get the second, just replace "$a + (n-1)d$" with *l*:

$$S_n = \frac{n}{2}[a + a + (n-1)d], \text{ so } S_n = \frac{n}{2}[a + l]$$

Now it's time to try out the sum formulas in some worked examples.

Example 1

Find the sum of the series with first term 3, last term 87 and common difference 4.

- You're told the last term, so use the S_n formula with l in: $S_n = n \times \dfrac{(a + l)}{2}$
- You know a (3) and l (87), but you don't know n yet.
- Find n by putting what you do know into the 'nth term' formula:

$$a + (n - 1)d = 87$$
$$3 + (n - 1)4 = 87$$
$$4n - 1 = 87$$
$$n = 22$$

- You're now all set to plug the values for a, l and n into the S_n formula:

$n = 22$ means that there are 22 terms in the series.

$$S_n = n \times \frac{(a + l)}{2}$$
$$S_{22} = 22 \times \frac{(3 + 87)}{2}$$
$$= 22 \times 45$$
$$= 990$$

The sum of the series is **990**.

Example 2

This question is about the sequence −5, −2, 1, 4, 7…

a) Is 67 a term in the sequence? If it is, give its position.

First, find the formula for the nth term of the sequence:

$$n^{th} \text{ term} = a + (n - 1)d$$
$$= -5 + (n - 1)3 \qquad a = -5 \text{ and } d = 3$$
$$= 3n - 8$$

Put 67 into the formula and see if this gives a whole number for n:

$$67 = 3n - 8$$
$$3n = 75 \Rightarrow n = 25$$

67 **is** a term in the sequence. It's the **25th** term.

b) Find the sum of the first 20 terms.

We know $a = -5$, $d = 3$ and $n = 20$, so plug these values into the formula $S_n = \frac{n}{2}[2a + (n - 1)d]$:

$$S_{20} = \frac{20}{2}[2(-5) + (20 - 1)3]$$
$$S_{20} = 10[-10 + 19 \times 3]$$
$$S_{20} = 470$$

The sum of the first 20 terms is **470**.

Tip: This question could just have easily been "about the series −5 + −2 + −1 + 4 + 7 + …" — the working would have been exactly the same.

Don't worry too much about the distinction between sequences and series in this type of question.

Example 3

Find the possible numbers of terms in the arithmetic series starting $21 + 18 + 15...$ if the sum of the series is 75.

- You're told the first term, a, is 21 and the sum of the series, S_n, is 75. You can see that the common difference, d, is -3. What you need to work out is n, the number of terms in the series.

- With a bit of rearranging, you can use the S_n formula for this:

$$S_n = \frac{n}{2}[2a + (n - 1)d]$$

$$S_n = \frac{n}{2}[2(21) + (n - 1) \times -3]$$

$$75 = \frac{n}{2}[42 - 3n + 3]$$

$$75 = \frac{45n}{2} - \frac{3n^2}{2}$$

$$-3n^2 + 45n - 150 = 0 \quad \longleftarrow \quad \text{Divide through by } -3 \text{ to simplify the quadratic}$$

$$n^2 - 15n + 50 = 0$$

$$(n - 5)(n - 10) = 0$$

$$n = 5 \text{ or } n = 10$$

> There are **5** or **10** terms in the series.

Tip: There are two answers to this one. It's because the series goes into negative numbers, so the sum of 75 is reached twice. Look at the first 10 terms of the series written out in full and you'll see what I mean: $21 + 18 + 15 + 12 + 9 + 6 + 3 + 0 + (-3) + (-6)$.

Example 4

Genetically modified super-chickens lay eggs for 7 days. The number of eggs they lay each day will always form an arithmetic sequence.

A super-chicken lays 19 times as many eggs on the seventh day as it did on the first day, and lays 350 eggs in total over the week.

How many extra eggs does it lay each day compared to the previous?

- You've been asked to find the common difference, d, of the series. You know that S_n is 350, and that there are 7 numbers in the series (so $n = 7$). Call the first term a, and the last term $19a$.

- Plug these values into the formula: $S_n = n \times \dfrac{(a + l)}{2}$

$$350 = 7 \times \frac{(a + 19a)}{2}$$

$$100 = 20a$$

$$a = 5$$

- The last term, l, is $19a$, so $l = 95$.
- You're now just one step from finding the common difference, d.

$$l = a + (n - 1)d$$

$$95 = 5 + (7 - 1)d$$

$$d = 15$$

> **15** more eggs are laid each day than the day before.

Tip: Examiners like to put numbers in contexts. Whether the context is super-chickens, money or something else, start by seeing what you know out of a, d, n, l and S_n.

Sigma notation

So far, the letter S has been used for the sum. The Greeks did a lot of work on this — their capital letter for S is Σ or **sigma**. This is used today, together with the general term, to mean the sum of the series.

For example, the following means the sum of the series with n^{th} term $2n + 3$.

...and ending with $n = 15$

$$\sum_{n=1}^{15}(2n + 3)$$

Starting with $n = 1$...

Example 5

Find $\displaystyle\sum_{n=1}^{15}(2n + 3)$.

- The first term ($n = 1$) is 5, the second term ($n = 2$) is 7, the third is 9, ... and the last term ($n = 15$) is 33. So in other words, you need to find $5 + 7 + 9 + ... + 33$. This gives $a = 5$, $d = 2$, $n = 15$ and $l = 33$.
- You know all of a, d, n and l, so you can use either formula:

$$S_n = n\frac{(a + l)}{2}$$
$$S_{15} = 15\frac{(5 + 33)}{2}$$
$$S_{15} = 15 \times 19$$
$$S_{15} = 285$$

It makes no difference which formula you use.

$$S_n = \frac{n}{2}[2a + (n - 1)d]$$
$$S_{15} = \frac{15}{2}[2 \times 5 + 14 \times 2]$$
$$S_{15} = \frac{15}{2}[10 + 28]$$
$$S_{15} = 285$$

Exercise 2.1

Q1 An arithmetic series has first term 8 and common difference 3. Find the 10th term and the sum of the first 10 terms.

Q2 In an arithmetic series $u_2 = 16$ and $u_5 = 10$. Find a, d and S_8.

Q3 In an arithmetic series $a = 12$ and $d = 6$. Find u_{100} and S_{100}.

Q4 Find $\displaystyle\sum_{n=1}^{12}(5n - 2)$.

Q5 Find $\displaystyle\sum_{n=1}^{9}(20 - 2n)$.

Q6 "Cornflake Collector" magazine sells 6 000 copies in its first month of publication, 8 000 in its second month and 10 000 in its third month. If this pattern continues, how many copies will it sell in the first year of publication?

Q7 In an arithmetic series $a = 3$ and $d = 2$. Find n if $S_n = 960$.

Q8 Given that $\displaystyle\sum_{n=1}^{k}(5n + 2) = 553$ show that the value of k is 14.

Q9 An arithmetic sequence begins $x + 11$, $4x + 4$, $9x + 5$, ... Find the sum of the first 11 terms.

Q9 Hint: You're eventually going to need to find a and d (or l) so you can use them in the sum formula, but start off by writing down what you know, and don't be put off by the x's.

Sum of the first n natural numbers

You probably know that the **natural numbers** are the positive whole numbers, i.e. 1, 2, 3, 4...

They form a very simple arithmetic progression with $a = 1$ and $d = 1$. So you could find the sum to any number of terms using one of the sum formulas from the previous pages. But there's actually a separate formula that's normally used for doing this.

The sum of the first n natural numbers is:

$$S_n = \frac{1}{2}n(n + 1)$$

This formula can be easily derived from the previous sum formulas just by plugging in values, like this:

> The sum of the first n natural numbers looks like this:
> $$S_n = 1 + 2 + 3 + \ldots + (n - 2) + (n - 1) + n$$
> So $a = 1$, $l = n$ and also $n = n$.
> $$S_n = n \times \frac{(a + l)}{2} \longrightarrow S_n = \frac{1}{2}n(n + 1)$$

You can also derive the formula from first principles — the proof is almost identical to the one for a general arithmetic series on p.103.

- $S_n = 1 + 2 + 3 + \ldots + (n - 2) + (n - 1) + n$ ①

- Rewrite ① with the terms reversed:
  $S_n = n + (n - 1) + (n - 2) + \ldots + 3 + 2 + 1$ ②

- ① + ② gives:
  $$2S_n = (n + 1) + (n + 1) + (n + 1) + \ldots + (n + 1) + (n + 1) + (n + 1)$$
  $$\Rightarrow 2S_n = n(n + 1)$$
  $$\Rightarrow S_n = \frac{1}{2}n(n + 1)$$

Tip: You could be asked to prove any of these sum formulas, so make sure you know these steps.

Example 1

Find the sum of the first 100 natural numbers.

$$S_n = \frac{1}{2}n(n + 1)$$
$$S_{100} = \frac{1}{2} \times 100 \times 101$$
$$S_{100} = \mathbf{5050}$$

Sum of the first 100 natural numbers = **5050**

Tip: Easy peasy.

Example 2

The sum of the first k natural numbers is 861. Find the value of k.

- Form an equation in k:

$$\frac{1}{2}k(k+1) = 861$$

- Expand the brackets and rearrange:

$$k^2 + k = 1722$$
$$k^2 + k - 1722 = 0$$

- So we got a quadratic in k to solve.
  We're looking for a whole number for k, so it should factorise.

$$k^2 + k - 1722 = 0$$
$$(k\quad)(k\quad) = 0$$

- It looks tricky to factorise, but notice that '$b = 1$', so we're just looking for two numbers that are 1 apart and multiply to 1722.

$$(k + 42)(k - 41) = 0$$
$$k = -42 \ \text{ or } \ k = 41$$

- We can ignore the negative solution here, so the answer is $\boxed{k = 41}$.

Tip: In this question we have k numbers added together, so an answer of $k = -42$ wouldn't make any sense.

Exercise 2.2

Q1 Find the sum of the first: **a)** 10, **b)** 2000 natural numbers.

Q2 Find $\sum\limits_{n=1}^{32} n$.

Q3 Hint: This Q uses a handy little tricky for finding series sums that don't start from $n = 1$.

Q3 Find $\sum\limits_{n=1}^{10} n$ and $\sum\limits_{n=1}^{20} n$. Hence find $\sum\limits_{n=11}^{20} n$.

Q4 Frazer draws one dot in the first square of his calendar for July, two dots in the second square, and so on up to 31 dots in the last day of the month. How many dots does he draw in total?

Q5 The sum of the first n natural numbers is 66. Find n.

Q6 Find k if $\sum\limits_{n=1}^{k} n = 120$.

Q7 Find the sum of the series $16 + 17 + 18 + \dots + 35$.

Q8 How many natural numbers are needed for the sum to exceed 1 000 000?

Q8-9 Hint: These will get quite tricky without a calculator, so it's OK to use one here — but in the exam, the numbers will be nicer.

Q9 Laura puts 1p in her jar on the first day, 2p in on the second day, 3p in on the third day, etc. How many days will it take her to collect over £10?

Review Exercise — Chapter 5

Q1 Find the nth term for each of the following sequences:
    a) 2, 6, 10, 14, ...
    b) 0.2, 0.7, 1.2, 1.7, ...
    c) 21, 18, 15, 12, ...
    d) 76, 70, 64, 58, ...

Q2 Find the 10th term of the sequence with n^{th} term $(n-1) \div (n+2)$.

Q3 Find the 8th term of the sequence $x_n = n^2 - 3$.

Q4 The rth term of the sequence $a_n = n^3$ is 64. Find the value of r.

Q5 In the sequence $u_n = n^2 + 3n + 4$, $u_k = 44$. Find the value of k.

Q6 Find the first 5 terms of the sequence $u_n = (-1)^n n$.

Q7 A sequence has the form $u_n = an^2 + bn$, where a and b are constants.
If the 3rd term is 18, and the 7th term is 70, find the values of a and b.

Q8 Describe the sequence 32, 37, 42, 47, ... using a recurrence relation.

Q9 Find the first 5 terms of the sequence in which:
    a) $x_1 = 7$ and $x_{n+1} = x_n + 3$ for $n \geq 1$.
    b) $u_1 = 2$ and $u_{n+1} = 6 \div u_n$ for $n \geq 1$.

Q10 Find a recurrence relation which generates the sequence:
    a) 65 536, 256, 16, 4, 2, . . .
    b) 40, 38, 34, 28, 20, . . .
    c) 1, 1, 2, 3, 5, 8, . . . (the Fibonacci sequence)

Q11 In a sequence $u_1 = 5$, $u_2 = 7$ and $u_{n+2} = u_{n+1} - u_n$ for $n \geq 1$.
Find the first 10 terms and describe the behaviour of the sequence.

Q12 In a sequence $u_1 = 2$, $u_2 = 8$ and $u_3 = 26$. If the recurrence relation is of
the form $u_{n+1} = au_n + b$, find the values of the constants a and b.

Q13 A sequence is generated by a recurrence relation of the form $u_{n+1} = ku_n + 3$,
where k is a constant. If $u_1 = 4$ and $u_2 = 11$, find the values of k, u_3 and u_4.

Q14 A sequence is generated by $u_1 = 8$ and $u_{n+1} = 18 - u_n$ for $n \geq 1$.
Find the first 5 terms and a formula for u_n in terms of n.

Q15 Find the common difference in a sequence that starts with –2, ends with 19 and has 29 terms.

Q16 In the first week of release, "Extreme Excitement 7" takes £3 million at the box office.
In the second week it only takes £2.8 million, and in the third week it takes £2.6 million.
If this pattern continues, how much will it make in the 10th week of release?

Q17 In an arithmetic series, $u_7 = 8$ and $u_{11} = 10$. Find u_3.

Q18 A new shop takes £300 on its first day of business, £315 on its second day and £330
on its third day. If this pattern continues, on which day will the shop first take over £500?

Q19 In an arithmetic series, $u_3 = 15$ and $u_7 = 27$. Find the value of k if $u_k = 66$.

Q20 A series has seventh term 36 and tenth term 30.
Find the sum of the first five terms and the nth term.

Q21 Jordan is following a 12 week training plan to prepare for a half marathon.
He does a 30 minute run in the first week and a 40 minute run in the second.
If the run lengths increase by 10 minutes each week, how much will he have to do in the
last week of training? How many hours will he have run in total at the end of the training?

Q22 Find $\sum_{n=1}^{20}(3n - 1)$.

Q23 a) Find the sum of the first 24 natural numbers.

b) Find $\sum_{n=13}^{24} n$.

Q24 Hussain puts one stone on the wall on his way to school on the first day of term,
two stones on the wall on the second day of term and three on the third day of term.
The term has 13 weeks of 5 days each. If he continues like this, how many stones
will he have put on the wall in total by the holiday?

Q25 Find k if $\sum_{n=1}^{k} n = 630$.

1   A sequence is defined by the recurrence relation: $h_{n+1} = 2h_n + 2$ when $n \geq 1$.

    a)   Given that $h_1 = 5$, find the values of h_2, h_3, and h_4.

            (3 marks)

    b)   Calculate the value of $\displaystyle\sum_{r=3}^{6} h_r$.

            (3 marks)

2   Ned has 15 cuboid pots that need filling with soil. Each pot is taller than the one before it. The different capacities of his 15 pots form an arithmetic sequence with first term (representing the smallest pot) a ml and the common difference d ml.
The 7th pot is 580 ml and he will need a total of exactly 9525 ml of soil to fill all of them.

    Find the value of a and the value of d.

            (7 marks)

3   The first term of an arithmetic sequence is 22 and the common difference is -1.1.

    a)   Find the value of the 31st term.

            (2 marks)

    b)   If the kth term of the sequence is 0, find k.

            (2 marks)

    c)   The sum to n terms of the sequence is S_n.
         Find the value of n at which S_n first becomes negative.

            (3 marks)

4   David's personal trainer gives him a timetable to improve his upper-body strength, which increases the number of push-ups David does each day by equal amounts.
The timetable for the first four days is shown below:

Day:	Mon	Tue	Wed	Thur
Number of push-ups:	6	14	22	30

    a)   Find an expression, in terms of n, for the number of push-ups he will have to do on day n.

            (3 marks)

    b)   David follows his exercise routine for 10 days. Calculate how many push-ups he has done in total over the 10 days.

            (3 marks)

    His personal trainer recommends that David takes a break from his exercise routine when he has done a cumulative total of 2450 push-ups. Given that David does all his exercises on day k, then reaches the recommended limit part-way through day $(k + 1)$,

    c)   Show that k satisfies $(2k - 49)(k + 25) < 0$.

            (3 marks)

    d)   Find the value of k.

            (2 marks)

1. The Gradient of a Curve

Differentiation is an algebraic process that finds the gradient of a curve. It is useful for finding out how fast one thing changes with respect to another.

Finding the gradient of a curve

The **gradient** of a curve is just how **steep** it is. Unlike a straight line, the steepness of a curve **changes** as you move along it — you can only give an **exact value** for the gradient at a **particular point** on the curve.

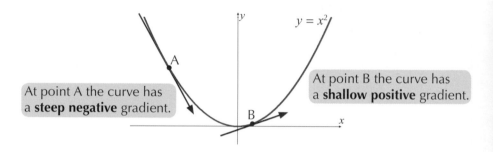

At point A the curve has a **steep negative** gradient.

At point B the curve has a **shallow positive** gradient.

Tip: For a reminder about gradients of straight lines, see p.68.

At a **point**, the gradient of a curve is the same as the gradient of the **tangent line** to the curve at that point.

- The tangent line is a **straight line** which **just touches** the curve at that point, without going through it.

- Sadly, you can't work out the gradient of this tangent using the normal method of picking **two points** and finding the change in $y \div$ change in x. This is because you only know **one point** on the line — the point where the tangent **meets the curve**.

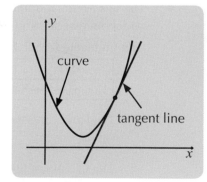

- So we need another method to find the gradient of a curve — it's known as **differentiation**.

Differentiating produces an **algebraic expression** for the gradient as a **function of x** — its numerical value **changes** as you move along the curve.

Before we get started with differentiation, there's some important **notation** to learn:

- The function you get from differentiating y with respect to x is called the derivative of y with respect to x and it's written $\frac{dy}{dx}$.

- $\frac{dy}{dx}$ represents the rate of change of y with x or the gradient of the curve.

- The notation $f'(x)$ means the derivative of $y = f(x)$ with respect to x. It's sometimes used instead of $\frac{dy}{dx}$.

Tip: $\frac{dy}{dx}$ is **not** a fraction, it is just notation for a derivative.

Differentiating from first principles

To find the derivative of a function you need to find its gradient as a function of x.

You can get **close** to the gradient of the tangent (and so the curve) at a point $(x, f(x))$, by finding the gradient of the line joining $(x, f(x))$ and another point **close to** it on the curve.

- On the diagram, the point $(x + h, f(x + h))$ is a small distance further along the curve from $(x, f(x))$.

- As h gets smaller, the distance between the two points gets smaller.

- The closer the points, the **closer** the line joining them will be **to the tangent line**.

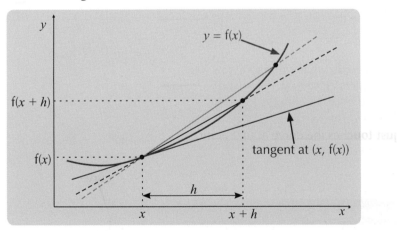

Now you can write an expression for the gradient of the **straight line** joining the two points $(x, f(x))$ and $(x + h, f(x + h))$ like this:

$$\frac{f(x + h) - f(x)}{(x + h) - x}$$

And you know that as h gets **smaller**, the gradient of the straight line gets **closer and closer** to the gradient of the **curve** at $(x, f(x))$.
So you can write an expression for the gradient of the curve $y = f(x)$ like this:

$$f'(x) = \lim_{h \to 0}\left[\frac{f(x + h) - f(x)}{(x + h) - x}\right]$$

This method of differentiation is known as differentiating from **first principles** and the formula can be used to find the gradient of a curve as a function of x.

Tip: Remember the gradient of a line which passes through points (x_1, y_1) and (x_2, y_2) is given by:
$$\frac{y_2 - y_1}{x_2 - x_1}$$

Tip: $\lim_{h \to 0}$ in front of the function just means 'what the function goes towards as h goes towards zero'.

Find an expression for the gradient of the function $f(x) = x^2$ by differentiating from first principles.

- Write down the formula for differentiating from first principles. $\longrightarrow$ $f'(x) = \lim\limits_{h\to 0}\left[\dfrac{f(x+h) - f(x)}{(x+h) - x}\right]$

- Use the fact that $f(x) = x^2$. $\longrightarrow$ $= \lim\limits_{h\to 0}\left[\dfrac{(x+h)^2 - x^2}{(x+h) - x}\right]$

- Multiply out and simplify. $\longrightarrow$ $= \lim\limits_{h\to 0}\left[\dfrac{x^2 + 2xh + h^2 - x^2}{x + h - x}\right]$

  $= \lim\limits_{h\to 0}\left[\dfrac{2xh + h^2}{h}\right]$

- Now decide what will happen as h gets close to 0. $\longrightarrow$ $= \lim\limits_{h\to 0}[2x + h]$

- In this case $2x + h$ gets close to $2x$. $\longrightarrow$ $= \boxed{2x}$

Find the gradient of the curve $y = 0.5x$ by differentiating from first principles.

$$\dfrac{dy}{dx} = \lim\limits_{h\to 0}\left[\dfrac{f(x+h) - f(x)}{(x+h) - x}\right]$$

- Use the fact that $y = f(x)$ with $f(x) = 0.5x$. $\longrightarrow$ $= \lim\limits_{h\to 0}\left[\dfrac{0.5(x+h) - 0.5x}{(x+h) - x}\right]$

  $= \lim\limits_{h\to 0}\left[\dfrac{0.5h}{h}\right]$

- Decide what will happen as h gets close to 0. There are no h's so the limit is just 0.5. $\longrightarrow$ $= \lim\limits_{h\to 0}[0.5] = \boxed{0.5}$

Tip: A straight line will always have a constant gradient.

Exercise 1.1

Q1 Hint: It's OK to use a calculator for this question.

Q1 The curve C is given by $y = f(x)$ where $f(x) = x^3$.

a) Find the gradient of the straight line joining the point on the curve where $x = 1$ and the point on the curve where:

  (i) $x = 2$

  (ii) $x = 1.5$

  (iii) $x = 1.1$

b) The gradient of the curve at the point $(1, 1)$ is 3. What do you notice about the gradient of the straight lines in part a) as the value of x moves closer to 1?

Q2 Derive from first principles expressions for the gradients of the following curves:

  a) $y = x$ b) $f(x) = x^3$ c) $f(x) = 2x$

2. Differentiating $y = f(x)$

Differentiating from first principles can take a long time, especially if there are large powers involved. Luckily, there's a formula that will do it quickly for you.

Differentiating x^n

Expressions are much easier to **differentiate** when they're written using **powers of x** — like writing $\sqrt{x}$ as $x^{\frac{1}{2}}$ or $\frac{3}{x^2}$ as $3x^{-2}$.

When you've done this, you can use this **formula** to differentiate:

$$\text{If } y = x^n, \text{ then } \frac{dy}{dx} = nx^{n-1}$$

It comes from differentiating x^n from **first principles**, like on the page before.

Example 1

Differentiate each of the following using the formula for powers of x.

a) $y = x^2$

For 'normal' powers, n is just the power of x. Here $n = 2$.

$$\frac{dy}{dx} = nx^{n-1}$$
$$= 2x^1$$
$$= \boxed{2x}$$

b) $y = \sqrt{x}$

First write the square root as a fractional power of x. $\longrightarrow$

$$y = x^{\frac{1}{2}} \left(n = \frac{1}{2}\right)$$
$$\frac{dy}{dx} = nx^{n-1}$$
$$= \frac{1}{2}x^{\left(-\frac{1}{2}\right)}$$
$$= \boxed{\frac{1}{2\sqrt{x}}}$$

c) $y = \frac{1}{x^2}$

Write the fraction as a negative power of x. $\longrightarrow$

$$y = x^{-2} \ (n = -2)$$
$$\frac{dy}{dx} = nx^{n-1}$$
$$= -2x^{-3}$$
$$= \boxed{-\frac{2}{x^3}}$$

d) $y = 4x^3$

This is just a normal power with $n = 3$, but there's a constant (a number) in front of it.

$$y = 4x^3$$
$$\frac{dy}{dx} = 4(nx^{n-1})$$

If there's a number in front of the x^n term — multiply the derivative by it. Formally:

$$\text{If } y = ax^n, \ \frac{dy}{dx} = anx^{n-1}$$

$$= 4(3x^2)$$
$$= \boxed{12x^2}$$

Learning Objectives:

- Be able to differentiate powers of x.
- Be able to differentiate sums and differences of powers of x.
- Be able to differentiate more complicated functions containing powers of x.
- Be able to find tangents and normals to a curve.

Tip: When it says 'differentiate', it actually means 'differentiate **with respect to x**' as it's a function of x you're differentiating.

Tip: Differentiation's much easier if you know the Laws of Indices really well. Like knowing that $x^1 = x$ and $\sqrt{x} = x^{\frac{1}{2}}$ See page 10.

Example 2

Differentiate $y = 5$ using the formula for powers of x.

There are no powers of x in this expression for y so multiply by $x^0 = 1$.

$y = 5x^0$, $n = 0$

$\dfrac{dy}{dx} = 5(nx^{n-1})$

$= 5(0x^{-1})$

$= \boxed{0}$

You could be asked to **use** your gradient function to work out the **numerical value** of the gradient at a **particular point** on the curve.

Example 3

Find the gradient of the curve $y = x^2$ at $x = 1$ and $x = -2$.

You need the gradient of the graph of $y = x^2$, so differentiate this function to get $\dfrac{dy}{dx} = 2x$.

Now when $x = 1$, $\dfrac{dy}{dx} = 2$,

And so the $\boxed{\text{gradient of the graph at } x = 1 \text{ is } 2.}$

And when $x = -2$, $\dfrac{dy}{dx} = -4$,.

So the $\boxed{\text{gradient of the graph at } x = -2 \text{ is } -4.}$

Exercise 2.1

Q1 Differentiate to find $\dfrac{dy}{dx}$ for:

a) $y = x^6$ b) $y = x^3$ c) $y = x^{-2}$ d) $y = 3x^2$

e) $y = 7x$ f) $y = 3$ g) $y = 3\sqrt{x}$ h) $y = 2x^{-1}$

Q2 Differentiate to find $f'(x)$ for:

a) $f(x) = x^5$ b) $f(x) = x^7$ c) $f(x) = x^{-4}$ d) $f(x) = 4x^3$

e) $f(x) = 8\sqrt{x}$ f) $f(x) = 3\sqrt[3]{x}$ g) $f(x) = -7$ h) $f(x) = 4x^{-2}$

Q3 Find the gradient of each of the following functions:

a) $y = 2x^2$ when $x = 4$ b) $y = x^{-1}$ when $x = 2$

c) $y = -4x^5$ when $x = 1$ d) $f(x) = 2\sqrt{x}$ at the point $(9, 6)$

e) $f(x) = x^4$ at the point $(-2, 16)$ f) $f(x) = -2x^3$ when $f(x) = -250$

Differentiating functions

Even if there are **loads** of terms in the expression, it doesn't matter.

Differentiate each bit **separately** and you'll be fine.

Formally, this means:

$$f'(x^m + x^n) = f'(x^m) + f'(x^n)$$

Example 1

a) **Differentiate $y = 3x^2 + 2x$.**

Differentiate each bit separately.

$$y = 3x^2 + 2x$$

$$\frac{dy}{dx} = 3(2x) + 2 = \boxed{6x + 2}$$

Tip: Remember — if there's a number in front of the function, multiply the derivative by the same number.

b) **Differentiate $f(x) = x^4 + 6x - 2$.**

Differentiate each bit separately.

$$f(x) = x^4 + 6x - 2$$

$$f'(x) = 4x^3 + 6 - 0 = \boxed{4x^3 + 6}$$

c) **Find $\dfrac{d}{dx}\left(6x^2 + \dfrac{4}{\sqrt[3]{x}} - \dfrac{2}{x^2} + 1\right)$.**

This notation just means the derivative with respect to x of the thing in the brackets.

Rewrite the function first to get powers of x. Then differentiate each bit separately.

$x^0 = 1$

$$6x^2 + \frac{4}{\sqrt[3]{x}} - \frac{2}{x^2} + 1 = 6x^2 + 4x^{-\frac{1}{3}} - 2x^{-2} + x^0$$

$$\frac{d}{dx}\left(6x^2 + \frac{4}{\sqrt[3]{x}} - \frac{2}{x^2} + 1\right) = 6(2x) + 4\left(-\frac{1}{3}x^{-\frac{4}{3}}\right) - 2(-2x^{-3}) + 0x^{-1}$$

$$= \boxed{12x - \frac{4}{3\sqrt[3]{x^4}} + \frac{4}{x^3}}$$

You'll often need to **simplify** a function before you can differentiate it by multiplying out **brackets** or simplifying **fractions**. If you have a fraction to simplify, check first whether the denominator is a **factor** of the numerator, otherwise you'll need to **split it up** into terms.

Example 2

a) **Differentiate $y = x(x + 3)(x - 4) + 4(2 - x^2)$.**

- Multiply out all brackets and simplify to powers of x.

$$
\begin{aligned}
y &= x(x + 3)(x - 4) + 4(2 - x^2) \\
&= x(x^2 - x - 12) + 8 - 4x^2 \\
&= x^3 - x^2 - 12x + 8 - 4x^2 \\
&= x^3 - 5x^2 - 12x + 8
\end{aligned}
$$

- Differentiate term-by-term.

$$
\begin{aligned}
\frac{dy}{dx} &= 3x^2 - 10x - 12 + 0 \\
&= 3x^2 - 10x - 12
\end{aligned}
$$

b) **Find $f'(x)$ for the function $f(x) = (\frac{1}{2}x + 5)(\frac{1}{2}x - 1)$.**

$$
\begin{aligned}
f(x) &= (\tfrac{1}{2}x + 5)(\tfrac{1}{2}x - 1) \\
&= \tfrac{1}{4}x^2 - \tfrac{1}{2}x + \tfrac{5}{2}x - 5 \\
&= \tfrac{1}{4}x^2 + \tfrac{4}{2}x - 5 \\
&= \tfrac{1}{4}x^2 + 2x - 5
\end{aligned}
$$

- x^2 is multiplied by $\frac{1}{4}$ so multiply the derivative by $\frac{1}{4}$ as well and simplify.

$$
\begin{aligned}
f'(x) &= \tfrac{1}{4}(2x) + 2 - 0 \\
&= \tfrac{x}{2} + 2
\end{aligned}
$$

Example 3

Tip: If the denominator is an expression instead of just one term, chances are the numerator will have a factor that cancels with the denominator.

a) **Differentiate $y = \dfrac{x^3 - 5x^2 + 6x}{x - 2}$.**

The numerator of this fraction will factorise and then one of the factors will cancel with the denominator.

$$
\begin{aligned}
y &= \frac{x^3 - 5x^2 + 6x}{x - 2} \\
&= \frac{x(x^2 - 5x + 6)}{x - 2} \\
&= \frac{x(x - 3)(x - 2)}{x - 2} \\
&= x(x - 3) \\
&= x^2 - 3x
\end{aligned}
$$

$$
\frac{dy}{dx} = 2x - 3
$$

b) **Differentiate the function** $f(x) = \dfrac{x^3 + 4x + 1}{2x^2}$.

This numerator won't factorise. Instead, split the fraction up into three fractional terms and then write each term as a power of x.

$$
\begin{aligned}
f(x) &= \frac{x^3 + 4x + 1}{2x^2} \\
&= \frac{x^3}{2x^2} + \frac{4x}{2x^2} + \frac{1}{2x^2} \\
&= \frac{x}{2} + \frac{2}{x} + \frac{1}{2x^2} \\
&= \frac{1}{2}x + 2x^{-1} + \frac{1}{2}x^{-2}
\end{aligned}
$$

Differentiating....

$$
\begin{aligned}
f'(x) &= \frac{1}{2} + 2\left(-x^{-2}\right) + \frac{1}{2}\left(-2x^{-3}\right) \\
&= \frac{1}{2} - 2x^{-2} - x^{-3} \\
&= \frac{1}{2} - \frac{2}{x^2} - \frac{1}{x^3}
\end{aligned}
$$

> **Tip:** For any a, b, c & d:
>
> $$\dfrac{a + b + c}{d} = \dfrac{a}{d} + \dfrac{b}{d} + \dfrac{c}{d}$$
>
> You can split up fractions using this rule.

Exercise 2.2

Q1 Differentiate these functions:

a) $y = 4x^3 - x^2$

b) $y = x + \dfrac{1}{x}$

c) $y = 3x^2 + \sqrt{x} - 5$

d) $f(x) = -2x^5 + 4x - \dfrac{1}{x^2}$

e) $f(x) = \sqrt{x^3} - x$

f) $f(x) = 5x - \dfrac{2}{x^3} + \sqrt[3]{x}$

Q2 Find:

a) $\dfrac{d}{dx}(x(x^6 - 1))$

b) $\dfrac{d}{dx}((x - 3)(x + 4))$

c) $\dfrac{d}{dx}(x(x - 1)(x - 2))$

d) $\dfrac{d}{dx}((x - 3)(x + 4)(x - 1))$

e) $\dfrac{d}{dx}(x^2(x - 4)(3 - x^3))$

f) $\dfrac{d}{dx}((x - 3)^2(x^2 - 2))$

> **Q2 Hint:** Remember that $\dfrac{d}{dx}(\ \ )$ means the derivative with respect to x of the thing in brackets.

Q3 Find the gradient of each of the following curves:

a) $y = x^4 - x^2 + 2$ when $x = 3$

b) $y = 2x^5 + \dfrac{1}{x}$ when $x = -2$

c) $y = x(x - 1)(x - 2)$ when $x = -3$

d) $y = 5(x^2 - 1)(3 - x)$ when $x = 0$

e) $y = \sqrt{x}\,(x - 1)$ at $(4, 6)$

f) $f(x) = x^3(x^2 - 5)$ at $(-1, 4)$

g) $f(x) = \dfrac{1}{x^2}(x^3 - x)$ at $x = 5$

h) $f(x) = \dfrac{3x^3 + 18x^2 + 24x}{x + 4}$ at $(-2, 0)$

Q4 a) Find the coordinates of the point on the curve $y = (x + 3)(x + 4)$ where $\frac{dy}{dx} = 3$.

b) Find the coordinates of the point on the curve $y = (x + 3)(x - 5)$ where $\frac{dy}{dx} = 2$.

c) Find the coordinates of the point on the curve $y = x^2 + 8x$ where $\frac{dy}{dx} = 4$.

d) Find the coordinates of the point on the curve $y = \frac{x^3 - 3x^2 + 2x}{x - 1}$ where $\frac{dy}{dx} = -6$.

Q5 For each of the following functions, find the coordinates of the point or points where the gradient is 0:

a) $y = x^2 - 2x$

b) $y = 3x^2 + 4x$

c) $y = 5x^2 - 3x$

d) $y = 9x - 3x^3$

e) $y = 2x^3 - x^2$

f) $y = 2x^3 + 3x^2 - 12x$

Q6 Differentiate these functions:

a) $y = \frac{x^2 - 3x - 4}{x + 1}$

b) $f(x) = \frac{x^4 - 9}{x^2 + 3}$

c) $f(x) = \frac{x^5 - 16x^3}{x + 4}$

d) $y = \frac{1}{x}(x - 3)(x - 4)$

e) $y = \sqrt{x}(x^3 - \sqrt{x})$

f) $f(x) = \frac{3 - \sqrt{x}}{\sqrt{x}}$

g) $f(x) = \frac{x + 5\sqrt{x}}{\sqrt{x}}$

h) $f(x) = \frac{x - 3\sqrt{x} + 2}{\sqrt{x} - 1}$

Q6 Hint: Where there's a fraction with an expression in the denominator, try to take the denominator out of the numerator as a factor.

Finding tangents and normals

Differentiation can be used to find the gradient at a point on a curve. When you've done this it's easy to find the equation for the **tangent** or **normal** at that point.

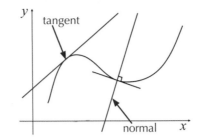

- You already know that a **tangent** is a straight line that just **touches** the curve and has the **same gradient** as the curve at that point.
- A **normal** is a straight line that is **perpendicular** (at right angles) to the curve at a particular point.

Now, there's one key fact to remember for normals — tangents and normals are perpendicular, and as a result, their **gradients multiply to give –1**:

$$\text{gradient of tangent} \times \text{gradient of normal} = -1$$

$$\text{gradient of normal} = \frac{-1}{\text{gradient of tangent}}$$

Tip: This rule for the gradients of perpendicular lines was introduced back in Chapter 4 on p75.

Armed with this rule, we can write down a step-by-step method for finding the equation of a tangent or normal to a curve...

To find the equation of the tangent or normal to a curve at a point:
- Differentiate the function.
- Find the gradient of the curve at that point.
- Use this to deduce the gradient, m, of the tangent or normal:

$$\text{gradient of the tangent} = \text{gradient of the curve}$$

$$\text{gradient of the normal} = -\frac{1}{\text{gradient of the curve}}$$

- Write the equation of the tangent or normal in the form $y = mx + c$.
- Work out the constant value c in the equation by using the coordinates of the point (which you know lies on the tangent/normal).

Tip: The tangent and normal are always straight lines, so their equations can be written $y = mx + c$. They can also be written in the form $y - y_1 = m(x - x_1)$ if you prefer.

Example 1

Find the equation of the tangent to the curve $y = (4 - x)(x + 2)$ at the point (2, 8), giving your answer in the form $ax + by + c = 0$, where a, b and c are integers.

- Write the curve in a form you can differentiate...

$$\begin{aligned} y &= (4 - x)(x + 2) \\ &= 4x + 8 - x^2 - 2x \\ &= 8 + 2x - x^2 \end{aligned}$$

...and differentiate it.

$$\begin{aligned} \frac{dy}{dx} &= 0 + 2 - 2x \\ &= 2 - 2x \end{aligned}$$

- Find the gradient of the curve at (2, 8).

$$x = 2 \Rightarrow \frac{dy}{dx} = 2 - (2 \times 2) = 2 - 4 = -2$$

So the gradient of the curve is -2 at (2, 8)

- Gradient of the tangent = gradient of the curve, so $m = -2$

- So the equation of the tangent is $y = -2x + c$.

- Use the point (2, 8) to work out the value of c:

$$x = 2, y = 8 \Rightarrow 8 = -4 + c \Rightarrow c = 12$$

So the tangent has equation $y = -2x + 12$.

Rearranging into the form $ax + by + c = 0$ gives:

$$2x + y - 12 = 0$$

Example 2

Find the equation of the normal to the curve $y = x(x - 3)(x + 2)$ at the point (2, –8), giving your answer in the form $y = mx + c$.

Tip: Make sure you always check whether the question wants a normal or a tangent.

- Simplify and differentiate.

$$\begin{aligned} y &= x(x - 3)(x + 2) \\ &= x^3 - x^2 - 6x \\ \frac{dy}{dx} &= 3x^2 - 2x - 6 \end{aligned}$$

- Find the gradient of the curve at (2, –8).

$$x = 2 \Rightarrow \frac{dy}{dx} = 3(2^2) - 2(2) - 6 = 2$$

So the gradient of the curve is 2 at (2, –8)

- Gradient of the normal at (2, –8) is

$$m = -\frac{1}{\text{gradient of the curve at } (2, -8)} = -\frac{1}{2}$$

- So the equation of the normal is $y = -\frac{1}{2}x + c$.

- Use the point (2, –8) to work out the value of c.

$$x = 2, y = -8 \Rightarrow -8 = -1 + c \Rightarrow c = -7$$

So the normal has equation:

$$y = -\frac{1}{2}x - 7$$

Example 3

Find the equation of the normal to the curve $y = \dfrac{(x+2)(x+4)}{6\sqrt{x}}$ at the point (4, 4), giving your answer in the form $ax + by + c = 0$, where a, b and c are integers.

- Simplify and differentiate.

$$y = \frac{(x+2)(x+4)}{6\sqrt{x}}$$

> Denominator is one term so it'll probably need splitting up.

$$= \frac{x^2 + 6x + 8}{6x^{\frac{1}{2}}}$$

$$= \frac{x^2}{6x^{\frac{1}{2}}} + \frac{6x}{6x^{\frac{1}{2}}} + \frac{8}{6x^{\frac{1}{2}}}$$

$$= \frac{1}{6}x^{\frac{3}{2}} + x^{\frac{1}{2}} + \frac{4}{3}x^{-\frac{1}{2}}$$

$$\frac{dy}{dx} = \frac{1}{6}\left(\frac{3}{2}x^{\frac{1}{2}}\right) + \frac{1}{2}x^{-\frac{1}{2}} + \frac{4}{3}\left(-\frac{1}{2}x^{-\frac{3}{2}}\right)$$

$$= \frac{1}{4}\sqrt{x} + \frac{1}{2\sqrt{x}} - \frac{2}{3\sqrt{x^3}}$$

- Find the gradient of the curve at (4, 4).

$$x = 4 \Rightarrow \frac{dy}{dx} = \frac{1}{4}\sqrt{4} + \frac{1}{2\sqrt{4}} - \frac{2}{3\sqrt{4^3}}$$

$$= \frac{1}{2} + \frac{1}{4} - \frac{1}{12} = \frac{2}{3}$$

So the gradient of the curve is $\frac{2}{3}$ at (4, 4)

- Gradient of the normal line at (4, 4) is

$$m = -\frac{1}{\text{gradient of the curve at (4, 4)}} = -\frac{3}{2}$$

- So the equation of the normal is $y = -\frac{3}{2}x + c$.

- Use the point (4, 4) to work out the value of c.

$$x = 4, y = 4 \Rightarrow 4 = -\frac{3}{2}4 + c \Rightarrow c = 10$$

So the tangent has equation $y = -\frac{3}{2}x + 10$.

Rearranging into the form $ax + by + c = 0$ gives:

$$3x + 2y - 20 = 0$$

Tip: Rewriting the answer in the form the question asks for will get you easy marks.

Q1 Find the equation of the tangent to each of these curves at the given point. Give your answer in the form $y = mx + c$.

a) $y = 9x - 2x^2$, $(1, 7)$

b) $y = x^3 - 2x + 3$, $(2, 7)$

c) $y = (x + 2)(2x - 3)$, $(2, 4)$

d) $y = x(x - 1)^2$, $(-1, -4)$

e) $y = x^2(x + 3) - 10$, $(2, 10)$

f) $y = x(2x + 4)(x - 3)$, $(-1, 8)$

Q2 Find the tangent to each of these curves at the given point, giving your answer in the form $ax + by + c = 0$, where a, b and c are integers.

a) $y = \frac{1}{x} + x + 3$, $(2, 5\frac{1}{2})$

b) $y = 4x^2 - 3\sqrt{x}$, $(1, 1)$

c) $y = \frac{3}{x} + 2\sqrt{x}$, $(4, 4\frac{3}{4})$

d) $y = \frac{1}{x} + \frac{4}{x^2}$, $(2, 1\frac{1}{2})$

e) $y = \frac{1}{3}x^2 - 4\sqrt{x} - \frac{1}{3}$, $(4, -3)$

f) $y = x - \frac{2}{x} + \frac{3}{x^2}$, $(-3, -2)$

Q3 Find the normal to each of these curves at the given point, giving your answer in the form $ax + by + c = 0$, where a, b and c are integers.

a) $y = 3x^2 - 4x + 2$, $(2, 6)$

b) $y = x^2(x + 4) - 5x$, $(-1, 8)$

c) $y = x(x - 1)(x - 2)$, $(3, 6)$

d) $y = x(x - 3)(x + 4) - 10$, $(-2, 10)$

e) $y = \frac{x^3 - 5x^2 - 14x}{x + 2}$, $(5, -10)$

Q4 Find the normal to each of these curves at the given point, giving your answer in an appropriate form.

a) $y = \frac{2x^5 - 2x^4}{3x^3}$, $(-2, 4)$

b) $y = \frac{5x^2 - 2x + 3}{x^2}$, $(2, 4\frac{3}{4})$

c) $y = \frac{3x - x^2}{\sqrt{x}}$, $(4, -2)$

d) $y = \frac{1}{x} - \frac{3}{x^2} - \frac{4}{x^3} + \frac{7}{4}$, $(-2, 1)$

e) $y = \frac{x^3 - 5x^2 - 4x}{x\sqrt{x}}$, $(4, -4)$

Q5 Consider the curve with equation $y = f(x)$ where $f(x) = x^3 - 3x^2 + 3$.

a) Find the coordinates of the point where $f'(x) = 9$ and $x > 0$.

b) Find the equation of the tangent to the curve at this point, giving your answer in the form $y = mx + c$.

c) Find the equation of the normal to the curve at this point, giving your answer in the form $ax + by + c = 0$, where a, b and c are integers.

Q6 a) Show that the curve $y = \frac{x^3 + x^2 + x + 5}{x^2}$ passes through the point $\left(-2, -\frac{1}{4}\right)$.

b) Find the equation of the tangent to the curve at this point, giving your answer in the form $ax + by + c = 0$, where a, b and c are integers.

c) Find the equation of the normal to the curve at this point, giving your answer in the form $ax + by + c = 0$, where a, b and c are integers.

3. Second Order Derivatives

Second order derivatives have lots of useful applications in later modules, like finding maximum and minimum points of graphs.
For now you just need to know what they are and how to find them.

Learning Objectives:

- Be able to find the second derivative of functions.
- Be able to solve real life problems about rates of change.

Finding second order derivatives

- If you differentiate y with respect to x, you get the derivative $\frac{dy}{dx}$.

- If you then differentiate $\frac{dy}{dx}$ with respect to x, you get the **second order derivative**, denoted $\frac{d^2y}{dx^2}$.

- The **second derivative** gives the **rate of change** of the **gradient** of the curve with respect to x.

- In function notation, the **second derivative** is written $f''(x)$.

Example 1

a) **For the function $f(x) = 2x^3 + 4x^2 + x$ find $f'(x)$ and $f''(x)$**

$$f(x) = 2x^3 + 4x^2 + x$$

$$f'(x) = 2(3x^2) + 4(2x) + 1 \quad \longleftarrow \boxed{\text{Differentiate for } f'(x).}$$
$$= 6x^2 + 8x + 1$$

$$f''(x) = 6(2x) + 8 \quad \longleftarrow \boxed{\text{Differentiate again to get the second derivative.}}$$
$$= 12x + 8$$

b) **For the equation $y = (3x + 5)(2x - 1)$, find $\frac{dy}{dx}$ and $\frac{d^2x}{dy^2}$.**

$$y = (3x + 5)(2x - 1) \quad \longleftarrow \boxed{\text{Multiply the brackets...}}$$
$$= 6x^2 + 7x - 5$$

$$\frac{dy}{dx} = 6(2x) + 7 - 0 \quad \longleftarrow \boxed{\text{Differentiate for } \frac{dy}{dx}.}$$
$$= 12x + 7$$

$$\frac{d^2y}{dx^2} = 12 + 0 \quad \longleftarrow \boxed{\text{Differentiate again to get the second derivative.}}$$
$$= 12$$

Until now, all the examples have been about differentiating functions of x to find gradients of curves. But **real life** examples often involve a function of t, time, and you'll need to differentiate to find the **rate of change** over time. The maths is **the same**, the **letters** are just different.

The next example looks at the **distance** a car has travelled as a function of **time**.

Example 2

A sports car pulls off from a junction and drives away, travelling x metres in t seconds. For the first 10 seconds, its journey can be described by the equation $x = 2t^2$.

a) Find the speed of the car after 8 seconds

Speed is the rate of change of distance with respect to time — it can be found by differentiating the expression for distance with respect to time.

So to work out the speed as a function of t, differentiate x to find $\frac{dx}{dt}$.

$$x = 2t^2$$

$$\frac{dx}{dt} = 4t$$

You've got speed as a function of t, so just put 8 seconds into the expression.

$$\text{When } t = 8, \frac{dx}{dt} = 32$$

So, the car is travelling at $\boxed{32 \text{ ms}^{-1}}$ after 8 seconds.

b) Find the car's acceleration during this period.

Acceleration is the rate of change of speed with respect to time — it can be found by differentiating the expression for speed with respect to time.

The speed is $\frac{dx}{dt}$ so differentiate again to get the second derivative $\frac{d^2x}{dt^2}$.

$$\frac{dx}{dt} = 4t$$

$$\frac{d^2x}{dt^2} = 4$$

This means that the car's acceleration during this period is $\boxed{4 \text{ ms}^{-2}}$.

Tip: Just like in all the other questions, $\frac{dx}{dt}$ is a gradient. If you were to draw a distance–time graph, it would just be the gradient of the graph as a function of t.

Tip: Careful with the units here — acceleration is measured in metres per second^2.

Q1 Find $\dfrac{dy}{dx}$ and $\dfrac{d^2y}{dx^2}$ for each of these functions:

a) $y = x^3$ b) $y = x^5$ c) $y = x^4$ d) $y = x$

e) $y = \dfrac{1}{x}$ f) $y = \sqrt{x}$ g) $y = \dfrac{1}{x^2}$ h) $y = x\sqrt{x}$

Q2 Find $f'(x)$ and $f''(x)$ for each of these functions:

a) $f(x) = x(4x^2 - x)$ b) $f(x) = (x^2 - 3)(x - 4)$

c) $f(x) = \dfrac{4x^5 + 12x^3 - 40x}{4(x^2 + 5)}$ d) $f(x) = 3\sqrt{x} + x\sqrt{x}$

e) $f(x) = \dfrac{1}{x}(3x^4 - 2x^3)$ f) $f(x) = \dfrac{x^2 - x\sqrt{x} + 7x}{\sqrt{x}}$

Q3 Find the value of the second derivative at the given value for x.

a) $f(x) = x^3 - x^2$, $x = 3$ b) $y = x\sqrt{x} - \dfrac{1}{x}$, $x = 4$

c) $f(x) = x^2(x - 5)(x^2 + x)$, $x = -1$ d) $y = \dfrac{x^5 + 4x^4 - 12x^3}{x + 6}$, $x = 5$

e) $f(x) = \dfrac{9x^2 + 3x}{3\sqrt{x}}$, $x = 1$ f) $y = (\dfrac{1}{x^2} + \dfrac{1}{x})(5 - x)$, $x = -3$

Q4 A particle moves along a path described by the equation $x = 3t^2 - 7t$, where t is the time in seconds and x is the distance in metres.

a) Find the speed, $\dfrac{dx}{dt}$, of the particle as a function of t.

b) What is the speed of the particle in ms^{-1} at:

    (i) $t = 2$ seconds   (ii) $t = 5$ seconds

c) Find the value of t when the speed is 17 ms^{-1}.

d) Find the acceleration $\dfrac{d^2x}{dt^2}$ of the particle as a function of t.

Q5 A particle moves along a path described by the equation $x = 2t^3 - 4t^2$, $t > 0$, where t is the time in seconds and x is the distance in metres.

a) Find the speed of the particle after t seconds.

b) Find x and t when the speed is 30 ms^{-1}.

c) Find the acceleration of the particle after t seconds.

d) Find the acceleration at $t = 5$ seconds in ms^{-2}.

e) Find the speed when the acceleration is 16 ms^{-2}.

> **Q5 Hint:** For part e), use the information you've been given to work out the value of t and then put the t value into the expression for speed.

Review Exercise — Chapter 6

Q1 Differentiate the following functions from first principles:
a) $y = x + 1$
b) $y = 4x^2$
c) $y = \dfrac{3}{x}$

Q2 Write down the formula for differentiating any power of x.

Q3 Differentiate these functions with respect to x:
a) $y = x^2 + 2$,
b) $y = x^4 + \sqrt{x}$,
c) $y = \dfrac{7}{x^2} - \dfrac{3}{\sqrt{x}} + 12x^3$

Q4 What's the connection between the gradient of a curve at a point and the gradient of the tangent to the curve at the same point?

Q5 What's the connection between the gradient of a curve at a point and the gradient of the normal to the curve at the same point?

Q6 Find the gradients of these graphs at $x = 2$:

a)
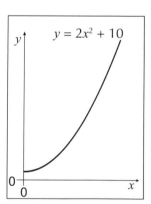
$y = 2x^2 + 10$

b)
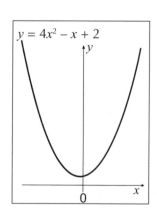
$y = 4x^2 - x + 2$

c)
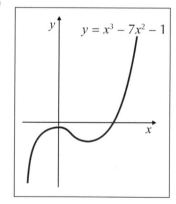
$y = x^3 - 7x^2 - 1$

Q7 Water is poured into a bowl. The volume (v) of water in the bowl (in ml) after t seconds is given by the function: $v = 3t^2 + 4$.
a) How much water is in the bowl initially?
b) Find the rate at which water is being poured into the bowl when $t = 4$ seconds.

Q8 Find the equations of the tangent and the normal to the curve $y = \sqrt{x^3} - 3x - 10$ at $x = 16$.

Q9 Find the equation of the tangent to the curve $y = x^3 + \dfrac{4}{x} + 2\sqrt{x}$ at $x = 1$.

Q10 Show that the graphs of $y = \frac{x^3}{3} - 2x^2 - 4x + \frac{86}{3}$ and $y = \sqrt{x}$ both go through the point $(4, 2)$, and are perpendicular at that point.

Q11 Consider the curve C given by the equation $y = x^2 - 6$ and the line L given by the equation $y = 3$.
    a) Find the coordinates of the points, A and B, where C and L intersect.
    b) Find the gradient of C at points A and B.
    c) Find the equations of the normals to C at A and B.

    The normals at points A and B meet the point D.
    d) Find the coordinates of the point D.

Q12 Consider the curve C given by the equation $y = x^3 - 2x^2 + 1$, $x > 0$, and the line L given by the equation $y = 1$.
    a) Write down the gradient of the line L for any x.
    b) Find the point at which the curve C has the same gradient as the line L.
    c) Hence give the equation of the tangent to C at this point.

Q13 Find the equations of the tangent and the normal to the curve $y = 1 + \sqrt{x^3}$ at $x = 16$.

Q14 A particle moves along a path described by the equation $x = t^3 - 8t$, $t > 0$, where t is the time in seconds and x is the distance in metres.
    a) Find the speed $\frac{dx}{dt}$ of the particle as a function of t.
    b) Find x and t when the speed is 19 ms^{-1}.
    c) Find the acceleration $\frac{d^2x}{dt^2}$ of the particle as a function of t.
    d) Find the acceleration, in ms^{-2}, after 2 seconds.
    e) Find the speed, in ms^{-1}, when the acceleration is 18 ms^{-2}.

Q15 Consider the curve with equation $y = f(x)$, where $f(x) = x^3 - 3x$.
    a) Work out the gradient of this curve when $x = -1$.
    b) Show that $2f''(x) - 3f'(x) + f(x) = x^3 + 9(1 + x - x^2)$.

Q16 Let $f(x) = x^4$. Find $f''(x) + 2f'(x) - 4f(x)$.

1   Differentiate with respect to x:

   a) $f(x) = 2\sqrt{x} + \frac{1}{x}$

                                               (3 marks)

   b) $g(x) = \dfrac{(x + 2)(x + 1)}{\sqrt{x}}$

                                               (4 marks)

2   Given that $y = x^7 + \dfrac{2}{x^3}$, find:

   a) $\dfrac{dy}{dx}$

                                               (2 marks)

   b) $\dfrac{d^2y}{dx^2}$

                                               (2 marks)

3   The curve C is given by the equation $y = 2x^3 - 4x^2 - 4x + 12$.

   a)   Find $\dfrac{dy}{dx}$.

                                               (2 marks)

   b)   Find the gradient of the tangent to the curve at the point where $x = 2$.

                                               (1 mark)

   c)   Hence find an equation for the normal to the curve at this point.

                                               (3 marks)

4   Find the gradient of the curve $y = \dfrac{1}{\sqrt{x}} + \dfrac{1}{x}$ at the point $\left(4, \frac{3}{4}\right)$.

                                               (5 marks)

5   a)   Show that the expression $\dfrac{x^2 + 3x^{\frac{3}{2}}}{\sqrt{x}}$ can be written in the form $x^p + 3x^q$, and state the values of p and q.

                                               (3 marks)

   b)   Now let $y = 3x^3 + 5 + \dfrac{x^2 + 3x^{\frac{3}{2}}}{\sqrt{x}}$.
       Find $\dfrac{dy}{dx}$, giving each coefficient in its simplest form.

                                               (4 marks)

6   Given that $f(x) = \frac{1}{4}x^4 + 7 + \frac{3\sqrt{x}}{x^2}$ and $x > 0$, find:

   a) $f'(x)$ *(3 marks)*

   b) $f''(x)$ *(3 marks)*

7   The curve C is given by the equation $y = mx^3 - x^2 + 8x + 2$, for a constant m.

   a)   Find $\frac{dy}{dx}$.

                                                       (2 marks)

   The point P lies on C, and has the x-value 5.
   The normal to C at P is parallel to the line given by the equation $y + 4x - 3 = 0$.

   b)   Find the gradient of curve C at P.

                                                       (3 marks)

   Hence find:

   c)   (i)   the value of m,

                                                       (3 marks)

       (ii)   the y-value at P.

                                                       (2 marks)

8   The curve C is given by $y = f(x)$, where $f(x) = 3x + 4 + x^4$, $x > 0$.

   a)   Find $f'(x)$.

                                                       (1 mark)

   b)   Given that $f'(x) = 111$, find x.

                                                       (2 marks)

9   For $x \geq 0$ and $y \geq 0$, x and y satisfy the equation $2x - y = 6$.

   a)   If $W = x^2y^2$, show that $W = 4x^4 - 24x^3 + 36x^2$.

                                                       (2 marks)

   b)   (i)   Show that $\frac{dW}{dx} = k(2x^3 - 9x^2 + 9x)$, and find the value of the integer k.
                                                       (4 marks)

       (ii)   Find the value of $\frac{dW}{dx}$ when $x = 1$.

                                                       (1 mark)

   c)   Find $\frac{d^2W}{dx^2}$ and give its value when $x = 1$.

                                                       (2 marks)

1. Integration

Integration is just the process of getting from $\dfrac{dy}{dx}$ back to y itself.

Indefinite integration

Integration is the '**opposite**' of differentiation. When you integrate something, you're trying to find a function that returns to **what you started with** when you differentiate it. This function is called an **integral**.

The integral of a **function** f(x) with respect to **x** is written:

$\int$ means **the integral of**. $\int f(x)\, dx$ dx means **with respect to** x.

For example, 'the integral of $2x$ with respect to x' is written $\int 2x\, \mathbf{dx}$. The answer could be **any function** which differentiates to give $2x$.

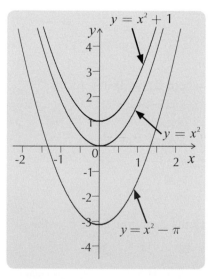

From Chapter 6, we know that:

$$\frac{d}{dx}(x^2) = 2x$$

$$\frac{d}{dx}(x^2 + 1) = 2x$$

$$\frac{d}{dx}(x^2 - \pi) = 2x$$

If you differentiate any of these functions, you get $2x$ — they're **all possible integrals** because they all have the **same gradient**.

In fact, if you differentiate **any** function which is of the form $x^2 +$ **'a constant'** — you'll get $2x$.

So the answer to this integral is actually...

$$\int 2x\, dx = x^2 + C$$

C is a constant representing 'any number'— it's known as the **constant of integration**.

This is an example of **indefinite integration** — a good way to remember this is that C can take an **indefinite number** of values. There are **lots of answers** to an indefinite integral, so you need to add a **constant of integration** to show that it could be **any number**.

Integrating x^n

The formula below tells you how to integrate **any power of x** (except x^{-1}).

$$\int x^n \, \mathrm{d}x = \frac{x^{n+1}}{n+1} + C$$

This just says:

To integrate a power of x:
(i) **Increase the power** by one — then divide by it.
and (ii) Add a **constant**.

> **Tip:** You can't use this formula for $\frac{1}{x} = x^{-1}$. When you increase the power by 1 and then divide by the power you get:
> $$\int x^{-1} \, \mathrm{d}x = \frac{x^0}{0}$$
> This is undefined since you can't divide by 0.

Example 1

Find the following integrals:

a) $\int x^3 \, \mathrm{d}x$.

Increase the power to 4...

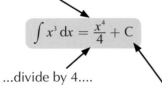

$$\int x^3 \, \mathrm{d}x = \frac{x^4}{4} + C$$

...divide by 4....

...and add a constant of integration.

> **Tip:** It's easy to forget the constant of integration and lose easy marks. Make sure you get used to adding it on.

You can always check that you've got the right answer by differentiating it — you should end up with the thing you started with:

$$\frac{\mathrm{d}}{\mathrm{d}x}\left(\frac{x^4}{4} + C\right) = \frac{\mathrm{d}}{\mathrm{d}x}\left(\frac{x^4}{4}\right) + \frac{\mathrm{d}}{\mathrm{d}x}(C) = x^3 + 0 = x^3$$

b) $\int \frac{1}{x^3} \, \mathrm{d}x$.

Increase the power by 1 to –2...

$$\int \frac{1}{x^3} \, \mathrm{d}x = \int x^{-3} \, \mathrm{d}x = \frac{x^{-2}}{-2} + C = -\frac{1}{2x^2} + C$$

...divide by –2...

...and add a constant of integration.

Check your answer is correct by differentiating:

$$\frac{\mathrm{d}}{\mathrm{d}x}\left(-\frac{1}{2x^2} + C\right) = \frac{\mathrm{d}}{\mathrm{d}x}\left(-\frac{1}{2}x^{-2}\right) + \frac{\mathrm{d}}{\mathrm{d}x}(C) = x^{-3} + 0 = \frac{1}{x^3}$$

c) $\int \sqrt[3]{x^4}\, dx$.

Add 1 to the power...

$$\int \sqrt[3]{x^4}\, dx = \int x^{\frac{4}{3}}\, dx = \frac{x^{\frac{7}{3}}}{\left(\frac{7}{3}\right)} + C = \frac{3\sqrt[3]{x^7}}{7} + C$$

...then divide by $\frac{7}{3}$...

...and add a constant of integration.

Check your answer is correct by differentiating:

$$\frac{d}{dx}\left(\frac{3\sqrt[3]{x^7}}{7} + C\right) = \frac{d}{dx}\left(\frac{3}{7}x^{\frac{7}{3}}\right) + \frac{d}{dx}(C) = x^{\frac{4}{3}} + 0 = \sqrt[3]{x^4}$$

Example 2

Find $\int 4\, dx$.

There's no x^n here, but $x^0 = 1$, so you can multiply by x^0 without changing anything.

$$\int 4\, dx = \int 4x^0\, dx$$

Increase the power from 0 to 1.

$$= \frac{4x^1}{1} + C$$

Divide by the power.

$$= 4x + C$$

Exercise 1.1

Q1 Find an expression for y when $\frac{dy}{dx}$ is the following:

a) x^7 b) $2x^3$ c) $8x$ d) $-5x^4$ e) x^{-3}

f) $4x^{-4}$ g) $-6x^{-5}$ h) -12 i) $x^{\frac{1}{2}}$ j) $x^{\frac{1}{3}}$

Q2 Find the following:

a) $\int x^{\frac{2}{3}}\, dx$

b) $\int 7x^{\frac{4}{3}}\, dx$

c) $\int x^{-\frac{1}{2}}\, dx$

d) $\int 2x^{-\frac{1}{3}}\, dx$

e) $\int 14x^{0.4}\, dx$

f) $\int -1.2x^{-0.6}\, dx$

g) $\int -2x^{-\frac{5}{4}}\, dx$

h) $\int -\frac{3}{2}x^{-\frac{1}{2}}\, dx$

i) $\int -\frac{4}{3}x^{-\frac{4}{3}}\, dx$

Integrating functions

Just like differentiating, if there are **lots of terms** in an expression, you can just integrate each bit **separately**. If the terms are multiplied by **constants**, take them **outside** the integral like this:

$$\int ax^n \, dx = a \int x^n \, dx$$

Examples

Find $\int \left(3x^2 - \frac{2}{\sqrt{x}} + \frac{7}{x^2}\right) dx$.

Write as powers of x.

$$\int \left(3x^2 - \frac{2}{\sqrt{x}} + \frac{7}{x^2}\right) dx = \int \left(3x^2 - 2x^{-\frac{1}{2}} + 7x^{-2}\right) dx$$

Integrate each term separately.

Take the constants outside the integral.

$$= 3\int x^2 \, dx - 2\int x^{-\frac{1}{2}} \, dx + 7\int x^{-2} \, dx$$

$$= \frac{3x^3}{3} - \frac{2x^{\frac{1}{2}}}{\left(\frac{1}{2}\right)} + \frac{7x^{-1}}{-1} + C$$

Just add one constant of integration.

$$= x^3 - 4\sqrt{x} - \frac{7}{x} + C$$

Tip: When you're doing lots of separate integrations, you only need one constant of integration for the whole expression — if each integral gives a constant, you can just add them up to get a new constant.

Find y **if** $\frac{dy}{dx} = \frac{1}{2}x^3 - 4x^{\frac{3}{2}}x$.

$$y = \int \frac{dy}{dx} \, dx = \int \left(\frac{1}{2}x^3 - 4x^{\frac{3}{2}}x\right) dx$$

Integrate the derivative of y to get y.

$$= \int \left(\frac{1}{2}x^3 - 4x^{\frac{5}{2}}\right) dx = \frac{1}{2}\int x^3 \, dx - 4\int x^{\frac{5}{2}} \, dx$$

$$= \frac{1}{2} \times \frac{x^4}{4} + (-4) \times \frac{x^{\frac{7}{2}}}{\left(\frac{7}{2}\right)} + C$$

$$= \frac{x^4}{8} - \frac{8}{7}x^{\frac{7}{2}} + C$$

Find $\int \left(\frac{(x-1)^2}{\sqrt{x}}\right) dx$.

...and write as powers of x.

$$\int \left(\frac{(x-1)^2}{\sqrt{x}}\right) dx = \int \left(\frac{x^2 - 2x + 1}{x^{\frac{1}{2}}}\right) dx = \int \left(x^{\frac{3}{2}} - 2x^{\frac{1}{2}} + x^{-\frac{1}{2}}\right) dx$$

Split into separate terms...

Tip: Some expressions will need simplifying before you integrate with the formula for powers of x.

$$= \int x^{\frac{3}{2}} \, dx - 2\int (x^{\frac{1}{2}}) \, dx + \int x^{-\frac{1}{2}} \, dx$$

Do each of these bits separately.

$$= \frac{x^{\frac{5}{2}}}{\left(\frac{5}{2}\right)} - \frac{2x^{\frac{3}{2}}}{\left(\frac{3}{2}\right)} + \frac{x^{\frac{1}{2}}}{\left(\frac{1}{2}\right)} + C$$

$$= \frac{2(\sqrt{x})^5}{5} - \frac{4(\sqrt{x})^3}{3} + 2\sqrt{x} + C$$

Q1 Hint: Remember f'(x) is just another way of saying $\frac{dy}{dx}$.

When you integrate f'(x) you get f(x) and when you differentiate f(x) you get f'(x).

Q1   Find f(x) when f'(x) is given by the following:

a) $5x + 3x^{-4}$

b) $4x(x^2 - 1)$

c) $(x - 3)^2$

d) $x\left(6x + \frac{4}{x^4}\right)$

e) $\left(x + \frac{2}{x}\right)^2$

f) $x\left(3x^{\frac{1}{2}} - \frac{2}{x^{\frac{4}{3}}}\right)$

g) $6\sqrt{x} - \frac{1}{x^2}$

h) $\frac{2}{\sqrt{x}} - 7x^2\sqrt{x}$

i) $5(\sqrt{x})^3 - \frac{3x}{\sqrt{x}}$

Q2   Find the following integrals:

a) $\int (0.55x^{0.1} - 3x^{-1.5}x)\, dx$

b) $\int \left(8x^3 - \frac{2}{\sqrt{x}} + \frac{5}{x^2}\right) dx$

c) $\int \left((\sqrt{x})^5 + \frac{1}{2\sqrt{x}}\right) dx$

d) $\int \left(\sqrt{x}\left(7x^2 - 1 - \frac{2}{x}\right)\right) dx$

e) $\int (3x - 5\sqrt{x})^2\, dx$

f) $\int \left(\frac{2x^3 - \sqrt{x}}{x}\right) dx$

g) $\int \left(\frac{10x^2 + 3x + 4}{\sqrt{x}}\right) dx$

h) $\int \left(\frac{(5x - 3)^2}{\sqrt{x}}\right) dx$

i) $\int (\sqrt{x}(3 - \sqrt{x})^2)\, dx$

j) $\int (x^{\frac{1}{2}} + 1)(x^{-\frac{1}{2}} - 3)\, dx$

Q3   Given that $\frac{dy}{dx} = 1.5x^2 - \frac{4}{x^3}$, find y.

Q4   Given that $f'(x) = \frac{4}{3\left(x^{\frac{1}{3}}\right)^4} + 5x^{\frac{3}{2}}$, find f(x).

Q5   Find $\int \left(\sqrt{x}\left(\frac{3x^3}{2} - \frac{1}{x^2}\right)\right) dx$.

Q6   Find $\int \left(\frac{(\sqrt{x} + 3)(\sqrt{x} - 1)}{\sqrt{x}}\right) dx$.

Q7   Find $\int \left(\sqrt{x}\left(\sqrt{x} - \frac{1}{\sqrt{x}}\right)^2\right) dx$.

Integrating to find equations of curves

As you saw in Chapter 6, **differentiating** the equation of a curve gives its **gradient**. **Integrating** the gradient of a curve does the **opposite** — it gives you the **equation** of the curve.

But integrating actually gives you **many** possible curves because of the **constant of integration**, C. C can take any value and each different value represents a different curve (all vertically shifted copies of each other).

So to find the equation of a **particular curve** by integration you need to know the coordinates of **one point** on it, which you can use to find C.

Example 1

The curve $y = f(x)$ goes through the point (2, 16) and $\dfrac{dy}{dx} = 2x^3$.
Find the equation of the curve.

You know the derivative $\dfrac{dy}{dx}$ and need to find y.

$$\frac{dy}{dx} = 2x^3$$

So integrating gives...

$$y = \int 2x^3 \, dx = \frac{2x^4}{4} + C = \boxed{\frac{x^4}{2} + C}$$

Check this is correct by differentiating it and making sure you get what you started with.

$$y = \frac{x^4}{2} + C$$
$$\frac{dy}{dx} = \frac{1}{2}(4x^3) + 0$$
$$\frac{dy}{dx} = 2x^3$$

So this function's got the correct derivative — but you've not finished yet. You now need to find C — and you do this by using the fact that it goes through the point (2, 16).

$$y = \frac{x^4}{2} + C$$

Putting $x = 2$ and $y = 16$ in the above equation gives...

$$16 = \frac{2^4}{2} + C$$
$$\Rightarrow 16 = 2^3 + C$$
$$\Rightarrow \boxed{C = 8}$$

So the solution you need is:

$$\boxed{y = \frac{x^4}{2} + 8}$$

Example 2

The curve $y = f(x)$ goes through the point (2, 8) and $f'(x) = 6x(x - 1)$. Find $f(x)$.

You know $f'(x)$ and need to find the function $f(x)$.

$$f'(x) = 6x(x - 1) = 6x^2 - 6x$$

So integrate...

$$f(x) = \int (6x^2 - 6x)\, dx$$
$$\Rightarrow f(x) = \frac{6x^3}{3} - \frac{6x^2}{2} + C$$
$$\Rightarrow f(x) = 2x^3 - 3x^2 + C$$

Check this is correct by differentiating...

$$f(x) = 2x^3 - 3x^2 + C$$
$$f'(x) = 2(3x^2) - 3(2x^1)$$
$$f'(x) = 6x^2 - 6x$$

You now need to find C using the point (2, 8).

Put $x = 2$ and $y = 8$ into $f(x) = 2x^3 - 3x^2 + C$.

$$8 = (2 \times 2^3) - (3 \times 2^2) + C$$
$$\Rightarrow 8 = 16 - 12 + C$$
$$\Rightarrow C = 4$$

Tip: It may seem odd to substitute the value of y into an equation without any y's, but remember that y is just the same as $f(x)$, so put the value for y wherever you see $f(x)$.

So the answer is: $f(x) = 2x^3 - 3x^2 + 4$

It's a cubic equation — and the graph looks like this...

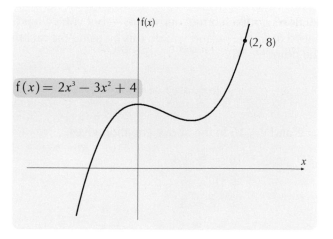

$f(x) = 2x^3 - 3x^2 + 4$

(2, 8)

Q1 For each of the following, the curve $y = f(x)$ passes through the given point. Find $f(x)$.

a) $f'(x) = 4x^3$, $(0, 5)$

b) $f'(x) = 3x^2 - 4x + 3$, $(1, -3)$

c) $f'(x) = 6x(x + 2)$, $(-1, 1)$

d) $f'(x) = \dfrac{5}{x^2} + 2x$, $(5, 4)$

e) $f'(x) = 3x^2(x - 4)$, $(2, -10)$

f) $f'(x) = (3x + 1)(x - 1)$, $(3, -3)$

g) $f'(x) = x(x + \dfrac{3}{x^3})$, $(-3, 5)$

h) $f'(x) = \dfrac{9x^3 + 2x^{-2}}{x}$, $(-1, 2)$

Q2 A curve that passes through the point $(2, -3)$ has derivative
$$\frac{dy}{dx} = (x - 2)(3x - 4)$$
Find the equation of the curve.

Q3 A curve $y = f(x)$ that passes through the point $(4, 9)$ has gradient function
$$f'(x) = \frac{3}{\sqrt{x}} + 2x$$
Find the equation of the curve.

Q3 Hint: The gradient function is just the function which tells you the gradient — the derivative.

Q4 The gradient function of a curve is given by
$$\frac{dy}{dx} = 3\sqrt{x} + \frac{1}{x^2}$$
Find the equation of the curve if it passes through the point $(1, 7)$.

Q5 Consider $\dfrac{dy}{dt} = (\sqrt{t} - 3)^2$.

Given that $y = 9$ when $t = 4$, find y as a function of t.

Q6 The curve $y = f(x)$ goes through the point $\left(1, \dfrac{1}{3}\right)$ and $f'(x) = \sqrt{x}\,(5x - 1)$. Find $f(x)$.

Q7 The curve $y = f(x)$ has derivative $f'(x) = x^2 + \dfrac{2}{x^{\frac{3}{2}}}$ and passes through the point $\left(1, -\dfrac{5}{3}\right)$. Find the equation of the curve.

Q8 The gradient function of a curve is given by $\dfrac{dy}{dx} = \dfrac{x - 6}{x^3} + 2$.

Find the equation of the curve if it passes through the point $(3, -1)$.

Review Exercise — Chapter 7

Q1 Find f(x) in each case below. Give each term in its simplest form.

a) $f'(x) = x^{-\frac{1}{2}} + 4 - 5x^3$

b) $f'(x) = 2x + \dfrac{3}{x^2}$

c) $f'(x) = 6x^2 - \dfrac{1}{3\sqrt{x}}$

Q2 Work out the equation of the curve that has derivative $\dfrac{dy}{dx} = 6x - 7$ and goes through the point (1, 0).

Q3 Find $\displaystyle\int\left(4x^2 + \dfrac{3}{\sqrt{x}} - 2\right)dx$.

Q4 Find $\displaystyle\int (3\sqrt{x} + 3)^2\, dx$.

Q5 The gradient function of a curve is given by
$$\frac{dy}{dx} = 2(3x - 6.5)$$
The curve passes through the point (1, 2).

a) Find the equation of the curve.

b) Sketch the curve, stating the coordinates of the points where the curve crosses the axes.

Q6 A curve $y = f(x)$ that passes through the origin has derivative
$$\frac{dy}{dx} = 6x^2 + 6x - 5$$

a) Find the equation of the curve.

b) Factorise and hence sketch the curve, showing the points where the curve cuts the axes.

Q7 The gradient of a curve C is given by
$$\frac{dy}{dx} = \frac{(x+2)(x-2)}{\sqrt{x}}, \quad x > 0$$

a) Show that $\dfrac{dy}{dx}$ can be written in the form $Ax^{\frac{3}{2}} + Bx^{-\frac{1}{2}}$, where A and B are integers.

b) The point $\left(1, \dfrac{7}{5}\right)$ lies on C. Find the equation of C.

Q8 The curve C with equation $y = f(x)$ has derivative
$$f'(x) = 6x^2 - 12 - \frac{8}{x^2}, \quad x > 0$$
and passes through the point P with coordinates (–2, 5).
Find the equation of the curve C.

Q9 The curve $y = f(x)$ passes through the point P with coordinates (1, –9).
Given that
$$f'(x) = \frac{5x^2 + 1}{x^{\frac{1}{2}}} - 10, \quad x > 0,$$
find the equation of the curve.

1 a) Show that $(5 + 2\sqrt{x})^2$ can be written in the form $a + b\sqrt{x} + cx$,
       stating the values of the constants a, b and c.

       (3 marks)

   b) Find $\int (5 + 2\sqrt{x})^2 \, dx$.

       (3 marks)

2 The curve C has the equation $y = f(x)$, $x > 0$. $f'(x)$ is given as $2x + 5\sqrt{x} + \dfrac{6}{x^2}$.

   A point P on curve C has the coordinates $(3, 7)$.

   Find $f(x)$, giving your answer in its simplest form.

   (6 marks)

3 $f'(x) = \dfrac{1}{\sqrt{36x}} - 2\left(\sqrt{\dfrac{1}{x^3}}\right)$ where $x > 0$.

   a) Show that $f'(x) = Ax^{-\frac{1}{2}} - Bx^{-\frac{3}{2}}$ and give the values of A and B.

       (3 marks)

   b) The curve C is given by $y = f(x)$ and goes through point $P(1, 7)$.
       Find the equation of the curve.

       (4 marks)

4 Curve C has equation $y = f(x)$, $x \neq 0$, where the derivative is given by $f'(x) = x^3 - \dfrac{2}{x^2}$.

   The point $P(1, 2)$ lies on C.

   a) Find the equation for the tangent to C at the point P, giving your answer
       in the form $y = mx + c$, where m and c are integers.

       (4 marks)

   b) Find $f(x)$.

       (5 marks)

5   $f'(x) = (x - 1)(3x - 1)$ where $x > 0$.

    a)   The curve C is given by $y = f(x)$ and goes through point P (3, 10). Find $f(x)$.

        (6 marks)

    b)   The equation for the normal to C at the point P can be written
        in the form $y = \dfrac{a - x}{b}$ where a and b are integers.
        Find the values of a and b.

        (4 marks)

6   The curve C passes through the point P with coordinates (4, 1) and has derivative
$$f'(x) = 2x - 3\sqrt{x} + \frac{16}{x^2}, \ x > 0.$$

    a)   Find f(x), simplifying your answer.

        (6 marks)

    b)   Find the equation of the tangent to C at P,
        giving your answer in the form $y = mx + c$.

        (4 marks)

7   Consider the equation $y^{\frac{1}{2}} = 1 + 3\sqrt{x}$.

    a)   Show that y can be written in the form $y = ax + bx^{\frac{1}{2}} + c$.

        (2 marks)

    b)   Hence find $\int y \, dx$.

        (3 marks)

8   A curve passes through the point P with coordinates (4, –6).
    Given that
$$\frac{dy}{dx} = 3\sqrt{x} - \frac{5}{\sqrt{x}}, x > 0.$$

    a)   Find the equation of the curve in the form $y = f(x)$.

        (5 marks)

    b)   Find the equation of the normal to the curve at P, giving your
        answer in the form $ax + by + c = 0$, where a, b and c are integers.

        (4 marks)

Glossary

A

Algebraic expression
An **expression** which contains **constants** and / or **variables**.

Arithmetic sequence / series
A **sequence** or **series** where successive terms have a common difference.

Asymptote
A **line** which a curve gets infinitely closer to, but **never** touches.

C

Coefficient
The **constant** multiplying the **variable(s)** in an algebraic **term**.

Common denominator
A denominator (i.e. bottom of a fraction) which is shared by all fractions in an **expression**.

Common difference
The difference between two successive terms in an arithmetic progression.

Common factor
A factor which is shared by all the **terms** in an **expression**.

Completing the square
Rewriting a **quadratic function** as: $p(x + q)^2 + r$. Useful for solving equations or sketching curves.

Constant
A fixed numerical value in an **expression**.

Constant of integration
A constant term in an **integral** representing any number.

Cubic equation
An **equation** that can be written $ax^3 + bx^2 + cx + d = 0$ (where $a \neq 0$).

D

Derivative
The result you get when you **differentiate** something

Differentiation
An algebraic process for finding the **gradient** of a function.
 $\frac{dy}{dx}$ is 'derivative of y with respect to x'

Discriminant
The discriminant of a **quadratic** function $ax^2 + bx + c$ is the value of $b^2 - 4ac$.

E

Elimination
Method for **solving** linear simultaneous equations, by matching coefficients and then **eliminating** a variable.

Equation
A mathematical statement containing an '=' sign and at least one **variable** or **constant**.

Expression
Any combination of numbers, **variables**, **functions** and operations (+, −, ×, ÷ etc.) Unlike an **equation**, it doesn't have an equals sign.

F

Factor
A factor of a **term** or **expression** is something which divides into it.

Factorising
The opposite of multiplying out brackets. **Brackets** are put in to write an expression as a product of its **factors**.

Formula
A standard **equation** used to calculate a quantity or measure, e.g. volume.

f′(x)
The derivative of f(x) with respect to x.

f″(x)
The second order derivative of f(x) with respect to x.

Function
A function gives different 'outputs' for different 'inputs'. They are usually defined by an **algebraic expression** — plugging in different input values for the **variable** produces different output values.

Function notation f(x)
Standard way of referring to functions. E.g. function g defined by g(x) = x^2 + 5.

G

Gradient
A number representing the steepness of a straight line or of a curve at a given point.

Gradient function
A **function** that can be used to find the **gradient** at any point on a curve.

I

Identity
An **equation** that is true for all values of the **variable**, usually denoted by the '≡' sign.

Index
For a^n, n is the index and is often referred to as a **power**.

Inequality
An **expression** which contains one of the following symbols: >, <, ≥, ≤. Like an equation, but produces a range of solutions.

Integer
A positive or negative whole number (including 0).

Integral
The result you get when you **integrate** something.

Integration
Process for finding the equation of a function, given its **gradient function** — the opposite of **differentiation**.

Intercept
The coordinates at which the graph of a function crosses one of the axes.

Irrational number
A number that can't be expressed as the **quotient** (division) of two **integers**. Examples include **surds** and π.

Linear inequality
An inequality that can be written as $ax + b > cx + d$.

Maximum
The highest point on a graph, or on a section of a graph (this is a local maximum).

Minimum
The lowest point on a graph or on a section of a graph (this is a local minimum).

Normal
A straight line passing through a curve that is perpendicular (at right angles) to the curve at the point it crosses it.

nth term
A formula that gives any term in a sequence or series from its position n.

Power
Another word for **index**.

Progression
Another word for **sequence**.

Quadratic equation
An **equation** that can be written $ax^2 + bx + c = 0$ where $a \neq 0$.

Quadratic formula
A formula for solving a **quadratic equation** $ax^2 + bx + c = 0$ given by $x = \dfrac{-b \pm \sqrt{b^2 - 4ac}}{2a}$.

Quadratic inequality
An **inequality** that can be written as $ax^2 + bx + c \geq 0$, where $a \neq 0$. It can be solved by looking at the shape of the quadratic graph.

Quotient
Fancy word for the result of a division.

Rational number
A number that can be written as the **quotient** (division) of two **integers**, where the denominator is non-zero.

Rationalising the denominator
The process of removing **surds** from the denominator of a fraction.

Reciprocal function
A function of the form $y = \dfrac{k}{x^n}$ ($n > 0$), where k is a constant.

Recurrence relation
A formula or rule for a sequence that shows how each term can be found from the previous one.

Repeated root
If a quadratic (or cubic) when **factorised** has the same factor twice (or three times), this gives a repeated **root**.

Root
The roots of a function f(x) are the values of x where f(x) = 0.

Second order derivative
The result of **differentiating** a function twice — it tells you the rate of change of the gradient of a function. $\dfrac{d^2 y}{dx^2}$ means 'second order derivative of y with respect to x'.

Sequence
An ordered list of numbers (referred to as terms) that follow a set pattern. E.g. 2, 6, 10, ... or –4, 1, –4, 1, ...

Series
An ordered list of numbers, just like a **sequence**, but where the terms are being added together (to find a sum).

Sigma notation
Used for the sum of series. E.g. $\displaystyle\sum_{n=1}^{15}(2n + 3)$ is the sum of the first 15 terms of the series with nth term $2n + 3$.

Simultaneous equations
A set of equations containing two or more unknown quantities, often x and y, for which the same set of values satisfy each equation.

Solution
The value or values (usually of a **variable**) that satisfy a problem, e.g. an **equation** or **inequality**.

Substitution
Method for **solving** simultaneous equations, where you replace each occurrence of one unknown with an expression in terms of the other unknown.

Surd
A number that can only be expressed precisely by using a square root sign.

Tangent
A straight line which just touches a curve at a point. Its **gradient** is the same as the curve's gradient at that point.

Term
A collection of numbers, **variables** and brackets all multiplied or divided together.

Variable
A letter in an expression representing an unknown which, unlike a **constant**, can take on different values.

Vertex
Turning point of a graph — the max or min point for a quadratic graph.

Answers

Chapter 1: Algebra
1. Algebraic Expressions
Exercise 1.1 — Expanding brackets

Q1 **a)** $5(x + 4) = 5x + (5 \times 4) = 5x + 20$

b) $a(4 - 2b) = 4a + (a \times -2b) = 4a - 2ab$

c) $-2(x^2 + y) = -2x^2 - 2y$

d) $pq(r - q) = pqr - pqq = pqr - pq^2$

e) $6mn(m + 1) = 6mnm + 6mn = 6m^2n + 6mn$

f) $7z^2(2 + z) = 14z^2 + 7z^2z = 14z^2 + 7z^3$

g) $3xy(3 - x^2 - xy)$
$$= (3xy \times 3) + (3xy \times -x^2) + (3xy \times -xy)$$
$$= 9xy - 3x^3y - 3x^2y^2$$

h) $-4ht(t^2 - 2ht - 3h^3)$
$$= -4ht \times t^2 + (-4ht \times -2ht) + (-4ht \times -3h^3)$$
$$= -4ht^3 + 8h^2t^2 + 12h^4t$$

i) $7xy(x^2 + z^2) = (7xy \times x^2) + (7xy \times z^2)$
$$= 7x^3y + 7xyz^2$$

j) $4(x + 2) + 3(x - 5) = 4x + 8 + 3x - 15$
$$= 7x - 7$$

k) $p(3p^2 - 2q) + (q + 4p^3)$
$$= (p \times 3p^2) + (p \times -2q) + q + 4p^3$$
$$= 3p^3 - 2pq + q + 4p^3 = 7p^3 - 2pq + q$$

Don't forget to simplify your answer if possible.

Q2 **a)** $(x + 5)(x - 3) = x^2 - 3x + 5x - 15$
$$= x^2 + 2x - 15$$

b) $(2z + 3)(3z - 2) = 6z^2 - 4z + 9z - 6$
$$= 6z^2 + 5z - 6$$

c) $(u + 8)^2 = (u + 8)(u + 8)$
$$= u^2 + 8u + 8u + 64$$
$$= u^2 + 16u + 64$$

d) $(ab + cd)(ac + bd)$
$$= abac + abbd + cdac + cdbd$$
$$= a^2bc + ab^2d + ac^2d + bcd^2$$

e) $(10 + f)(2f^2 - 3g)$
$$= 20f^2 - 30g + 2f^3 - 3fg$$

f) $(7 + q)(7 - q) = 49 - 7q + 7q - q^2$
$$= 49 - q^2$$

g) $(2 - 3w)^2 = (2 - 3w)(2 - 3w)$
$$= 2^2 - 6w - 6w + 9w^2$$
$$= 4 - 12w + 9w^2$$

h) $(4rs^2 + 3)^2 = (4rs^2 + 3)(4rs^2 + 3)$
$$= 16r^2s^4 + 12rs^2 + 12rs^2 + 9$$
$$= 16r^2s^4 + 24rs^2 + 9$$

i) $(5k^2l - 2kn)^2 = (5k^2l - 2kn)(5k^2l - 2kn)$
$$= 25k^4l^2 - 10k^3nl - 10k^3nl + 4k^2n^2$$
$$= 25k^4l^2 - 20k^3ln + 4k^2n^2$$

In parts c), g), h) and i), you could get straight to the answer by using $(a + b)^2 = a^2 + 2ab + b^2$.

Q3 **a)** $(l + 5)(l^2 + 2l + 3)$
$$= l(l^2 + 2l + 3) + 5(l^2 + 2l + 3)$$
$$= l^3 + 2l^2 + 3l + 5l^2 + 10l + 15$$
$$= l^3 + 7l^2 + 13l + 15$$

b) $(2 + q)(3 - q + 4q^2)$
$$= 2(3 - q + 4q^2) + q(3 - q + 4q^2)$$
$$= 6 - 2q + 8q^2 + 3q - q^2 + 4q^3$$
$$= 6 + q + 7q^2 + 4q^3$$

c) $(m + 1)(m + 2)(m - 4)$
$$= (m^2 + 2m + m + 2)(m - 4)$$
$$= (m^2 + 3m + 2)(m - 4)$$
$$= m^2(m - 4) + 3m(m - 4) + 2(m - 4)$$
$$= m^3 - 4m^2 + 3m^2 - 12m + 2m - 8$$
$$= m^3 - m^2 - 10m - 8$$

d) $(r + s)^3 = (r + s)(r + s)(r + s)$
$$= (r^2 + rs + sr + s^2)(r + s)$$
$$= (r^2 + 2rs + s^2)(r + s)$$
$$= r^2(r + s) + 2rs(r + s) + s^2(r + s)$$
$$= r^3 + r^2s + 2r^2s + 2rs^2 + rs^2 + s^3$$
$$= r^3 + 3rs^2 + 3r^2s + s^3$$

e) $(4 + x + y)(1 - x - y)$
$$= 4(1 - x - y) + x(1 - x - y) + y(1 - x - y)$$
$$= 4 - 4x - 4y + x - x^2 - xy + y - xy - y^2$$
$$= 4 - 3x - 3y - 2xy - x^2 - y^2$$

f) $(2c^2 - cd + d)(2d - c - 5c^2)$
$$= 2c^2(2d - c - 5c^2) - cd(2d - c - 5c^2)$$
$$\qquad\qquad\qquad + d(2d - c - 5c^2)$$
$$= 4c^2d - 2c^3 - 10c^4 - 2cd^2 + c^2d + 5c^3d$$
$$\qquad\qquad\qquad + 2d^2 - dc - 5c^2d$$
$$= -10c^4 - 2c^3 + 5c^3d - 2cd^2 - cd + 2d^2$$

Exercise 1.2 — Factorising

Q1 **a)** $9k + 15l = (3 \times 3k) + (3 \times 5l) = 3(3k + 5l)$

b) $u^2 - uv = u(u - v)$

c) $10w + 15 = (5 \times 2w) + (5 \times 3) = 5(2w + 3)$

d) $2x^2y - 12xy^2 = (2xy \times x) - (2xy \times 6y)$
$$= 2xy(x - 6y)$$

e) $f^2g^2 - fg = (fg \times fg) - (fg \times 1)$
$$= fg(fg - 1)$$

f) $3u^2v^2 + 5u^4v^4 + 12u^2v$
$$= (u^2v \times 3v) + (u^2v \times 5u^2v^3) + (u^2v \times 12)$$
$$= u^2v(3v + 5u^2v^3 + 12)$$

g) $p^3 + 3pq^3 + 2p$
$$= (p \times p^2) + (p \times 3q^3) + (p \times 2)$$
$$= p(p^2 + 3q^3 + 2)$$

h) $abcde - bcdef - cdefg$
$$= (cde \times ab) - (cde \times bf) - (cde \times fg)$$
$$= cde(ab - bf - fg)$$

i) $11xy^2 - 11x^2y - 11x^2y^2$
$$= (11xy \times y) - (11xy \times x) - (11xy \times xy)$$
$$= 11xy(y - x - xy)$$

j) $mnp^2 + 7m^2np^3 = (mnp^2 \times 1) + (mnp^2 \times 7mp)$
$$= mnp^2(1 + 7mp)$$

Q2 **a)** $x^2 - y^2 = (x + y)(x - y)$
This is just using the formula for the 'difference of two squares'.

b) $9a^2 - 4b^2 = (3a)^2 - (2b)^2 = (3a + 2b)(3a - 2b)$

c) $25x^2 - 49z^2 = (5x)^2 - (7z)^2 = (5x + 7z)(5x - 7z)$

d) $a^2c - 16b^2c = c(a^2 - 16b^2)$
$$= c(a^2 - (4b)^2) = c(a + 4b)(a - 4b)$$

Q3 **a)** $(4 - z)^2(2 - z) + p(2 - z)$
$$= (2 - z)[(4 - z)^2 + p]$$

b) $(r - d)^3 + 5(r - d)^2 = (r - d)^2[(r - d) + 5]$
$$= (r - d)^2(r - d + 5)$$

c) $(b + c)^5(a + b) - (b + c)^5$
$$= (b + c)^5[(a + b) - 1]$$
$$= (b + c)^5(a + b - 1)$$

d) $l^2m(a - 2x) + rp^2(2x - a)$
$$= l^2m(a - 2x) + rp^2(-(a - 2x))$$
$$= l^2m(a - 2x) - rp^2(a - 2x)$$
$$= (a - 2x)(l^2m - rp^2)$$
You might have factorised this slightly differently and ended up with $(2x - a)(rp^2 - l^2m)$ instead.

Q4 **a)** $(p + q)^2 + 2q(p + q) = (p + q)[(p + q) + 2q]$
$$= (p + q)(p + 3q)$$

b) $2(2x - y)^2 - 6x(2x - y)$
$$= 2(2x - y)[(2x - y) - 3x]$$
$$= -2(2x - y)(x + y)$$

---

c) $(r + 6s)^2 - (r + 6s)(r - s)$
$$= (r + 6s)[(r + 6s) - (r - s)]$$
$$= (r + 6s)(7s) = 7s(r + 6s)$$

d) $(l + w + h)^2 - l(l + w + h)$
$$= (l + w + h)[(l + w + h) - l]$$
$$= (l + w + h)(w + h)$$

Q5 **a)** $(m + 5)(m^2 - 5m + 25)$
$$= m(m^2 - 5m + 25) + 5(m^2 - 5m + 25)$$
$$= m^3 - 5m^2 + 25m + 5m^2 - 25m + 125$$
$$= m^3 + 125$$

b) $(p - 2q)(p^2 + 2pq + 4q^2)$
$$= p(p^2 + 2pq + 4q^2) - 2q(p^2 + 2pq + 4q^2)$$
$$= p^3 + 2p^2q + 4pq^2 - 2p^2q - 4pq^2 - 8q^3$$
$$= p^3 - 8q^3$$
Parts a) and b) were likely to need the brackets expanding because the quadratic in the second bracket won't factorise.

c) $(u - v)(u + v) - (u + v)^2$
$$= (u + v)[(u - v) - (u + v)]$$
$$= (u + v)(-2v) = -2v(u + v)$$

d) $(c + d)^3 - c(c + d)^2 - d(c + d)^2$
$$= (c + d)^2[(c + d) - c - d]$$
$$= (c + d)^2(0) = 0$$

Exercise 1.3 — Algebraic fractions

Q1 **a)** The common denominator is 3×4:
$$\frac{x}{3} + \frac{x}{4} = \frac{4x}{12} + \frac{3x}{12} = \frac{7x}{12}$$

b) The common denominator is t^2:
$$\frac{2}{t} + \frac{13}{t^2} = \frac{2t}{t^2} + \frac{13}{t^2} = \frac{2t + 13}{t^2}$$

c) The common denominator is $2 \times p \times 5 \times q = 10pq$:
$$\frac{1}{2p} - \frac{1}{5q} = \frac{5q}{10pq} - \frac{2p}{10pq} = \frac{5q - 2p}{10pq}$$

d) The common denominator is $a \times b \times c$:
$$\frac{ab}{c} + \frac{bc}{a} + \frac{ca}{b} = \frac{abab}{abc} + \frac{bcbc}{abc} + \frac{caca}{abc}$$
$$= \frac{a^2b^2 + b^2c^2 + c^2a^2}{abc}$$

e) The common denominator is mn:
$$\frac{2}{mn} - \frac{3m}{n} + \frac{n^2}{m} = \frac{2}{mn} - \frac{3m^2}{mn} + \frac{n^3}{mn}$$
$$= \frac{2 - 3m^2 + n^3}{mn}$$

f) The common denominator is $a^3 \times b^3 = a^3b^3$:
$$\frac{2}{ab^3} - \frac{9}{a^3b} = \frac{2a^2}{a^3b^3} - \frac{9b^2}{a^3b^3} = \frac{2a^2 - 9b^2}{a^3b^3}$$

Q2 a) The common denominator is $(y-1)(y-2)$:

$$\frac{5}{y-1} + \frac{3}{y-2}$$

$$= \frac{5(y-2)}{(y-1)(y-2)} + \frac{3(y-1)}{(y-1)(y-2)}$$

$$= \frac{5(y-2) + 3(y-1)}{(y-1)(y-2)}$$

$$= \frac{5y - 10 + 3y - 3}{(y-1)(y-2)}$$

$$= \frac{8y - 13}{(y-1)(y-2)}$$

b) The common denominator is $(r-5)(r+3)$:

$$\frac{7}{r-5} - \frac{4}{r+3} = \frac{7(r+3)}{(r-5)(r+3)} - \frac{4(r-5)}{(r-5)(r+3)}$$

$$= \frac{7(r+3) - 4(r-5)}{(r-5)(r+3)}$$

$$= \frac{7r + 21 - 4r + 20}{(r-5)(r+3)}$$

$$= \frac{3r + 41}{(r-5)(r+3)}$$

c) The common denominator is $p(p-3)$:

$$\frac{8}{p} - \frac{1}{p-3} = \frac{8(p-3)}{p(p-3)} - \frac{p}{p(p-3)}$$

$$= \frac{8p - 24 - p}{p(p-3)} = \frac{7p - 24}{p(p-3)}$$

d) The common denominator is $2(w-2)(w-7)$:

$$\frac{w}{2(w-2)} + \frac{3w}{w-7}$$

$$= \frac{w(w-7)}{2(w-2)(w-7)} + \frac{3w \times 2(w-2)}{2(w-2)(w-7)}$$

$$= \frac{w^2 - 7w}{2(w-2)(w-7)} + \frac{6w(w-2)}{2(w-2)(w-7)}$$

$$= \frac{w^2 - 7w + 6w(w-2)}{2(w-2)(w-7)}$$

$$= \frac{w^2 - 7w + 6w^2 - 12w}{2(w-2)(w-7)}$$

$$= \frac{7w^2 - 19w}{2(w-2)(w-7)}$$

e) The common denominator is $(z+2)(z+4)$:

$$\frac{z+1}{z+2} - \frac{z+3}{z+4}$$

$$= \frac{(z+1)(z+4)}{(z+2)(z+4)} - \frac{(z+2)(z+3)}{(z+2)(z+4)}$$

$$= \frac{(z+1)(z+4) - (z+2)(z+3)}{(z+2)(z+4)}$$

$$= \frac{(z^2 + 5z + 4) - (z^2 + 5z + 6)}{(z+2)(z+4)}$$

$$= \frac{-2}{(z+2)(z+4)}$$

f) The common denominator is $(q+1)(q-2)$:

$$\frac{1}{q+1} + \frac{3}{q-2}$$

$$= \frac{(q-2)}{(q+1)(q-2)} + \frac{3(q+1)}{(q+1)(q-2)}$$

$$= \frac{(q-2) + 3(q+1)}{(q+1)(q-2)}$$

$$= \frac{q - 2 + 3q + 3}{(q+1)(q-2)}$$

$$= \frac{4q + 1}{(q+1)(q-2)}$$

Q3 a) $\dfrac{2x+10}{6} = \dfrac{2(x+5)}{6} = \dfrac{x+5}{3}$

b) $\dfrac{6a - 12b - 15c}{3} = \dfrac{3(2a - 4b - 5c)}{3}$

$$= 2a - 4b - 5c$$

c) $\dfrac{np^2 - 2n^2p}{np} = \dfrac{np(p - 2n)}{np} = p - 2n$

d) $\dfrac{4st + 6s^2t + 9s^3t}{2t} = \dfrac{st(4 + 6s + 9s^2)}{2t}$

$$= \frac{s(4 + 6s + 9s^2)}{2}$$

e) $\dfrac{10yz^3 - 40y^3z^3 + 60y^2z^3}{10z^2} = \dfrac{10yz^3(1 - 4y^2 + 6y)}{10z^2}$

$$= yz(1 - 4y^2 + 6y)$$

f) $\dfrac{12cd - 6c^2d + 3c^3d^2}{12c^2de} = \dfrac{3cd(4 - 2c + c^2d)}{12c^2de}$

$$= \frac{4 - 2c + c^2d}{4ce}$$

2. Laws of Indices

Exercise 2.1 — Laws of indices

Q1 a) $2^3 \times 2^4 = 2^{3+4} = 2^7$

b) $10 \times 10^4 = 10^{1+4} = 10^5$

c) $7^2 \times 7^5 \times 7^3 = 7^{2+5+3} = 7^{10}$

d) $p^6 \times p^{-4} \times p^5 = p^{6-4+5} = p^7$

e) $y^{-1} \times y^{-2} \times y^7 = y^{-1-2+7} = y^4$

f) $5^{\frac{1}{2}} \times 5^3 \times 5^{-\frac{3}{2}} = 5^{\frac{1}{2}+3-\frac{3}{2}} = 5^2$

g) $6^5 \div 6^2 = 6^{5-2} = 6^3$

h) $x^{10} \div x^9 = x^{10-9} = x^1 = x$

i) $3^4 \div 3^{-1} = 3^{4-(-1)} = 3^{4+1} = 3^5$

j) $\dfrac{7^{15}}{7^5} = 7^{15-5} = 7^{10}$

k) $\dfrac{6^{11}}{6} = 6^{11-1} = 6^{10}$

l) $\dfrac{r^2}{r^6} = r^{2-6} = r^{-4}$

m) $(3^2)^3 = 3^{2 \times 3} = 3^6$

n) $(10^6)^{-1} = 10^{6 \times (-1)} = 10^{-6}$

o) $(k^{-2})^5 = k^{(-2) \times 5} = k^{-10}$

p) $(t^8)^{\frac{1}{2}} = t^{8 \times \frac{1}{2}} = t^{\frac{8}{2}} = t^4$

q) $(z^4)^{-\frac{1}{8}} = z^{4 \times \left(-\frac{1}{8}\right)} = z^{-\frac{4}{8}} = z^{-\frac{1}{2}}$

r) $(8^{-6})^{-\frac{1}{2}} = 8^{-6 \times -\frac{1}{2}} = 8^{\frac{6}{2}} = 8^3$

s) $cd^2 \times c^3 d^4 = (c \times c^3) \times (d^2 \times d^4)$
$$= c^{1+3} \times d^{2 \times 4}$$
$$= c^{1+3} \times d^{2 \times 4}$$
$$= c^4 d^6$$

t) $\dfrac{p^5 q^4}{p^4 q} = (p^{5-4})(q^{4-1}) = p^1 q^3 = pq^3$

u) $\dfrac{c^{-1} d^{-2}}{c^2 d^4} = c^{-1-2} d^{-2-4} = c^{-3} d^{-6} = \dfrac{1}{c^3 d^6}$

v) $(ab^2)^2 = (a)^2 (b^2)^2 = a^2 b^{2 \times 2} = a^2 b^4$

w) $(x^2 y^3 z^4)^5 = (x^2)^5 (y^3)^5 (z^4)^5$
$$= (x^{2 \times 5})(y^{3 \times 5})(z^{4 \times 5}) = x^{10} y^{15} z^{20}$$

x) $\dfrac{12 y z^{-\frac{1}{2}}}{4 y z^{\frac{1}{2}}} = \left(\dfrac{12}{4}\right)\left(y^{1-1}\right)\left(z^{-\frac{1}{2}-\frac{1}{2}}\right) = 3 y^0 z^{-1} = \dfrac{3}{z}$

Q2 a) $4^{\frac{1}{2}} \times 4^{\frac{3}{2}} = 4^{\frac{1}{2}+\frac{3}{2}} = 4^2 = 16$

b) $\dfrac{2^3 \times 2}{2^5} = \dfrac{2^{3+1}}{2^5} = \dfrac{2^4}{2^5} = 2^{4-5} = 2^{-1} = \dfrac{1}{2}$

c) $\dfrac{7^5 \times 7^3}{7^6} = \dfrac{7^{5+3}}{7^6} = \dfrac{7^8}{7^6} = 7^{8-6} = 7^2 = 49$

d) $(3^2)^5 \div (3^3)^3 = 3^{2 \times 5} \div 3^{3 \times 3}$
$$= 3^{10} \div 3^9 = 3^{10-9} = 3^1 = 3$$

e) $\left(4^{-\frac{1}{2}}\right)^2 \times (4^{-3})^{-\frac{1}{3}} = 4^{-\frac{1}{2} \times 2} \times 4^{(-3) \times \left(-\frac{1}{3}\right)}$
$$= 4^{-1} \times 4^1 = 4^{-1+1}$$
$$= 4^0 = 1$$

f) $\dfrac{\left(2^{\frac{1}{2}}\right)^6 \times (2^{-2})^{-2}}{(2^{-1})^{-1}} = \dfrac{2^{\frac{1}{2} \times 6} \times 2^{(-2) \times (-2)}}{2^{(-1) \times (-1)}}$
$$= \dfrac{2^3 \times 2^4}{2^1} = \dfrac{2^{3+4}}{2^1}$$
$$= \dfrac{2^{3+4}}{2^1} = \dfrac{2^7}{2^1} = 2^6$$
$$= 64$$

g) $1^0 = 1$

h) $\left(\dfrac{4}{5}\right)^0 = 1$

i) $(-5.726324)^0 = 1$

Q3 a) $\dfrac{1}{p} = p^{-1}$

b) $\sqrt{q} = q^{\frac{1}{2}}$

c) $\sqrt{r^3} = (r^3)^{\frac{1}{2}} = r^{3 \times \frac{1}{2}} = r^{\frac{3}{2}}$

d) $\sqrt[4]{s^5} = (s^5)^{\frac{1}{4}} = s^{5 \times \frac{1}{4}} = s^{\frac{5}{4}}$

e) $\dfrac{1}{\sqrt[3]{t}} = \dfrac{1}{\left(t^{\frac{1}{3}}\right)} = t^{-\frac{1}{3}}$

Q4 a) $9^{\frac{1}{2}} = \sqrt{9} = 3$

b) $8^{\frac{1}{3}} = \sqrt[3]{8} = 2$

c) $4^{\frac{3}{2}} = 4^{\frac{1}{2} \times 3} = \left(4^{\frac{1}{2}}\right)^3 = (\sqrt{4})^3 = (2)^3 = 8$

d) $27^{-\frac{1}{3}} = \dfrac{1}{27^{\frac{1}{3}}} = \dfrac{1}{\sqrt[3]{27}} = \dfrac{1}{3}$

e) $16^{-\frac{3}{4}} = \dfrac{1}{16^{\frac{3}{4}}} = \dfrac{1}{\left(16^{\frac{1}{4}}\right)^3} = \dfrac{1}{(\sqrt[4]{16})^3} = \dfrac{1}{(2)^3} = \dfrac{1}{8}$

3. Surds

Exercise 3.1 — The laws of surds

Q1 a) $\sqrt{8} = \sqrt{4 \times 2} = \sqrt{4}\sqrt{2} = 2\sqrt{2}$

b) $\sqrt{24} = \sqrt{4 \times 6} = \sqrt{4}\sqrt{6} = 2\sqrt{6}$

c) $\sqrt{50} = \sqrt{25 \times 2} = \sqrt{25}\sqrt{2} = 5\sqrt{2}$

d) $\sqrt{63} = \sqrt{9 \times 7} = \sqrt{9}\sqrt{7} = 3\sqrt{7}$

e) $\sqrt{72} = \sqrt{36 \times 2} = \sqrt{36}\sqrt{2} = 6\sqrt{2}$

f) $\sqrt{\dfrac{5}{4}} = \dfrac{\sqrt{5}}{\sqrt{4}} = \dfrac{\sqrt{5}}{2}$

g) $\sqrt{\dfrac{7}{100}} = \dfrac{\sqrt{7}}{\sqrt{100}} = \dfrac{\sqrt{7}}{10}$

h) $\sqrt{\dfrac{11}{9}} = \dfrac{\sqrt{11}}{\sqrt{9}} = \dfrac{\sqrt{11}}{3}$

Q2 a) $2\sqrt{3} \times 4\sqrt{3} = 2 \times 4 \times \sqrt{3} \times \sqrt{3}$
$$= 8\sqrt{3}\sqrt{3} = 8 \times 3 = 24$$

b) $\sqrt{5} \times 3\sqrt{5} = 3\sqrt{5}\sqrt{5} = 3 \times 5 = 15$

c) $(\sqrt{7})^2 = \sqrt{7}\sqrt{7} = 7$

d) $2\sqrt{2} \times 3\sqrt{5} = 2 \times 3 \times \sqrt{2} \times \sqrt{5}$
$$= 6\sqrt{2}\sqrt{5} = 6\sqrt{10}$$

e) $(2\sqrt{11})^2 = (2\sqrt{11})(2\sqrt{11}) = 4\sqrt{11}\sqrt{11}$
$$= 4 \times 11 = 44$$

f) $5\sqrt{8} \times 2\sqrt{2} = 5\sqrt{4 \times 2} \times 2\sqrt{2}$
$$= 5 \times 2\sqrt{2} \times 2\sqrt{2}$$
$$= 5 \times 4 \times \sqrt{2} \times \sqrt{2}$$
$$= 20 \times 2 = 40$$

g) $4\sqrt{3} \times 2\sqrt{27} = 4 \times 2 \times \sqrt{3}\sqrt{27}$
$$= 8\sqrt{3 \times 27} = 8\sqrt{81}$$
$$= 8 \times 9 = 72$$

h) $2\sqrt{6} \times 5\sqrt{24} = 2 \times 5 \times \sqrt{6} \times \sqrt{24}$
$$= 10\sqrt{6 \times 24} = 10\sqrt{144}$$
$$= 10 \times 12 = 120$$

i) $\dfrac{\sqrt{10}}{6} \times \dfrac{12}{\sqrt{5}} = \dfrac{12\sqrt{10}}{6\sqrt{5}} = \dfrac{12}{6} \times \dfrac{\sqrt{10}}{\sqrt{5}}$

$\qquad = 2 \times \sqrt{\dfrac{10}{5}} = 2\sqrt{2}$

j) $\dfrac{\sqrt{12}}{3} \times \dfrac{2}{\sqrt{27}} = \dfrac{2\sqrt{12}}{3\sqrt{27}} = \dfrac{2}{3} \times \dfrac{\sqrt{12}}{\sqrt{27}}$

$\qquad = \dfrac{2}{3} \times \dfrac{\sqrt{4 \times 3}}{\sqrt{9 \times 3}} = \dfrac{2}{3} \times \dfrac{\sqrt{4}\sqrt{3}}{\sqrt{9}\sqrt{3}}$

$\qquad = \dfrac{2}{3} \times \dfrac{2\sqrt{3}}{3\sqrt{3}} = \dfrac{2}{3} \times \dfrac{2}{3} = \dfrac{4}{9}$

Q3 a) $\sqrt{20} + \sqrt{5} = \sqrt{4 \times 5} + \sqrt{5} = \sqrt{4}\sqrt{5} + \sqrt{5}$

$\qquad = 2\sqrt{5} + \sqrt{5} = 3\sqrt{5}$

b) $\sqrt{32} - \sqrt{8} = \sqrt{16 \times 2} - \sqrt{4 \times 2}$

$\qquad = \sqrt{16}\sqrt{2} - \sqrt{4}\sqrt{2}$

$\qquad = 4\sqrt{2} - 2\sqrt{2} = 2\sqrt{2}$

c) $\sqrt{27} + 4\sqrt{3} = \sqrt{9 \times 3} + 4\sqrt{3} = \sqrt{9}\sqrt{3} + 4\sqrt{3}$

$\qquad = 3\sqrt{3} + 4\sqrt{3} = 7\sqrt{3}$

d) $2\sqrt{8} - 3\sqrt{2} = 2\sqrt{4 \times 2} - 3\sqrt{2}$

$\qquad = 2\sqrt{4}\sqrt{2} - 3\sqrt{2}$

$\qquad = 4\sqrt{2} - 3\sqrt{2} = \sqrt{2}$

e) $3\sqrt{10} + \sqrt{250} = 3\sqrt{10} + \sqrt{25 \times 10}$

$\qquad = 3\sqrt{10} + \sqrt{25}\sqrt{10}$

$\qquad = 3\sqrt{10} + 5\sqrt{10}$

$\qquad = 8\sqrt{10}$

f) $4\sqrt{27} + 2\sqrt{48} + 5\sqrt{108}$

$\qquad = 4\sqrt{9 \times 3} + 2\sqrt{16 \times 3} + 5\sqrt{36 \times 3}$

$\qquad = 4\sqrt{9}\sqrt{3} + 2\sqrt{16}\sqrt{3} + 5\sqrt{36}\sqrt{3}$

$\qquad = 12\sqrt{3} + 8\sqrt{3} + 30\sqrt{3} = 50\sqrt{3}$

Q4 a) $(1 + \sqrt{2})(2 + \sqrt{2}) = 2 + \sqrt{2} + 2\sqrt{2} + \sqrt{2}\sqrt{2}$

$\qquad = 2 + 3\sqrt{2} + 2 = 4 + 3\sqrt{2}$

b) $(3 + 4\sqrt{3})(2 - \sqrt{3})$

$\qquad = 6 - 3\sqrt{3} + 8\sqrt{3} - 4\sqrt{3}\sqrt{3}$

$\qquad = 6 + 5\sqrt{3} - 12 = 5\sqrt{3} - 6$

c) By the difference of two squares rule:

$\qquad (\sqrt{11} + 2)(\sqrt{11} - 2) = (\sqrt{11})^2 - 2^2$

$\qquad\qquad = 11 - 4 = 7$

d) By the difference of two squares rule:

$\qquad (9 - 2\sqrt{5})(9 + 2\sqrt{5}) = 9^2 - (2\sqrt{5})^2$

$\qquad\qquad = 81 - 20 = 61$

e) $(\sqrt{3} + 2)^2 = (\sqrt{3} + 2)(\sqrt{3} + 2)$

$\qquad = \sqrt{3}\sqrt{3} + 2\sqrt{3} + 2\sqrt{3} + 4$

$\qquad = 3 + 4\sqrt{3} + 4 = 7 + 4\sqrt{3}$

f) $(3\sqrt{5} - 4)^2 = (3\sqrt{5} - 4)(3\sqrt{5} - 4)$

$\qquad = (3\sqrt{5})^2 - 12\sqrt{5} - 12\sqrt{5} + 16$

$\qquad = 45 - 24\sqrt{5} + 16$

$\qquad = 61 - 24\sqrt{5}$

You could have used the rule $(a + b)^2 = a^2 + 2ab + b^2$ for parts e and f.

Q5 You may want to draw the triangle:

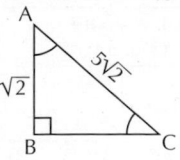

Using Pythagoras:

$(\sqrt{2})^2 + (BC)^2 = (5\sqrt{2})^2$

So, $2 + (BC)^2 = 50$

$\Rightarrow (BC)^2 = 48$

$\Rightarrow BC = \sqrt{48} = \sqrt{16 \times 3} = 4\sqrt{3}$

Exercise 3.2 — Rationalising the denominator

Q1 a) $\dfrac{6}{\sqrt{3}} = \dfrac{6\sqrt{3}}{\sqrt{3}\sqrt{3}} = \dfrac{6\sqrt{3}}{3} = 2\sqrt{3}$

b) $\dfrac{21}{\sqrt{7}} = \dfrac{21\sqrt{7}}{\sqrt{7}\sqrt{7}} = \dfrac{21\sqrt{7}}{7} = 3\sqrt{7}$

c) $\dfrac{30}{\sqrt{5}} = \dfrac{30\sqrt{5}}{\sqrt{5}\sqrt{5}} = \dfrac{30\sqrt{5}}{5} = 6\sqrt{5}$

d) $\sqrt{45} + \dfrac{15}{\sqrt{5}} = \sqrt{45} + \dfrac{15\sqrt{5}}{\sqrt{5}\sqrt{5}}$

$\qquad = \sqrt{45} + \dfrac{15\sqrt{5}}{5}$

$\qquad = \sqrt{9 \times 5} + 3\sqrt{5}$

$\qquad = \sqrt{9}\sqrt{5} + 3\sqrt{5}$

$\qquad = 3\sqrt{5} + 3\sqrt{5} = 6\sqrt{5}$

e) $\dfrac{\sqrt{54}}{3} - \dfrac{12}{\sqrt{6}} = \dfrac{\sqrt{9 \times 6}}{3} - \dfrac{12\sqrt{6}}{\sqrt{6}\sqrt{6}}$

$\qquad = \dfrac{\sqrt{9}\sqrt{6}}{3} - \dfrac{12\sqrt{6}}{6}$

$\qquad = \dfrac{3\sqrt{6}}{3} - \dfrac{12\sqrt{6}}{6}$

$\qquad = \sqrt{6} - 2\sqrt{6} = -\sqrt{6}$

f) $\dfrac{\sqrt{300}}{5} + \dfrac{30}{\sqrt{12}} = \dfrac{\sqrt{100 \times 3}}{5} + \dfrac{30\sqrt{12}}{\sqrt{12}\sqrt{12}}$

$\qquad = \dfrac{\sqrt{100}\sqrt{3}}{5} + \dfrac{30\sqrt{4 \times 3}}{12}$

$\qquad = \dfrac{10\sqrt{3}}{5} + \dfrac{30\sqrt{4}\sqrt{3}}{12}$

$\qquad = 2\sqrt{3} + \dfrac{60\sqrt{3}}{12}$

$\qquad = 2\sqrt{3} + 5\sqrt{3} = 7\sqrt{3}$

Q2 a) $\dfrac{4}{1 + \sqrt{3}} = \dfrac{4(1 - \sqrt{3})}{(1 + \sqrt{3})(1 - \sqrt{3})}$

$\qquad = \dfrac{4 - 4\sqrt{3}}{1 - 3} = \dfrac{4 - 4\sqrt{3}}{-2} = -2 + 2\sqrt{3}$

The denominator was simplified by using the difference of two squares rule. It will be used in almost every question in the rest of this exercise, so watch out for it and make sure you understand what's going on.

b) $\dfrac{11}{4 - \sqrt{5}} = \dfrac{11(4 + \sqrt{5})}{(4 - \sqrt{5})(4 + \sqrt{5})} = \dfrac{44 + 11\sqrt{5}}{16 - 5}$

$= \dfrac{44 + 11\sqrt{5}}{11} = 4 + \sqrt{5}$

c) $\dfrac{8}{\sqrt{7} + 3} = \dfrac{8(\sqrt{7} - 3)}{(\sqrt{7} + 3)(\sqrt{7} - 3)} = \dfrac{8\sqrt{7} - 24}{7 - 9}$

$= \dfrac{8\sqrt{7} - 24}{-2} = \dfrac{24 - 8\sqrt{7}}{2} = 12 - 4\sqrt{7}$

d) $\dfrac{8}{-1 + \sqrt{5}} = \dfrac{8(-1 - \sqrt{5})}{(-1 + \sqrt{5})(-1 - \sqrt{5})}$

$= \dfrac{-8 - 8\sqrt{5}}{1 - 5} = \dfrac{-8 - 8\sqrt{5}}{-4}$

$= 2 + 2\sqrt{5}$

e) $\dfrac{1}{\sqrt{26} - 5} = \dfrac{\sqrt{26} + 5}{(\sqrt{26} - 5)(\sqrt{26} + 5)} = \dfrac{\sqrt{26} + 5}{26 - 25}$

$= \dfrac{\sqrt{26} + 5}{1} = 5 + \sqrt{26}$

f) $\dfrac{18}{\sqrt{10} - 4} = \dfrac{18(\sqrt{10} + 4)}{(\sqrt{10} - 4)(\sqrt{10} + 4)} = \dfrac{18\sqrt{10} + 72}{10 - 16}$

$= \dfrac{18\sqrt{10} + 72}{-6} = -12 - 3\sqrt{10}$

Q3 **a)** $\dfrac{\sqrt{2} + 1}{\sqrt{2} - 1} = \dfrac{(\sqrt{2} + 1)(\sqrt{2} + 1)}{(\sqrt{2} - 1)(\sqrt{2} + 1)}$

$= \dfrac{2 + \sqrt{2} + \sqrt{2} + 1}{2 - 1}$

$= \dfrac{2\sqrt{2} + 3}{1} = 3 + 2\sqrt{2}$

b) $\dfrac{\sqrt{5} + 3}{\sqrt{5} - 2} = \dfrac{(\sqrt{5} + 3)(\sqrt{5} + 2)}{(\sqrt{5} - 2)(\sqrt{5} + 2)}$

$= \dfrac{5 + 2\sqrt{5} + 3\sqrt{5} + 6}{5 - 4}$

$= \dfrac{11 + 5\sqrt{5}}{1} = 11 + 5\sqrt{5}$

c) $\dfrac{3 - \sqrt{3}}{4 + \sqrt{3}} = \dfrac{(3 - \sqrt{3})(4 - \sqrt{3})}{(4 + \sqrt{3})(4 - \sqrt{3})}$

$= \dfrac{12 - 3\sqrt{3} - 4\sqrt{3} + 3}{16 - 3}$

$= \dfrac{15 - 7\sqrt{3}}{13} = \dfrac{15}{13} - \dfrac{7}{13}\sqrt{3}$

d) $\dfrac{3\sqrt{5} - 1}{2\sqrt{5} - 3} = \dfrac{(3\sqrt{5} - 1)(2\sqrt{5} + 3)}{(2\sqrt{5} - 3)(2\sqrt{5} + 3)}$

$= \dfrac{(2\sqrt{5})(3\sqrt{5}) + 9\sqrt{5} - 2\sqrt{5} - 3}{(2\sqrt{5})^2 - 9}$

$= \dfrac{27 + 7\sqrt{5}}{(2\sqrt{5})^2 - 9} = \dfrac{27 + 7\sqrt{5}}{11}$

$= \dfrac{27}{11} + \dfrac{7}{11}\sqrt{5}$

e) $\dfrac{\sqrt{2} + \sqrt{3}}{3\sqrt{2} - \sqrt{3}} = \dfrac{(\sqrt{2} + \sqrt{3})(3\sqrt{2} + \sqrt{3})}{(3\sqrt{2} - \sqrt{3})(3\sqrt{2} + \sqrt{3})}$

$= \dfrac{3\sqrt{2}\sqrt{2} + \sqrt{2}\sqrt{3} + 3\sqrt{3}\sqrt{2} + 3}{(3\sqrt{2})^2 - (\sqrt{3})^2}$

$= \dfrac{6 + \sqrt{2}\sqrt{3} + 3\sqrt{3}\sqrt{2} + 3}{18 - 3}$

$= \dfrac{9 + 4\sqrt{3}\sqrt{2}}{15} = \dfrac{9}{15} + \dfrac{4}{15}\sqrt{2}\sqrt{3}$

$= \dfrac{3}{5} + \dfrac{4}{15}\sqrt{6}$

f) $\dfrac{2\sqrt{7} - \sqrt{5}}{\sqrt{7} + 2\sqrt{5}} = \dfrac{(2\sqrt{7} - \sqrt{5})(\sqrt{7} - 2\sqrt{5})}{(\sqrt{7} + 2\sqrt{5})(\sqrt{7} - 2\sqrt{5})}$

$= \dfrac{2\sqrt{7}\sqrt{7} - 4\sqrt{7}\sqrt{5} - \sqrt{5}\sqrt{7} + 10}{7 - (2\sqrt{5})^2}$

$= \dfrac{14 - 4\sqrt{7}\sqrt{5} - \sqrt{5}\sqrt{7} + 10}{7 - 20}$

$= \dfrac{24 - 5\sqrt{35}}{-13} = -\dfrac{24}{13} + \dfrac{5}{13}\sqrt{35}$

Q4 $8 = (\sqrt{5} - 1)x$

$\Rightarrow x = \dfrac{8}{(\sqrt{5} - 1)} = \dfrac{8(\sqrt{5} + 1)}{(\sqrt{5} - 1)(\sqrt{5} + 1)}$

$= \dfrac{8\sqrt{5} + 8}{5 - 1} = \dfrac{8\sqrt{5} + 8}{4} = 2 + 2\sqrt{5}$

Q5 $5 + \sqrt{7} = (3 - \sqrt{7})y$

$\Rightarrow y = \dfrac{5 + \sqrt{7}}{3 - \sqrt{7}} = \dfrac{(5 + \sqrt{7})(3 + \sqrt{7})}{(3 - \sqrt{7})(3 + \sqrt{7})}$

$= \dfrac{15 + 5\sqrt{7} + 3\sqrt{7} + 7}{9 - 7}$

$= \dfrac{22 + 8\sqrt{7}}{2} = 11 + 4\sqrt{7}$

Q6 The area of a rectangle is given by area(A) = length(l) × width(w) so:

$(2 + \sqrt{2}) = l \times (3\sqrt{2} - 4)$

$\Rightarrow l = \dfrac{(2 + \sqrt{2})}{(3\sqrt{2} - 4)} = \dfrac{(2 + \sqrt{2})(3\sqrt{2} + 4)}{(3\sqrt{2} - 4)(3\sqrt{2} + 4)}$

$= \dfrac{6\sqrt{2} + 8 + 6 + 4\sqrt{2}}{(3\sqrt{2})^2 - 16}$

$= \dfrac{14 + 10\sqrt{2}}{18 - 16} = \dfrac{14 + 10\sqrt{2}}{2}$

$= (7 + 5\sqrt{2})\,\text{cm}$

Don't forget the units here.

Review Exercise — Chapter 1

Q1 A, C and D are identities because the left-hand side is identical to the right-hand side in each case — you can rearrange one side to get the other. B is not an identity because the left-hand side is only equal to the right-hand side for certain values of x and y, not all values.

Q2 **a)** $a^2 - b^2$ by the difference of two squares.

b) $a^2 + ab + ab + b^2 = a^2 + 2ab + b^2$

c) $35xy + 125y^2 + 175xy - 100y^2 = 25y^2 + 210xy$

d) $x(3x + y + 7) + 3y(3x + y + 7) + 2(3x + y + 7)$

$= 3x^2 + 10xy + 3y^2 + 13x + 23y + 14$

Q3 a) $xy(2x + a + 2y)$

b) $a^2x(1 + b^2x)$

c) $8(2y + xy + 7x)$

d) $(x - 2)(x - 3)$

Q4 a) The common denominator is $5 \times 12 = 60$:
$$\frac{2x \times 20}{60} + \frac{y \times 5}{60} + \frac{x \times 12}{60} = \frac{52x + 5y}{60}$$

b) The common denominator is x^2y^2:
$$\frac{5 \times x}{x^2y^2} - \frac{2 \times y}{x^2y^2} = \frac{5x - 2y}{x^2y^2}$$

c) The common denominator is
$x(x - y)(x + y) = x(x^2 - y^2)$ so :
$$\frac{1 \times (x^2 - y^2)}{x(x^2 - y^2)} + \frac{x \times x(x - y)}{x(x^2 - y^2)} + \frac{y \times x(x + y)}{x(x^2 - y^2)}$$
$$= \frac{x^3 + x^2 - y^2 + xy^2}{x(x^2 - y^2)}$$

Q5 a) $\dfrac{2a \times 2}{2b} - \dfrac{a}{2b} = \dfrac{4a}{2b} - \dfrac{a}{2b} = \dfrac{3a}{2b}$

b) $\dfrac{2p(p - q)}{(p + q)(p - q)} + \dfrac{2q(p + q)}{(p + q)(p - q)} = \dfrac{2(p^2 + q^2)}{p^2 - q^2}$

Q6 a) $x^{3 + 5} = x^8$ **b)** $a^{7 + 8} = a^{15}$ **c)** $x^{8 - 2} = x^6$

d) $a^{2 \times 4} = a^8$

e) $(x^{1 + 3})(y^{2 + 1})z = x^4y^3z$ **f)** $a^{-1}b^2c^5 = \dfrac{b^2c^5}{a}$

Q7 a) $\sqrt{16} = 4$ **b)** $\sqrt[3]{8} = 2$

c) $(\sqrt[4]{16})^3 = 2^3 = 8$ **d)** $x^0 = 1$

e) $\dfrac{1}{\sqrt{49}} = \dfrac{1}{7}$

Q8 a) $x^2 = 5 \Rightarrow x = \pm\sqrt{5}$

b) $(x + 2)^2 = 3 \Rightarrow x = -2 \pm \sqrt{3}$

Q9 a) $\sqrt{4 \times 7} = 2\sqrt{7}$ **b)** $\dfrac{\sqrt{5}}{\sqrt{36}} = \dfrac{\sqrt{5}}{6}$

c) $\sqrt{9 \times 2} = 3\sqrt{2}$ **d)** $\dfrac{\sqrt{9}}{\sqrt{16}} = \dfrac{3}{4}$

Q10 a) $\dfrac{8}{\sqrt{2}} = \dfrac{8}{\sqrt{2}} \times \dfrac{\sqrt{2}}{\sqrt{2}} = \dfrac{8\sqrt{2}}{2} = 4\sqrt{2}$

b) $\dfrac{\sqrt{2}}{2} = \dfrac{\sqrt{2}}{(\sqrt{2})^2} = \dfrac{1}{\sqrt{2}}$

Q11 $(6\sqrt{3} + 2\sqrt{7})(6\sqrt{3} + 2\sqrt{7})$
$= (6\sqrt{3})^2 + 2(2\sqrt{7})(6\sqrt{3}) + (2\sqrt{7})^2$
$= 108 + 24\sqrt{7}\sqrt{3} + 28$
$= 136 + 24\sqrt{21}$

Q12 $\dfrac{2(3 - \sqrt{7})}{(3 + \sqrt{7})(3 - \sqrt{7})} = \dfrac{6 - 2\sqrt{7}}{9 - 7} = 3 - \sqrt{7}$

Exam-Style Questions — Chapter 1

Q1 a) $27^{\frac{1}{3}} = \sqrt[3]{27}$
$= 3$ *[1 mark]*

b) $27^{\frac{4}{3}} = \left(27^{\frac{1}{3}}\right)^4$ *[1 mark]*
$= 3^4 = 3 \times 3 \times 3 \times 3 = 9 \times 9$
$= 81$ *[1 mark]*

Q2 a) $(5\sqrt{3})^2 = (5^2)(\sqrt{3})^2 = 25 \cdot 3$
$= 75$ *[1 mark]*

b) $(5 + \sqrt{6})(2 - \sqrt{6})$
$= 10 - 5\sqrt{6} + 2\sqrt{6} - 6$ *[1 mark]*
$= 4 - 3\sqrt{6}$ *[1 mark]*

Q3 $10000\sqrt{10} = 10^4 \cdot 10^{\frac{1}{2}}$ *[1 mark]*
$= 10^{4 + \frac{1}{2}}$ *[1 mark]*
$= 10^{\frac{9}{2}}$
so $k = \dfrac{9}{2}$ *[1 mark]*

Q4 Multiply top and bottom by $3 + \sqrt{5}$ to 'rationalise the denominator':
$$\frac{5 + \sqrt{5}}{3 - \sqrt{5}} = \frac{(5 + \sqrt{5})(3 + \sqrt{5})}{(3 - \sqrt{5})(3 + \sqrt{5})} \quad \textit{[1 mark]}$$
$$= \frac{15 + 5\sqrt{5} + 3\sqrt{5} + 5}{9 - 5} \quad \textit{[1 mark]}$$
$$= \frac{20 + 8\sqrt{5}}{4} \quad \textit{[1 mark]}$$
$$= 5 + 2\sqrt{5} \quad \textit{[1 mark]}$$

Q5 $2x^4 - 32x^2 = 2x^2(x^2 - 16)$
$= 2x^2(x + 4)(x - 4)$

[3 marks available in total — 1 mark for each correct factor]

Q6 $\dfrac{x + 5x^3}{\sqrt{x}} = x^{-\frac{1}{2}}(x + 5x^3)$ *[1 mark]*
$= x^{\frac{1}{2}} + 5x^{\frac{5}{2}}$ *[1 mark]*

Q7 $\dfrac{(5 + 4\sqrt{x})^2}{2x} = \dfrac{25 + 40\sqrt{x} + 16x}{2x}$ *[1 mark]*
$= \dfrac{1}{2}x^{-1}(25 + 40x^{\frac{1}{2}} + 16x)$ *[1 mark]*
$= \dfrac{25}{2}x^{-1} + 20x^{-\frac{1}{2}} + 8,$
so $P = 20$ and $Q = 8$ *[1 mark]*

Chapter 2:
Quadratics and Cubics

1. Quadratic Equations
Exercise 1.1 — Factorising a quadratic

Q1 a) $x^2 - 6x + 5 = (x - 5)(x - 1)$

b) $x^2 - 3x - 18 = (x - 6)(x + 3)$

c) $x^2 + 22x + 121 = (x + 11)(x + 11) = (x + 11)^2$

d) $x^2 - 12x = x(x - 12)$

Note that if every term contains an x, you can just take a factor of x out of the bracket.

e) $y^2 - 13y + 42 = (y - 6)(y - 7)$

f) $x^2 + 51x + 144 = (x + 48)(x + 3)$

g) $x^2 - 121 = (x + 11)(x - 11)$

If there is no 'b' term, see if the expression is a 'difference of two squares' (chances are it will be).

h) $x^2 + 2\sqrt{3}x + 3 = (x + \sqrt{3})(x + \sqrt{3}) = (x + \sqrt{3})^2$

Q2 a) $x^2 - 2x - 8 = 0$
$\Rightarrow (x - 4)(x + 2) = 0$
$\Rightarrow x - 4 = 0$ or $x + 2 = 0$
$\Rightarrow x = 4$ or $x = -2$

b) $2x^2 + 2x - 40 = 0$
$2(x^2 + x - 20) = 0$

This is an example of a question where you can simplify the equation before factorising. You can divide through by 2.

$x^2 + x - 20 = 0$
$\Rightarrow (x + 5)(x - 4) = 0$
$\Rightarrow x + 5 = 0$ or $x - 4 = 0$
$\Rightarrow x = -5$ or $x = 4$

c) $p^2 + 21p + 38 = 0$
$\Rightarrow (p + 19)(p + 2) = 0$
$\Rightarrow p + 19 = 0$ or $p + 2 = 0$
$\Rightarrow p = -19$ or $p = -2$

d) $x^2 - 15x + 54 = 0$
$\Rightarrow (x - 9)(x - 6) = 0$
$\Rightarrow x - 9 = 0$ or $x - 6 = 0$
$\Rightarrow x = 9$ or $x = 6$

e) $x^2 + 18x = -65$
$\Rightarrow x^2 + 18x + 65 = 0$
$\Rightarrow (x + 5)(x + 13) = 0$
$\Rightarrow x + 5 = 0$ or $x + 13 = 0$
$\Rightarrow x = -5$ or $x = -13$

f) $x^2 - x = 42$
$\Rightarrow x^2 - x - 42 = 0$
$\Rightarrow (x - 7)(x + 6) = 0$
$\Rightarrow x - 7 = 0$ or $x + 6 = 0$
$\Rightarrow x = 7$ or $x = -6$

g) $x^2 + 1100x + 100\,000 = 0$
$\Rightarrow (x + 100)(x + 1000) = 0$
$\Rightarrow x + 100 = 0$ or $x + 1000 = 0$
$\Rightarrow x = -100$ or $x = -1000$

h) $3x^2 - 3x - 6 = 0$
$\Rightarrow 3(x^2 - x - 2) = 0$
$\Rightarrow x^2 - x - 2 = 0$
$\Rightarrow (x - 2)(x + 1) = 0$
$\Rightarrow x - 2 = 0$ or $x + 1 = 0$
$\Rightarrow x = 2$ or $x = -1$

Q3 a) $4x^2 - 4x - 3 = (2x + 1)(2x - 3)$

b) $2x^2 + 23x + 11 = (2x + 1)(x + 11)$

c) $7x^2 - 19x - 6 = (7x + 2)(x - 3)$

d) $-x^2 - 5x + 36 = (-x + 4)(x + 9)$

e) $2x^2 - 2 = 2(x^2 - 1)$
$= 2(x + 1)(x - 1)$

f) $3x^2 - 3 = 3(x^2 - 1)$
$= 3(x + 1)(x - 1)$

Q4 a) $-5x^2 - 22x + 15 = 0$
$\Rightarrow 5x^2 + 22x - 15 = 0$
$\Rightarrow (5x - 3)(x + 5) = 0$
$\Rightarrow 5x - 3 = 0$ or $x + 5 = 0$
$\Rightarrow x = \frac{3}{5}$ or $x = -5$

If you want to get rid of the minus sign in front of the x^2 just multiply through by -1, the right hand side will remain O and the left hand side will change signs.

b) $32x^2 + 60x + 13 = 0$
$\Rightarrow (4x + 1)(8x + 13) = 0$
$\Rightarrow 4x + 1 = 0$ or $8x + 13 = 0$
$\Rightarrow x = -\frac{1}{4}$ or $x = -\frac{13}{8}$

c) $5a^2 + 12a = 9$
$\Rightarrow 5a^2 + 12a - 9 = 0$
$\Rightarrow (5a - 3)(a + 3) = 0$
$\Rightarrow 5a - 3 = 0$ or $a + 3 = 0$
$\Rightarrow a = \frac{3}{5}$ or $a = -3$

d) $8x^2 + 22x + 15 = 0$
$\Rightarrow (4x + 5)(2x + 3) = 0$
$\Rightarrow 4x + 5 = 0$ or $2x + 3 = 0$
$\Rightarrow x = -\frac{5}{4}$ or $x = -\frac{3}{2}$

Q5 $(x - 1)(x - 2) = 37 - x$

$\Rightarrow x^2 - 3x + 2 = 37 - x$

$\Rightarrow x^2 - 2x - 35 = 0$

$\Rightarrow (x - 7)(x + 5) = 0$

$\Rightarrow x - 7 = 0$ or $x + 5 = 0$

$\Rightarrow x = 7$ or $x = -5$

Q6 The function f(x) meets the x-axis when f(x) = 0 so set the expression for f(x) equal to 0.

$-x^2 + 7x + 30 = 0$

$\Rightarrow x^2 - 7x - 30 = 0$

$\Rightarrow (x - 10)(x + 3) = 0$

$\Rightarrow x - 10 = 0$ or $x + 3 = 0$

$\Rightarrow x = 10$ or $x = -3$

So the graph of f(x) meets the x-axis when $x = 10$ and $x = -3$.

Q7 *This question looks harder because it has y's in it as well as x's — just treat the y as a constant. You'll need two numbers which multiply to give $8y^2$ and add or subtract to give 6y.*

4y and 2y multiply to $8y^2$ and add to give 6y so these are the numbers you need.

$x^2 + 6xy + 8y^2 = (x + 4y)(x + 2y)$

Exercise 1.2 — The quadratic formula

Q1 a) $x^2 - 4x = -2$

$\Rightarrow x^2 - 4x + 2 = 0$

$a = 1, b = -4, c = 2$

$x = \dfrac{-b \pm \sqrt{b^2 - 4ac}}{2a}$

$= \dfrac{-(-4) \pm \sqrt{(-4)^2 - 4 \times 1 \times 2}}{2 \times 1}$

$= \dfrac{4 \pm \sqrt{16 - 8}}{2}$

$= \dfrac{4 \pm \sqrt{8}}{2}$

$= \dfrac{4 \pm 2\sqrt{2}}{2}$

$= 2 \pm \sqrt{2}$

b) $x^2 - 2x - 44 = 0$

$a = 1, b = -2, c = -44$

$x = \dfrac{-b \pm \sqrt{b^2 - 4ac}}{2a}$

$= \dfrac{-(-2) \pm \sqrt{(-2)^2 - 4 \times 1 \times (-44)}}{2 \times 1}$

$= \dfrac{2 \pm \sqrt{4 + (4 \times 1 \times 44)}}{2}$

$= \dfrac{2 \pm \sqrt{180}}{2}$

$= \dfrac{2 \pm \sqrt{36 \times 5}}{2}$

$= \dfrac{2 \pm 6\sqrt{5}}{2}$

$= 1 \pm 3\sqrt{5}$

c) $x^2 - 14x + 42 = 0$

$a = 1, b = -14, c = 42$

$x = \dfrac{-b \pm \sqrt{b^2 - 4ac}}{2a}$

$= \dfrac{-(-14) \pm \sqrt{(-14)^2 - 4 \times 1 \times 42}}{2 \times 1}$

$= \dfrac{14 \pm \sqrt{196 - 168}}{2}$

$= \dfrac{14 \pm \sqrt{28}}{2}$

$= \dfrac{14 \pm \sqrt{4 \times 7}}{2}$

$= \dfrac{14 \pm 2\sqrt{7}}{2}$

$= 7 \pm \sqrt{7}$

d) $4x^2 + 4x - 1 = 0$

$a = 4, b = 4, c = -1$

$x = \dfrac{-b \pm \sqrt{b^2 - 4ac}}{2a}$

$= \dfrac{-4 \pm \sqrt{(4)^2 - 4 \times 4 \times (-1)}}{2 \times 4}$

$= \dfrac{-4 \pm \sqrt{16 + 16}}{8}$

$= \dfrac{-4 \pm \sqrt{32}}{8}$

$= \dfrac{-4 \pm \sqrt{32}}{8}$

$= \dfrac{-4 \pm 4\sqrt{2}}{8}$

$= -\dfrac{1}{2} \pm \dfrac{1}{2}\sqrt{2}$

e) $x^2 - \dfrac{5}{6}x + \dfrac{1}{6} = 0$

$6x^2 - 5x + 1 = 0$

$a = 6, b = -5, c = 1$

$x = \dfrac{-b \pm \sqrt{b^2 - 4ac}}{2a}$

$= \dfrac{-(-5) \pm \sqrt{(-5)^2 - 4 \times 6 \times 1}}{2 \times 6}$

$= \dfrac{5 \pm \sqrt{25 - 24}}{12}$

$= \dfrac{5 \pm 1}{12}$

$= \dfrac{1}{2}$ or $\dfrac{1}{3}$

Removing the fractions right at the start here saves you lots of fraction headaches in the working. This one wasn't actually too hard to factorise — you'd get $(3x - 1)(2x - 1)$.

f) $x^2 - x - \frac{35}{2} = 0$

$a = 1,\ b = -1,\ c = -\frac{35}{2}$

$x = \dfrac{-b \pm \sqrt{b^2 - 4ac}}{2a}$

$= \dfrac{-(-1) \pm \sqrt{(-1)^2 - 4 \times 1 \times \left(-\frac{35}{2}\right)}}{2 \times 1}$

$= \dfrac{1 \pm \sqrt{1 + \left(4 \times 1 \times \frac{35}{2}\right)}}{2}$

$= \dfrac{1 \pm \sqrt{1 + 70}}{2}$

$= \dfrac{1 \pm \sqrt{71}}{2}$

Q2 a) $(x - 2 + \sqrt{5})(x - 2 - \sqrt{5})$

$= x(x - 2 - \sqrt{5})$
$\quad -2(x - 2 - \sqrt{5})$
$\quad + \sqrt{5}(x - 2 - \sqrt{5})$

$= x^2 - 2x - \sqrt{5}x$
$\quad - 2x + 4 + 2\sqrt{5}$
$\quad + \sqrt{5}x - 2\sqrt{5} - 5$

$= x^2 - 4x - 1$

Use the method for multiplying out long brackets from Chapter 1.

b) $x^2 - 4x - 1 = 0$

$a = 1,\ b = -4,\ c = -1$

$x = \dfrac{-b \pm \sqrt{b^2 - 4ac}}{2a}$

$= \dfrac{-(-4) \pm \sqrt{(-4)^2 - 4 \times 1 \times (-1)}}{2 \times 1}$

$= \dfrac{4 \pm \sqrt{16 + 4}}{2}$

$= \dfrac{4 \pm \sqrt{20}}{2}$

$= \dfrac{4 \pm 2\sqrt{5}}{2}$

$= 2 \pm \sqrt{5}$

c) The roots produced by the quadratic formula in part b) are the same as the numbers subtracted from x in the expression from a) — this is because it's just the factorised version of the same quadratic. If you put the factorised version equal to zero and solved the equation, you'd get the same roots.

Q3 $x^2 + 8x + 13 = 0$

$a = 1,\ b = 8,\ c = 13$

$x = \dfrac{-b \pm \sqrt{b^2 - 4ac}}{2a}$

$= \dfrac{-8 \pm \sqrt{8^2 - 4 \times 1 \times 13}}{2 \times 1}$

$= \dfrac{-8 \pm \sqrt{64 - 52}}{2}$

$= \dfrac{-8 \pm \sqrt{12}}{2}$

$= \dfrac{-8 \pm 2\sqrt{3}}{2}$

$= -4 \pm \sqrt{3}$

So A = -4 and B = 3.

Q4 a) $x^2 + x + \frac{1}{4} = 0$

$a = 1,\ b = 1,\ c = \frac{1}{4}$

$x = \dfrac{-b \pm \sqrt{b^2 - 4ac}}{2a}$

$= \dfrac{-1 \pm \sqrt{1^2 - 4 \times 1 \times \frac{1}{4}}}{2 \times 1}$

$= \dfrac{-1 \pm \sqrt{1 - 1}}{2}$

$= \dfrac{-1 \pm 0}{2}$

$= -\dfrac{1}{2}$

b) $25x^2 - 30x + 7 = 0$

$a = 25,\ b = -30,\ c = 7$

$x = \dfrac{-b \pm \sqrt{b^2 - 4ac}}{2a}$

$= \dfrac{-(-30) \pm \sqrt{(-30)^2 - 4 \times 25 \times 7}}{2 \times 25}$

$= \dfrac{30 \pm \sqrt{900 - 700}}{2 \times 25}$

$= \dfrac{30 \pm \sqrt{200}}{50}$

$= \dfrac{30 \pm 10\sqrt{2}}{50}$

$= \dfrac{30}{50} \pm \dfrac{10}{50}\sqrt{2}$

$= \dfrac{3}{5} \pm \dfrac{1}{5}\sqrt{2}$

c) $60x - 5 = -100x^2 - 3$

$\Rightarrow 100x^2 + 60x - 2 = 0$

$a = 100,\ b = 60,\ c = -2$

$x = \dfrac{-b \pm \sqrt{b^2 - 4ac}}{2a}$

$= \dfrac{-60 \pm \sqrt{60^2 - 4 \times 100 \times (-2)}}{2 \times 100}$

$= \dfrac{-60 \pm \sqrt{3600 + 800}}{200}$

$= \dfrac{-60 \pm \sqrt{4400}}{200}$

$= \dfrac{-60 \pm \sqrt{44 \times 100}}{200}$

$= \dfrac{-60 \pm \sqrt{4 \times 11 \times 100}}{200}$

$= \dfrac{-60 \pm \sqrt{4}\sqrt{100}\sqrt{11}}{200}$

$= \dfrac{-60 \pm 20\sqrt{11}}{200}$

$= -\dfrac{3}{10} \pm \dfrac{1}{10}\sqrt{11}$

d) $2x(x - 4) = 7 - 3x$

$\Rightarrow 2x^2 - 8x = 7 - 3x$

$\Rightarrow 2x^2 - 5x - 7 = 0$

$a = 2,\ b = -5,\ c = -7$

$x = \dfrac{-b \pm \sqrt{b^2 - 4ac}}{2a}$

$= \dfrac{-(-5) \pm \sqrt{(-5)^2 - 4 \times 2 \times (-7)}}{2 \times 2}$

$= \dfrac{5 \pm \sqrt{25 + 56}}{4}$

$= \dfrac{5 \pm \sqrt{81}}{4}$

$= \dfrac{5 \pm 9}{4}$

$= \dfrac{5 + 9}{4}$ or $\dfrac{5 - 9}{4}$

$= \dfrac{14}{4}$ or $\dfrac{-4}{4}$

$= \dfrac{7}{2}$ or -1

Exercise 1.3 — Completing the square

Q1 a) Take the square root of both sides to get:

$x + 4 = \pm\sqrt{25} \Rightarrow x = -4 \pm \sqrt{25} = -4 \pm 5$

So $x = 1$ or -9

b) Take the square root of both sides to get:

$5x - 3 = \pm\sqrt{21} \Rightarrow 5x = 3 \pm \sqrt{21} \Rightarrow x = \dfrac{3}{5} \pm \dfrac{\sqrt{21}}{5}$

Q2 a) $x^2 + 6x + 8 = (x + 3)^2 - 9 + 8 = (x + 3)^2 - 1$

b) $x^2 + 8x - 10 = (x + 4)^2 - 16 - 10 = (x + 4)^2 - 26$

c) $x^2 - 3x - 10 = \left(x - \dfrac{3}{2}\right)^2 - \dfrac{9}{4} - 10$

$= \left(x - \dfrac{3}{2}\right)^2 - \dfrac{9}{4} - \dfrac{40}{4} = \left(x - \dfrac{3}{2}\right)^2 - \dfrac{49}{4}$

d) $x^2 - 20x + 15 = (x - 10)^2 - 100 + 15$

$= (x - 10)^2 - 85$

e) $x^2 - 2mx + n = (x - m)^2 - m^2 + n$

$= (x - m)^2 + (-m^2 + n)$

f) $3x^2 - 12x + 7 = 3(x - 2)^2 - 12 + 7 = 3(x - 2)^2 - 5$

Q3 a) First complete the square of the expression:

$x^2 - 6x - 16 = (x - 3)^2 - 9 - 16 = (x - 3)^2 - 25$

Now set the completed square equal to zero:

$(x - 3)^2 - 25 = 0 \Rightarrow (x - 3)^2 = 25$

$\Rightarrow x - 3 = \pm\sqrt{25} \Rightarrow x = 3 \pm \sqrt{25} = 3 \pm 5$

$\Rightarrow x = 8$ or -2

b) Write the equation in standard quadratic form:

$p^2 - 10p = 200 \Rightarrow p^2 - 10p - 200 = 0$

Then complete the square of the expression:

$p^2 - 10p - 200 = (p - 5)^2 - 25 - 200$

$= (p - 5)^2 - 225$

Now set the completed square equal to zero:

$(p - 5)^2 - 225 = 0 \Rightarrow (p - 5)^2 = 225$

$\Rightarrow p - 5 = \pm\sqrt{225} \Rightarrow x = 5 \pm \sqrt{225} = 5 \pm 15$

$\Rightarrow p = 20$ or -10

c) First complete the square of the expression:

$x^2 + 2x + k = (x + 1)^2 - 1 + k = (x + 1)^2 + (k - 1)$

Now set the completed square equal to zero:

$(x + 1)^2 + (k - 1) = 0 \Rightarrow (x + 1)^2 = 1 - k$

$\Rightarrow x + 1 = \pm\sqrt{1 - k} \Rightarrow x = -1 \pm \sqrt{1 - k}$

d) Write the equation in standard quadratic form:

$9x^2 + 18x = 16 \Rightarrow 9x^2 + 18x - 16 = 0$

Then complete the square of the expression:

$9x^2 + 18x - 16 = 9(x + 1)^2 - 9 - 16$

$= 9(x + 1)^2 - 25$

Now set the completed square equal to zero:

$9(x + 1)^2 - 25 = 0 \Rightarrow 9(x + 1)^2 = 25$

$\Rightarrow (x + 1)^2 = \dfrac{25}{9}$

$\Rightarrow x + 1 = \pm\sqrt{\dfrac{25}{9}} \Rightarrow x = -1 \pm \sqrt{\dfrac{25}{9}}$

$\Rightarrow x = -1 \pm \dfrac{5}{3}$

So $x = \dfrac{2}{3}$ or $-\dfrac{8}{3}$

e) First complete the square of the expression:

$x^2 + 4x - 8 = (x + 2)^2 - 4 - 8 = (x + 2)^2 - 12$

Now set the completed square equal to zero:

$(x + 2)^2 - 12 = 0 \Rightarrow (x + 2)^2 = 12$

$\Rightarrow x + 2 = \pm\sqrt{12} \Rightarrow x = \pm\sqrt{12} - 2$

So $x = -2 \pm 2\sqrt{3}$

f) First complete the square of the expression:

$2x^2 - 12x + 9 = 2(x - 3)^2 - 18 + 9$

$= 2(x - 3)^2 - 9$

Now set the completed square equal to zero:

$2(x - 3)^2 - 9 = 0 \Rightarrow 2(x - 3)^2 = 9$

$\Rightarrow (x - 3)^2 = \dfrac{9}{2} \Rightarrow x - 3 = \pm\sqrt{\dfrac{9}{2}}$

$\Rightarrow x = 3 \pm \sqrt{\dfrac{9}{2}} \Rightarrow x = 3 \pm \dfrac{3}{\sqrt{2}} = 3 \pm \dfrac{3\sqrt{2}}{2}$

g) First divide through by 2:
$$x^2 - 6x - 27 = (x - 3)^2 - 9 - 27$$
$$= (x - 3)^2 - 36$$
Now set the completed square equal to zero:
$$(x - 3)^2 - 36 = 0 \Rightarrow (x - 3)^2 = 36$$
$$\Rightarrow x - 3 = \pm 6 \Rightarrow x = 3 \pm 6$$
So $x = 9$ or -3

h) First complete the square of the expression:
$$5x^2 - 3x + \frac{2}{5} = 5\left(x - \frac{3}{10}\right)^2 - \frac{9}{20} + \frac{2}{5}$$
$$= 5\left(x - \frac{3}{10}\right)^2 + \frac{-9 + 8}{20}$$
$$= 5\left(x - \frac{3}{10}\right)^2 - \frac{1}{20}$$
Now set the completed square equal to zero:
$$5\left(x - \frac{3}{10}\right)^2 - \frac{1}{20} = 0 \Rightarrow 5\left(x - \frac{3}{10}\right)^2 = \frac{1}{20}$$
$$\Rightarrow \left(x - \frac{3}{10}\right)^2 = \frac{1}{100} \Rightarrow x - \frac{3}{10} = \pm\sqrt{\frac{1}{100}}$$
$$\Rightarrow x - \frac{3}{10} = \pm\frac{1}{10} \Rightarrow x = \frac{3}{10} \pm \frac{1}{10}$$
So $x = \frac{2}{5}$ or $\frac{1}{5}$

Q4 First complete the square of the expression:
$$ax^2 + bx + c = a(x^2 + \frac{b}{a}x + \frac{c}{a})$$
$$= a\left(x + \frac{b}{2a}\right)^2 - \frac{b^2}{4a} + c$$

Now set the completed square equal to zero and rearrange to find the roots:
$$a\left(x + \frac{b}{2a}\right)^2 - \frac{b^2}{4a} + c = 0$$
$$\Rightarrow \left(x + \frac{b}{2a}\right)^2 = \frac{b^2}{4a^2} - \frac{c}{a}$$
$$\Rightarrow \left(x + \frac{b}{2a}\right)^2 = \frac{b^2 - 4ac}{4a^2}$$
$$\Rightarrow x + \frac{b}{2a} = \pm\sqrt{\frac{b^2 + 4ac}{4a^2}}$$
$$\Rightarrow x = -\frac{b}{2a} \pm \frac{\sqrt{b^2 - 4ac}}{2a}$$
$$\Rightarrow x = \frac{-b \pm \sqrt{b^2 - 4ac}}{2a}$$

This last question was quite tricky, but if you got there you should have noticed something quite special — you've just proved the quadratic formula... wow.

2. Quadratic Functions and Roots
Exercise 2.1
— The roots of a quadratic function
Q1 a) 2 real roots.

b) 1 real root.

c) no real roots.

d) 2 real roots.

Q2 Completing the square:
$$f(x) = x^2 + 6x + 10 = (x + 3)^2 - 9 + 10 = (x + 3)^2 + 1$$

The smallest the $(x + 3)^2$ bit can be is 0, and 1 is positive which means that f(x) is always positive and the smallest it can be is 1. So f(x) has no real roots.

Q3 $f(x) = -\left(x + \frac{7}{2}\right)^2 + \frac{25}{4} = 0$ when $\left(x + \frac{7}{2}\right)^2 = \frac{25}{4}$.
This can be solved by taking the square root (since the RHS is positive) — so it has real roots.

Exercise 2.2 — Using the discriminant
Q1 a) $a = 1$, $b = 8$, $c = 15$.
So $b^2 - 4ac = 8^2 - 4 \times 1 \times 15 = 64 - 60 = 4$.

b) $a = 1$, $b = 2\sqrt{3}$, $c = 3$.
So $b^2 - 4ac = (2\sqrt{3})^2 - 4 \times 1 \times 3 = 12 - 12 = 0$.

c) Write in standard form:
$(2x + 1)(5x - 3) = 10x^2 - x - 3$
so $a = 10$, $b = -1$ and $c = -3$.
$b^2 - 4ac = (-1)^2 - 4 \times 10 \times -3 = 1 + 120 = 121$

d) $a = -3$, $b = -\frac{11}{5}$, $c = -\frac{2}{5}$.
So $b^2 - 4ac = \left(-\frac{11}{5}\right)^2 - 4 \times (-3) \times \left(-\frac{2}{5}\right)$
$$= \frac{121}{25} - \frac{24}{5} = \frac{121}{25} - \frac{120}{25} = \frac{1}{25}$$

e) $a = 9$, $b = 20$, $c = 0$.
So $b^2 - 4ac = 20^2 - 4 \times 9 \times 0 = 400 - 0 = 400$.

f) $a = \frac{19}{16}$, $b = 0$, $c = -4$.
So $b^2 - 4ac = 0^2 - 4 \times \frac{19}{16} \times (-4) = 0 + 19 = 19$.

Q2 Find the discriminant of the equation by first writing it in standard form: $15x^2 + bx = 2 \Rightarrow 15x^2 + bx - 2 = 0$
$a = 15$, $b = b$, $c = -2$.
So $b^2 - 4ac = b^2 - 4 \times 15 \times (-2) = b^2 + 120$.
Now you know that the discriminant is 169 so let $b^2 + 120 = 169 \Rightarrow b^2 = 49 \Rightarrow b = \pm 7$.

Q3 First find the discriminant: $a = a$, $b = 7$, $c = \frac{1}{4}$.
So $b^2 - 4ac = 7^2 - 4 \times a \times \frac{1}{4} = 49 - a$.
The equation has one real root which means its discriminant must be 0. So $49 - a = 0 \Rightarrow a = 49$.

Q4 a) $a = 13$, $b = 8$, $c = 2$
so $b^2 - 4ac = 8^2 - 4 \times 13 \times 2 = 64 - 104 = -40$.
The discriminant is negative so the equation has no real roots.

b) $a = \frac{1}{3}$, $b = \frac{5}{2}$, $c = 3$
so $b^2 - 4ac = \left(\frac{5}{2}\right)^2 - 4 \times \frac{1}{3} \times 3 = \frac{25}{4} - 4$
$= \frac{25}{4} - \frac{16}{4} = \frac{9}{4}$
The discriminant is positive so the equation has two real roots.

Q5 $a = 1$, $b = -12$, $c = 27 + p$.
So $b^2 - 4ac = (-12)^2 - 4 \times 1 \times (27 + p)$
$= 144 - (108 + 4p) = 36 - 4p$.

If the equation has two distinct real roots, the discriminant must be positive so $36 - 4p > 0$
$\Rightarrow 36 > 4p \Rightarrow p < 9$.

Q6 $a = 10$, $b = -10$, $c = \frac{q}{2}$.

So $b^2 - 4ac = (-10)^2 - 4 \times 10 \times \frac{q}{2} = 100 - 20q$

If the equation has two distinct real roots, the discriminant must be positive so $100 - 20q > 0$
$\Rightarrow 100 > 20q \Rightarrow q < 5$.

Q7 $a = 2$, $b = 10p + 1$, $c = 5$.
So $b^2 - 4ac = (10p + 1)^2 - 4 \times 2 \times 5$
$= (100p^2 + 20p + 1) - 40$
$= 100p^2 + 20p - 39$.

If the equation has no real roots, the discriminant must be negative so $100p^2 + 20p - 39 < 0$
$\Rightarrow 100p^2 + 20p < 39 \Rightarrow 20p(5p + 1) < 39$
$\Rightarrow p(5p + 1) < \frac{39}{20}$.

Q8 First find the discriminant of the equation.
$a = -2$, $b = -2$, $c = k$.
So $b^2 - 4ac = (-2)^2 - 4 \times (-2) \times k = 4 + 8k$.

a) If the equation has two distinct real roots, the discriminant must be positive so $4 + 8k > 0$
$\Rightarrow 8k > -4 \Rightarrow k > -\frac{1}{2}$.

b) If the equation has one real root, the discriminant must be zero so $4 + 8k = 0 \Rightarrow k = -\frac{1}{2}$.

c) If the equation has no real roots, the discriminant must be negative so $4 + 8k < 0 \Rightarrow k < -\frac{1}{2}$.

Q9 a) First work out the discriminant:
$a = 1$, $b = k + 5$, $c = \frac{k^2}{4}$
So $b^2 - 4ac = (k + 5)^2 - 4 \times 1 \times \frac{k^2}{4}$
$= (k^2 + 10k + 25) - k^2$
$= 10k + 25$

The equation has no real roots so the discriminant is negative so $10k + 25 < 0$.

b) To find the range of values of k, solve the inequality in part a).

$10k + 25 < 0 \Rightarrow 10k < -25 \Rightarrow k < -\frac{25}{10} = -\frac{5}{2}$
So $k < -\frac{5}{2}$

Q10 a) $a = k - \frac{6}{5}$, $b = \sqrt{k}$, $c = \frac{5}{4}$
$b^2 - 4ac = (\sqrt{k})^2 - 4 \times \left(k - \frac{6}{5}\right) \times \frac{5}{4}$
$= k - 5\left(k - \frac{6}{5}\right)$
$= k - 5k + 6$
$= -4k + 6$

b) (i) For one real root, discriminant = 0:
$-4k + 6 = 0 \Rightarrow k = \frac{6}{4} = \frac{3}{2}$.

(ii) For no real roots, discriminant is negative:
$-4k + 6 < 0$ so $k > \frac{3}{2}$.

(iii) For two real roots, discriminant is positive:
$-4k + 6 > 0$ so $k < \frac{3}{2}$.

3. Quadratic Graphs
Exercise 3.1
— Sketching a quadratic graph
Q1 a) & b)

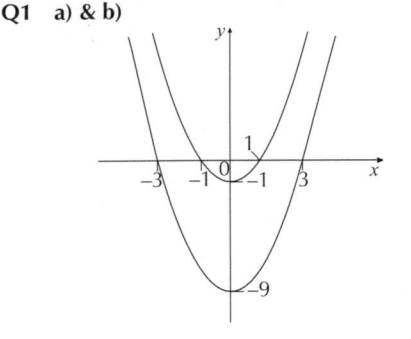

Q2 a) $f(x) = x^2 - 10x + 9 = (x - 9)(x - 1)$

b) & c)

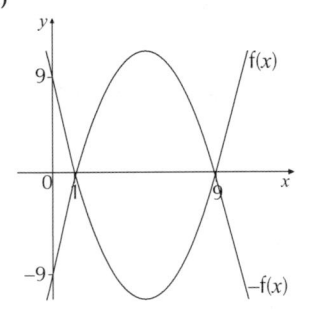

Q3 a) $y = -x^2 + 2x + 1$

(i) The x^2 coefficient is -1 so it is n-shaped.

(ii) Letting $x = 0$, $y = 1$ is the y-intercept.

(iii) Calculate the discriminant to work out the number of roots: $a = -1$, $b = 2$, $c = 1$.
$b^2 - 4ac = 2^2 - 4 \times (-1) \times 1 = 4 + 4 = 8$
The discriminant is positive so there are 2 distinct real roots.

(iv) To find the x-intercepts — find the roots:
$y = -x^2 + 2x + 1 = -(x - 1)^2 + 2$ by completing the square. Setting this equal to zero:
$-(x - 1)^2 + 2 = 0$ so $(x - 1)^2 = 2$
so $x - 1 = \pm\sqrt{2} \Rightarrow x = 1 \pm \sqrt{2}$.

(v) The vertex is a maximum since the graph's n-shaped. The maximum can be found by looking at the completed square
$y = -(x - 1)^2 + 2$. The highest value $-(x - 1)^2$ can take is 0, so the maximum is at $y = 2$ and $x = 1$ (to make the bracket 0).

(vi)

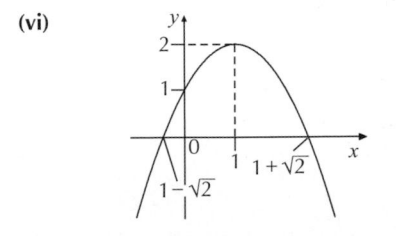

b) $y = x^2 - 7x + 15$

    (i) The x^2 coefficient is 1 so the graph's u-shaped.

    (ii) Letting $x = 0$, $y = 15$ is the y-intercept.

    (iii) Calculate the discriminant to work out the number of roots: $a = 1$, $b = -7$, $c = 15$.
$b^2 - 4ac = (-7)^2 - 4 \times 1 \times 15 = 49 - 60 = -11$
The discriminant is negative so there are no real roots.

    (iv) There are no real roots so the graph does not intersect the x-axis.

    (v) The vertex is a minimum since the graph's u-shaped. The minimum can be found by completing the square.
$y = x^2 - 7x + 15 = (x - \frac{7}{2})^2 + \frac{11}{4}$
The lowest value $(x - \frac{7}{2})^2$ can take is zero — so the minimum is at $y = \frac{11}{4}$ and so $x = \frac{7}{2}$ (to make the bracket 0).

    (vi)

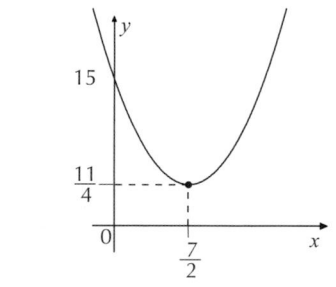

c) $y = 2x^2 + 4x - 9$

    (i) The x^2 coefficient is 2 so it is u-shaped.

    (ii) Letting $x = 0$, $y = -9$ is the y-intercept.

    (iii) Calculate the discriminant to work out the number of roots: $a = 2$, $b = 4$, $c = -9$.
$b^2 - 4ac = 4^2 - 4 \times 2 \times (-9) = 16 + 72 = 88$
The discriminant is positive so there are 2 distinct real roots.

    (iv) To find the x-intercepts, find the roots:
$2x^2 + 4x - 9 = 0$
Completing the square gives:
$2(x + 1)^2 - 2 - 9 = 0$
$2(x + 1)^2 - 11 = 0$
Solving:
$(x + 1)^2 = \frac{11}{2}$
$x = -1 \pm \sqrt{\frac{11}{2}}$

    (v) The vertex is a minimum since the graph is u-shaped. The minimum occurs when the square is 0, so it's $(-1, -11)$

    (vi)

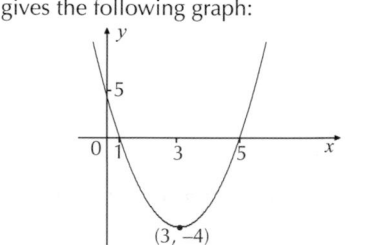

Q4 **a)** The minimum point is shown on the graph as $(-4, 2)$. The coordinates of the vertex of the function $f(x) = p(x + q)^2 + r$ are $(-q, r)$. In this case $p = 1$ and from the minimum on the graph you can see $-q = -4$, so $q = 4$ and $r = 2$.
So you can write the function $f(x) = (x + 4)^2 + 2$.

    b) $g(x) = (x + 4)^2$ is in the form $p(x + q)^2 + r$ with $p = 1$ so the graph is u-shaped and the minimum is at $(-q, r) = (-4, 0)$.

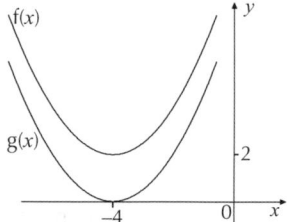

    c) $f(x)$ does not have any real roots as its graph does not touch the x-axis.

Q5 **a)** $x^2 - 6x + 5 = (x - 3)^2 - 9 + 5 = (x - 3)^2 - 4$

    b) $x^2 - 6x + 5 = 0 \Rightarrow (x - 3)^2 - 4 = 0 \Rightarrow (x - 3)^2 = 4$
$\Rightarrow x - 3 = \pm \sqrt{4} \Rightarrow x = 3 \pm \sqrt{4} = 3 \pm 2 = 5$ or 1

    c) The graph is u-shaped. The function has roots $x = 1$ and 5 so these are the x-intercepts. Putting $x = 0$ into the original equation gives $y = 5$, so this is the y-intercept. Completing the square gives the minimum as $(3, -4)$. Putting all this together gives the following graph:

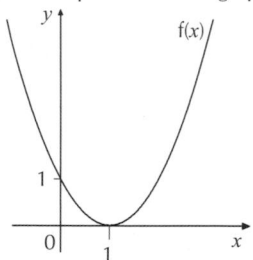

Q6 **a)** $f(x) = x^2 - 2x + 1 = (x - 1)^2$ so the function has one repeated root at $x = 1$. Letting $x = 0$ gives $f(x) = 1$ so the y-intercept is at 1. The graph is u-shaped.

    b) $f(x) = x^2 + x - 1 = (x + \frac{1}{2})^2 - \frac{5}{4}$ and solving $f(x) = 0$ gives $x = -\frac{1}{2} \pm \frac{\sqrt{5}}{2}$ as the x-intercepts. Letting $x = 0$ we get $f(x) = -1$ so this is the y-intercept. The graph is u-shaped.

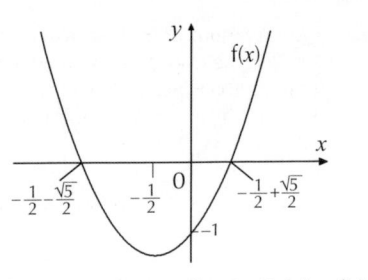

c) $f(x) = x^2 - 8x + 18 = (x - 4)^2 + 2$. Solving $f(x) = 0$ gives $x = 4 \pm \sqrt{-2}$ so there are no x-intercepts as you cannot take the square root of -2.

You could have worked out the discriminant to see that there were no real roots to save you trying to solve the equation.

Letting $x = 0$ gives $f(x) = 18$. The graph is u-shaped but it could be one of two graphs which are u-shaped with a y-intercept of 18. To find out which, work out the vertex. It has a minimum as it is u-shaped and from completing the square, the minimum is at $(4, 2)$.

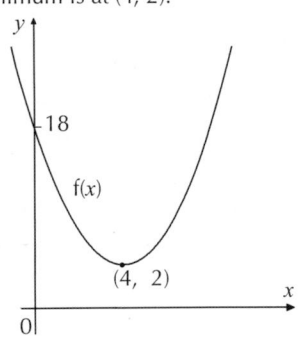

d) $f(x) = -x^2 + 3$ so setting $f(x) = 0$ gives $x = \pm\sqrt{3}$ as the x-intercepts. Letting $x = 0$ gives $f(x) = 3$ so 3 is the y-intercept. The graph is n-shaped.

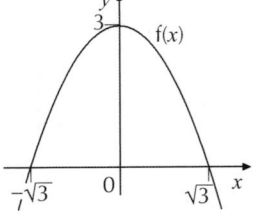

Q7 a) The roots of the quadratic function are the values of x where the graph crosses the x-axis. So the roots are $x = -2$ and $x = 1$.

b) One root of the equation is $x = -2$ which means $x + 2$ will be a factor. The other root $x = 1$ means that $x - 1$ will be a factor. So the quadratic function should be of the form $y = a(x + 2)(x - 1)$ for some value of a. But you know the equation has the form $y = -x^2 + px + q$. So a should be -1 to produce the term $-x^2$. So $y = -(x + 2)(x - 1)$ which gives $y = -x^2 - x + 2$, so $p = -1$ and $q = 2$.

The trickiest part of this question is realising you might also need a number factor, a, to form the factorised quadratic. Without it, you'd have got the wrong answer of $x^2 + x - 2$.

4. Factorising Cubics
Exercise 4.1
— Solving cubics by factorising

Q1 a) $x(x^2 + 5x + 6) = x(x + 2)(x + 3)$

b) $x(x^2 + 6x - 7) = x(x + 7)(x - 1)$

c) $x(x^2 - 18x + 81) = x(x - 9)(x - 9) = x(x - 9)^2$

d) $x(x^2 + 7x + 10) = x(x + 5)(x + 2)$

e) $-x(x^2 - 4x + 3) = -x(x - 3)(x - 1)$

f) $x(2x^2 + 15x + 25) = x(2x + 5)(x + 5)$

g) $x(x^2 - 49) = x(x + 7)(x - 7)$

h) $x(x^2 - \frac{9}{4}) = x(x + \frac{3}{2})(x - \frac{3}{2})$

Q2 a) $-x^3 + 2x^2 + 24x = 0$
$\Rightarrow -x(x^2 - 2x - 24) = 0$
$\Rightarrow -x(x - 6)(x + 4) = 0$
So either $-x = 0$, $x - 6 = 0$ or $x + 4 = 0$.
So the roots are $x = 0$, $x = 6$ and $x = -4$.

b) $x^3 - \frac{7}{9}x^2 + \frac{10}{81}x = 0$
$\Rightarrow x(x^2 - \frac{7}{9}x + \frac{10}{81}) = 0$
$\Rightarrow x(x - \frac{5}{9})(x - \frac{2}{9}) = 0$
So either $x = 0$, $x - \frac{5}{9} = 0$ or $x - \frac{2}{9} = 0$.
So the roots are $x = 0$, $x = \frac{5}{9}$ and $x = \frac{2}{9}$.

c) $2x^3 + 9x^2 + 4x = 0$
$\Rightarrow x(2x^2 + 9x + 4) = 0$
$\Rightarrow x(2x + 1)(x + 4) = 0$
So either $x = 0$, $2x + 1 = 0$ or $x + 4 = 0$.
So the roots are $x = 0$, $x = -\frac{1}{2}$ or $x = -4$.

d) $3x^3 - 3x^2 + 4x = 0$
$\Rightarrow x(3x^2 - 3x + 4) = 0$
This quadratic won't factorise — so use the quadratic formula: $a = 3$, $b = -3$, $c = 4$
$$x = \frac{-b \pm \sqrt{b^2 - 4ac}}{2a} = \frac{3 \pm \sqrt{(-3)^2 - 4 \times 3 \times 4}}{2 \times 3}$$
$$= \frac{3 \pm \sqrt{9 - 48}}{6} = \frac{3 \pm \sqrt{-39}}{6}$$
These aren't possible solutions since you can't take the square root of a negative number so the only solution is the one we get from the x that we factorised out at the start — $x = 0$.

e) $x^2(4x + 3) = x$
$\Rightarrow 4x^3 + 3x^2 = x$
$\Rightarrow 4x^3 + 3x^2 - x = 0$
$\Rightarrow x(4x^2 + 3x - 1) = 0$
$\Rightarrow x(4x - 1)(x + 1) = 0$
So either $x = 0$, $4x - 1 = 0$ or $x + 1 = 0$.
So the roots are $x = 0$, $x = \frac{1}{4}$ or $x = -1$.

f) $2x^3 + 8x^2 = -3x$
$\Rightarrow 2x^3 + 8x^2 + 3x = 0$
$\Rightarrow x(2x^2 + 8x + 3) = 0$

So one root is $x = 0$, but the quadratic won't factorise so use the quadratic formula.

Now $a = 2$, $b = 8$ and $c = 3$.

$$x = \frac{-b \pm \sqrt{b^2 - 4ac}}{2a} = \frac{-8 \pm \sqrt{8^2 - 4 \times 2 \times 3}}{4}$$

$$= \frac{-8 \pm \sqrt{40}}{4} = -2 \pm \frac{1}{2}\sqrt{10}$$

So the roots are $x = 0$ and $x = -2 \pm \frac{1}{2}\sqrt{10}$.

Review Exercise — Chapter 2

Q1 **a)** $(x + 1)^2$ **b)** $(x - 10)(x - 3)$

c) $(x + 2)(x - 2)$ **d)** $(3 - x)(x + 1)$

e) $(2x + 1)(x - 4)$ **f)** $(5x - 3)(x + 2)$

Q2 **a)** $(x - 2)(x - 1) = 0$, so $x = 2$ or 1

b) $(x + 4)(x - 3) = 0$, so $x = -4$ or 3

c) $(2 - x)(x + 1) = 0$, so $x = 2$ or -1

d) $(x + 4)(x - 4) = 0$, so $x = \pm 4$

e) $(3x + 2)(x - 7) = 0$, so $x = -\frac{2}{3}$ or 7

f) $(2x + 1)(2x - 1) = 0$, so $x = \pm\frac{1}{2}$

g) $(2x - 3)(x - 1) = 0$, so $x = \frac{3}{2}$ or 1

Q3 **a)** $(x - 2)^2 - 7$; minimum value $= -7$ at $x = 2$, and the graph crosses the x-axis at $x = 2 \pm \sqrt{7}$.

b) $\frac{21}{4} - \left(x + \frac{3}{2}\right)^2$; maximum value $= \frac{21}{4}$ at $x = -\frac{3}{2}$, and the graph crosses the x-axis at $-\frac{3}{2} \pm \frac{\sqrt{21}}{2}$.

c) $2(x - 1)^2 + 9$; minimum value $= 9$ at $x = 1$, and the graph doesn't cross the x-axis.

d) $4\left(x - \frac{7}{2}\right)^2 - 1$; minimum value $= -1$ at $x = \frac{7}{2}$, and the graph crosses the x-axis at $x = \frac{7}{2} \pm \frac{1}{2}$, i.e. $x = 4$ or $x = 3$.

Q4 **a)** $b^2 - 4ac = 16$, so 2 roots. Factorising gives: $(x + 1)(x - 3) = 0$

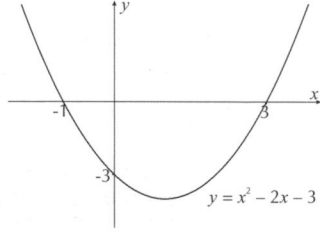
$y = x^2 - 2x - 3$

b) $b^2 - 4ac = 0$, so 1 root. Factorising gives: $(x - 3)^2 = 0$

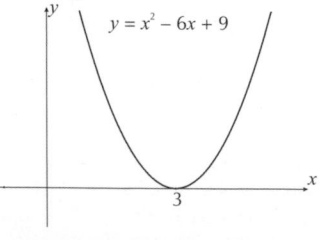
$y = x^2 - 6x + 9$

c) $b^2 - 4ac = -8$, so no roots. Completing the square gives: $2(x + 1)^2 + 1 = 0$, so vertex at $(-1, 1)$.

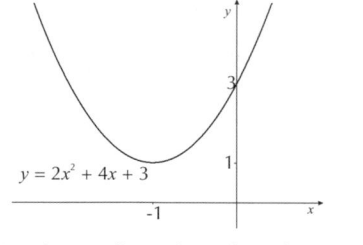
$y = 2x^2 + 4x + 3$

Q5 **a)** Using the quadratic formula with $a = 3$, $b = -7$ and $c = 3$:

$$x = \frac{-(-7) \pm \sqrt{(-7)^2 - (4 \times 3 \times 3)}}{(2 \times 3)}$$

$$= \frac{7 \pm \sqrt{49 - 36}}{6}$$

$$= \frac{7 \pm \sqrt{13}}{6}$$

so $x = \frac{7 + \sqrt{13}}{6}, x = \frac{7 - \sqrt{13}}{6}$.

b) First divide through by 2 to get: $x^2 - 3x - 1 = 0$

Now using the quadratic formula with $a = 1$, $b = -3$ and $c = -1$:

$$x = \frac{-(-3) \pm \sqrt{(-3)^2 - (4 \times 1 \times -1)}}{(2 \times 1)}$$

$$= \frac{3 \pm \sqrt{9 + 4}}{2}$$

$$= \frac{3 \pm \sqrt{13}}{2}$$

so $x = \frac{3 + \sqrt{13}}{2}, x = \frac{3 - \sqrt{13}}{2}$.

c) Using the quadratic formula with $a = 1$, $b = 4$ and $c = -6$:

$$x = \frac{-(4) \pm \sqrt{(4)^2 - (4 \times 1 \times -6)}}{(2 \times 1)}$$

$$= \frac{-4 \pm \sqrt{16 + 24}}{2}$$

$$= \frac{-4 \pm \sqrt{40}}{2}$$

$$= \frac{-4 \pm 2\sqrt{10}}{2}$$

$$= -2 \pm \sqrt{10}$$

so $x = -2 + \sqrt{10}, x = -2 - \sqrt{10}$.

Q6 $k^2 - (4 \times 1 \times 4) > 0$, so $k^2 > 16$ and so $k > 4$ or $k < -4$.

Q7 **a)** Let $f(x) = g(x)$ to find where the curves intersect:

$5x^3 - 13x^2 + 6x = -5x^3 + 7x^2 + 6x$

$\Rightarrow 5x^3 - 13x^2 + 6x + 5x^3 - 7x^2 - 6x = 0$

$\Rightarrow 10x^3 - 20x^2 = 0$

$\Rightarrow 10x^2(x - 2) = 0$

$\Rightarrow x = 0$ or $x = 2$.

Put $x = 0$, 2 into one of the expressions to find y:

$x = 0$ gives $y = 0$

$x = 2$ gives $y = 5(2^3) - 13(2^2) + 6(2)$

$\qquad = 40 - 52 + 12 = 0$

So the intersection points are $(0, 0)$ and $(2, 0)$.

b) In part a), you found that the graph of $y = f(x)$ passes through the points $(0, 0)$ and $(2, 0)$. So you actually found two roots of $f(x)$ since the roots are points where the graph meets the x-axis. These roots tell you that $f(x)$ will have factors of x and $(x - 2)$. So you only need to find one more factor. You know $5x^3 - 13x^2 + 6x = x(x - 2)(........)$ The third factor is found by noticing that you need $5x$ to make the $5x^3$ and -3 to make the $+6x$. So $5x^3 - 13x^2 + 6x = x(x - 2)(5x - 3)$.

Q8 a) Set the equations equal to each other to find the points where they intersect:
$x(x - 6)^2 = -x(2x - 31)$
$\Rightarrow x(x^2 - 12x + 36) = -2x^2 + 31x$
$\Rightarrow x^3 - 12x^2 + 36x = -2x^2 + 31x$
$\Rightarrow x^3 - 10x^2 + 5x = 0$

b) Solving the equation in part a):
$x^3 - 10x^2 + 5x = 0 \Rightarrow x(x^2 - 10x + 5) = 0$
This quadratic won't factorise so use the quadratic formula: $a = 1$, $b = -10$, $c = 5$

$x = \dfrac{-b \pm \sqrt{b^2 - 4ac}}{2a}$
$= \dfrac{10 \pm \sqrt{(-10)^2 - 4 \times 1 \times 5}}{2 \times 1}$
$= \dfrac{10 \pm \sqrt{100 - 20}}{2}$
$= \dfrac{10 \pm \sqrt{80}}{2} = \dfrac{10 \pm 4\sqrt{5}}{2} = 5 \pm 2\sqrt{5}$

So the points where the two curves meet are at $x = 0$ and $x = 5 \pm 2\sqrt{5}$.

Exam-Style Questions — Chapter 2

Q1 For equal roots, $b^2 - 4ac = 0$ *[1 mark]*
$a = 1$, $b = 2k$ and $c = 4k$
so $(2k)^2 - (4 \times 1 \times 4k) = 0$ *[1 mark]*
$4k^2 - 16k = 0$
$4k(k - 4) = 0$ *[1 mark]*
so $k = 4$ (as k is non-zero). *[1 mark]*

Q2 For distinct real roots, $b^2 - 4ac > 0$ *[1 mark]*
$a = p$, $b = 2p + 3$ and $c = p$, so:
$(2p + 3)^2 - (4 \times p \times p) > 0$ *[1 mark]*
$4p^2 + 12p + 9 - 4p^2 > 0$
$12p + 9 > 0$ *[1 mark]*
$p > -\dfrac{3}{4}$ *[1 mark]*

Q3 Expanding the brackets on the RHS gives the quadratic $mx^2 + 4mx + 4m + p$. Equating the coefficients of x^2 gives $m = 5$ *[1 mark]*. Equating the coefficients of x gives $n = 4m$, so $n = 20$ *[1 mark]*. Equating the constant terms gives $14 = 4m + p \Rightarrow p = -6$ *[1 mark]*.

Q4 a) Completing the square gives:
$(x - 6)^2 - 36 + 15$
$(x - 6)^2 - 21$
[1 mark for the square, 1 mark for '−21']

b) (i) The minimum occurs when the expression in brackets is equal to 0, which means the minimum is the value of b, which from (a) above is −21 *[1 mark]*.

(ii) From above, the minimum occurs when the expression in brackets is equal to 0, i.e. when $x = 6$ *[1 mark]*.

Part (b) is easy once you've completed the square — you can just take your values straight from there.

Q5 a) Put $a = 1$, $b = -14$ and $c = 25$ into the quadratic formula:
$x = \dfrac{-(-14) \pm \sqrt{(-14)^2 - (4 \times 1 \times 25)}}{(2 \times 1)}$
$= \dfrac{14 \pm \sqrt{196 - 100}}{2}$
$= \dfrac{14 \pm \sqrt{96}}{2}$
$= \dfrac{14 \pm 4\sqrt{6}}{2}$
$= 7 \pm 2\sqrt{6}$
so $x = 7 + 2\sqrt{6}$, $x = 7 - 2\sqrt{6}$
[3 marks available — 1 mark for putting correct values of a, b and c into the quadratic formula, 1 mark each for final x-value.]

b)

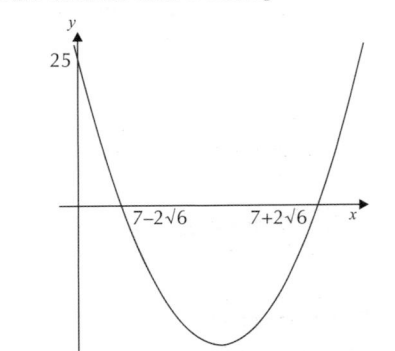

[3 marks available — 1 mark for drawing u-shaped curve, 1 mark for using answers from a) as x-axis intercepts and 1 mark for correct y-axis intercept (0, 25).]

c) As the graph is u-shaped, the function is < 0 when x is between the two intercepts,
$\Rightarrow 7 - 2\sqrt{6} \leq x \leq 7 + 2\sqrt{6}$ *[1 mark]*.
Quadratic inequalities like this are covered in detail in Chapter 3 — have a look if you want more info.

Q6 a) (i) First, rewrite the quadratic as:
$-x^2 + 10x - 27$
And complete the square $(a = -1)$:
$-(x - 5)^2 + 25 - 27$
$= -(x - 5)^2 - 2$
Rewrite the square in the form given in the question:
$-(-(5 - x))^2 - 2$
$= -(5 - x)^2 - 2$
[1 mark for m = 5, 1 mark for n = −2]
The last couple of steps are using the fact that $(-a)^2 = a^2$ to show that $(m - n)^2 = (n - m)^2$...

(ii) $(5-x)^2 \geq 0$ for all values of x, so $-(5-x)^2 \leq 0$.
Therefore: $(5-x)^2 - 2 < 0$ for all x,
i.e. the function is always negative. *[1 mark]*

b) (i) The y-coordinate is the maximum value, which is -2 *[1 mark]*, and this occurs when the expression in the brackets $= 0$.
The x-value that makes the expression in the brackets 0 is 5 *[1 mark]*, so the coordinates of the maximum point are $(5, -2)$.

(ii)

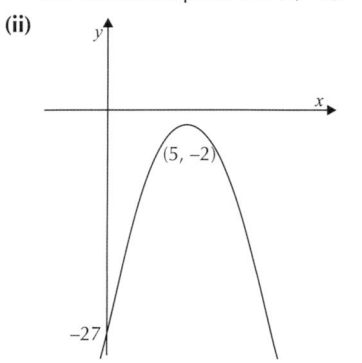

[2 marks available — 1 mark for drawing n-shaped curve that sits below the x-axis with the maximum roughly where shown (even if its position is not labelled), 1 mark for correct y-axis intercept (0, −27).]

Chapter 3: Inequalities and Simultaneous Equations

1. Inequalities
Exercise 1.1 — Linear inequalities

Q1 a) $2x - 1 < x + 4 \Rightarrow x < 5$

b) $4 - 3x \geq 10 - 5x \Rightarrow 2x \geq 6 \Rightarrow x \geq 3$

c) $5x + 7 > 3x + 1 \Rightarrow 2x > -6 \Rightarrow x > -3$

d) $3 - 2x \leq 5x - 4 \Rightarrow -7x \leq -7 \Rightarrow x \geq 1$

e) $9 - x \geq 7x + 5 \Rightarrow -8x \geq -4 \Rightarrow x \leq \frac{1}{2}$

Q2 a) $2(x + 3) > 3(x + 2)$
$\Rightarrow 2x + 6 > 3x + 6 \Rightarrow -x > 0 \Rightarrow x < 0$

b) $5(1 + 3x) \leq 7$
$\Rightarrow 5 + 15x \leq 7 \Rightarrow 15x \leq 2 \Rightarrow x \leq \frac{2}{15}$

Q3 a) $\frac{6 - 5x}{2} < \frac{4 - 8x}{3} \Rightarrow 3(6 - 5x) < 2(4 - 8x)$
$\Rightarrow 18 - 15x < 8 - 16x \Rightarrow x < -10$

b) $\frac{3x - 1}{4} \geq 2x \Rightarrow 3x - 1 \geq 8x \Rightarrow x \leq -\frac{1}{5}$

c) $\frac{x - 2}{2} - \frac{2x + 3}{3} < 7$
$\Rightarrow 3(x - 2) - 2(2x + 3) < 42$
$\Rightarrow 3x - 6 - 4x - 6 < 42 \Rightarrow -x < 54$
$\Rightarrow x > -54$

Q4 a) $-5 < 2x - 3 < 15$
$\Rightarrow -2 < 2x < 18 \Rightarrow -1 < x < 9$

b) $-5 \leq 4 - 3x < 19$
$\Rightarrow -9 \leq -3x < 15 \Rightarrow 3 \geq x > -5$
$\Rightarrow -5 < x \leq 3$

Q5 a) $2x \geq 3 - x \Rightarrow 3x \geq 3 \Rightarrow x \geq 1$

![number line, filled circle at 1, arrow to the right, labelled 1]

b) $5x - 1 < 3x + 5 \Rightarrow 2x < 6 \Rightarrow x < 3$

![number line, open circle at 3, arrow to the left, labelled 3]

c) $2x + 1 \geq 3x + 2 \Rightarrow -x \geq 1 \Rightarrow x \leq -1$

![number line, filled circle at −1, arrow to the left, labelled −1]

d) $3x - 1 \leq 5x - 7 \Rightarrow -2x \leq -6 \Rightarrow x \geq 3$

![number line, filled circle at 3, arrow to the right, labelled 3]

e) $9 - x \leq 3 - 4x \Rightarrow 3x \leq -6 \Rightarrow x \leq -2$

![number line, open circle at −2, arrow to the left, labelled −2]

f) $\frac{2(x - 3)}{3} + 1 < \frac{2x - 1}{2}$
$\Rightarrow 4(x - 3) + 6 < 3(2x - 1)$
$\Rightarrow 4x - 12 + 6 < 6x - 3 \Rightarrow -2x < 3 \Rightarrow x > -\frac{3}{2}$

![number line, open circle at −3/2, arrow to the right, labelled −3/2]

Q6 a) $7 \leq 3x - 2 < 16 \Rightarrow 9 \leq 3x \leq 18 \Rightarrow 3 \leq x < 6$

b)

![number line, filled circle at 3, open circle at 6, line segment between]

Q7 $4 - 2x < 10 \Rightarrow -2x < 6 \Rightarrow x > -3$
and
$3x - 1 < x + 7 \Rightarrow 2x < 8 \Rightarrow x < 4$

![two number lines showing x < 4 (open circle at 4, arrow left) and x > −3 (open circle at −3, arrow right), marked at −3 and 4]

The solutions overlap between −3 and 4, so:
$-3 < x < 4$

Q8 a) $2x \geq 3x - 5 \Rightarrow -x \geq -5 \Rightarrow x \leq 5$
and
$3x - 2 \geq x - 6 \Rightarrow 2x \geq -4 \Rightarrow x \geq -2$

![two number lines showing x ≤ 5 (filled circle at 5, arrow left) and x ≥ −2 (filled circle at −2, arrow right), marked at −2 and 5]

Solution: $-2 \leq x \leq 5$

b) $5x + 1 \le 11 \Rightarrow 5x \le 10 \Rightarrow x \le 2$

and

$2x - 3 < 5x - 6 \Rightarrow -3x < -3 \Rightarrow x > 1$

Solution: $1 < x \le 2$

c) $2x - 1 \le 3x - 5 \Rightarrow -x \le -4 \Rightarrow x \ge 4$

and

$5x - 6 > x + 22 \Rightarrow 4x > 28 \Rightarrow x > 7$

Solution: $x > 7$
Only these values satisfy both of the inequalities.

d) $3x + 5 < x + 1 \Rightarrow 2x < -4 \Rightarrow x < -2$

and

$6x - 1 \ge 3x + 5 \Rightarrow 3x \ge 6 \Rightarrow x \ge 2$

There is no solution that satisfies both inequalities.
The solutions don't overlap on the number line.

Exercise 1.2 — Quadratic inequalities

Q1 **a)** $-3 < x < 1$

b) $x < 0$ or $x > 4$

c) $2x^2 \ge 5 - 9x \Rightarrow 2x^2 + 9x - 5 \ge 0$

$\Rightarrow x \le -5$ or $x \ge \dfrac{1}{2}$

d) $x < 1 - \sqrt{6}$ or $x > 1 + \sqrt{6}$

Q2 **a)** Solve the equation $x^2 = 4$ to find the x-intercepts:

$x^2 = 4 \Rightarrow x^2 - 4 = 0 \Rightarrow (x - 2)(x + 2) = 0$

$x = -2$ or $x = 2$

Solution: $x^2 \le 4 \Rightarrow x^2 - 4 \le 0$

$\Rightarrow -2 \le x \le 2$

b) $13x = 3x^2 + 4 \Rightarrow -3x^2 + 13x - 4 = 0$

$\Rightarrow 3x^2 - 13x + 4 = 0 \Rightarrow (3x - 1)(x - 4) = 0$

$\Rightarrow x = \dfrac{1}{3}$ or $x = 4$

Solution: $13x < 3x^2 + 4 \Rightarrow -3x^2 + 13x - 4 < 0$

$\Rightarrow x < \dfrac{1}{3}$ or $x > 4$

c) $x^2 + 4 = 6x \Rightarrow x^2 - 6x + 4 = 0$

$\Rightarrow x = \dfrac{6 \pm \sqrt{36 - 16}}{2} = \dfrac{6 \pm \sqrt{20}}{2} = \dfrac{6 \pm 2\sqrt{5}}{2}$

$\Rightarrow x = 3 \pm \sqrt{5}$

Solution: $x^2 + 4 < 6x \Rightarrow x^2 - 6x + 4 < 0$

$\Rightarrow 3 - \sqrt{5} < x < 3 + \sqrt{5}$

Q3 **a)** $x^2 + 5x - 6 = 0 \Rightarrow (x + 6)(x - 1) = 0$

$\Rightarrow x = -6$ or $x = 1$

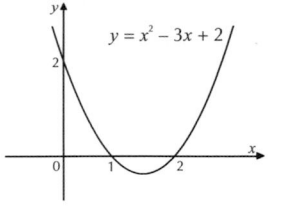

$x^2 + 5x - 6 \ge 0 \Rightarrow x \le -6$ or $x \ge 1$

b) $x^2 - 3x + 2 = 0 \Rightarrow (x - 1)(x - 2) = 0$

$\Rightarrow x = 1$ or $x = 2$

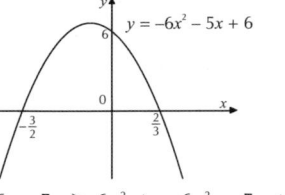

$x^2 - 3x + 2 < 0 \Rightarrow 1 < x < 2$

c) $6 - 5x = 6x^2 \Rightarrow -6x^2 - 5x + 6 = 0$

$\Rightarrow 6x^2 + 5x - 6 = 0 \Rightarrow (3x - 2)(2x + 3) = 0$

$\Rightarrow x = \dfrac{2}{3}$ or $x = -\dfrac{3}{2}$

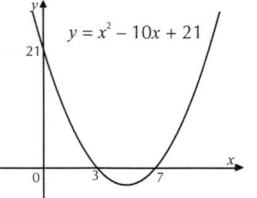

$6 - 5x > 6x^2 \Rightarrow -6x^2 - 5x + 6 > 0$

$\Rightarrow -\dfrac{3}{2} < x < \dfrac{2}{3}$

You could have rearranged the inequality into $6x^2 + 5x - 6 < 0$ and sketched the corresponding graph. You'd get the same final answer, but the graph would be the other way up.

d) $x^2 - 5x + 24 = 5x + 3 \Rightarrow x^2 - 10x + 21 = 0$

$\Rightarrow (x - 3)(x - 7) = 0 \Rightarrow x = 3$ or $x = 7$

$x^2 - 5x + 24 \le 5x + 3 \Rightarrow x^2 - 10x + 21 \le 0$

$\Rightarrow 3 \le x \le 7$

e) $36 - 4x^2 = 0 \Rightarrow 9 - x^2 = 0$

$\Rightarrow (3 - x)(3 + x) = 0 \Rightarrow x = \pm 3$

$36 - 4x^2 \le 0 \Rightarrow x \le -3$ or $x \ge 3$

f) $x^2 - 6x + 3 = 0 \Rightarrow x = \dfrac{6 \pm \sqrt{36 - 12}}{2}$

$\Rightarrow x = \dfrac{6 \pm \sqrt{24}}{2} = \dfrac{6 \pm 2\sqrt{6}}{2} = 3 \pm \sqrt{6}$

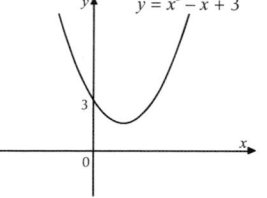

$x^2 - 6x + 3 > 0 \Rightarrow x < 3 - \sqrt{6}$ or $x > 3 + \sqrt{6}$

g) $x^2 - x + 3 = 0 \Rightarrow x = \dfrac{1 \pm \sqrt{1 - 12}}{2}$

$\Rightarrow$ no roots ($\sqrt{-11}$ is not real)

so the graph doesn't cross the x-axis.

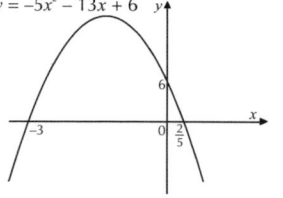

$x^2 - x + 3 > 0 \Rightarrow x$ can take any real value

h) $6 = 5x^2 + 13x \Rightarrow -5x^2 - 13x + 6 = 0$

$\Rightarrow 5x^2 + 13x - 6 = 0 \Rightarrow (5x - 2)(x + 3) = 0$

$\Rightarrow x = \dfrac{2}{5}$ or $x = -3$

$y = -5x^2 - 13x + 6$

$6 \geq 5x^2 + 13x \Rightarrow -5x^2 - 13x + 6 \geq 0$

$\Rightarrow -3 \leq x \leq \dfrac{2}{5}$

Again, you might have rearranged the inequality differently and ended up with the graph the other way up.

Q4 $(x - 9)(x - 6) > 28 \Rightarrow x^2 - 15x + 54 > 28$

$\Rightarrow x^2 - 15x + 26 > 0$

Now $x^2 - 15x + 26 = 0 \Rightarrow (x - 2)(x - 13) = 0$

$\Rightarrow x = 2$ or $x = 13$

$y = x^2 - 15x + 26$

$x^2 - 15x + 26 > 0 \Rightarrow x < 2$ or $x > 13$

But $x < 2$ would make the sides have negative lengths, so $x > 13$.

Q5 $x^2 - 6x + k = 0 \Rightarrow$
$a = 1,\ b = -6,\ c = k$
$b^2 - 4ac = (-6)^2 - (4 \times 1 \times k) = 36 - 4k$
The original equation has two distinct real solutions, so the discriminant must be > 0.
So $36 - 4k > 0 \Rightarrow 36 > 4k \Rightarrow 9 > k$, so $k < 9$.

Q6 $x^2 - kx + k = 0 \Rightarrow$
$a = 1,\ b = -k,\ c = k$
$b^2 - 4ac = (-k)^2 - (4 \times 1 \times k) = k^2 - 4k$
The original equation has no real solutions, so the discriminant must be < 0.
So $k^2 - 4k < 0$
Factorise the quadratic: $k^2 - 4k = k(k - 4)$
So the solutions of the equation are $k = 0$ and $k = 4$.

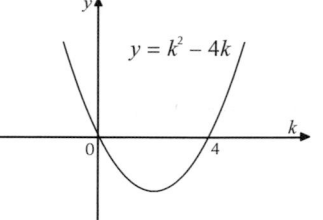

Solution: $0 < k < 4$

Q7 $4(3 - x) \geq 13 - 5x \Rightarrow 12 - 4x \geq 13 - 5x \Rightarrow x \geq 1$
and
$7x + 6 \geq 3x^2 \Rightarrow -3x^2 + 7x + 6 \geq 0$
$-3x^2 + 7x + 6 = 0 \Rightarrow 3x^2 - 7x - 6 = 0$
$\Rightarrow (3x + 2)(x - 3) = 0$
$\Rightarrow x = -\dfrac{2}{3}$ or $x = 3$

$y = -3x^2 + 7x + 6$

$\Rightarrow -\dfrac{2}{3} \leq x \leq 3$

So, for both inequalities:

$x = 1 \qquad y = -3x^2 + 7x + 6$

Solution that satisfies both inequalities:
$\Rightarrow 1 \leq x \leq 3$
Your graphs might be the other way up if you rearranged the inequality differently at the start.

2. Simultaneous Equations
Exercise 2.1 — Simultaneous equations — both linear

Q1 **a)** (1) $\qquad 2x - 3y = 3$

(2) $\qquad x + 3y = 6$

(1) + (2) $\qquad 3x = 9 \Rightarrow x = 3$

$x = 3$ in (2) $3 + 3y = 6 \Rightarrow 3y = 3 \Rightarrow y = 1$

So the solution is $x = 3$, $y = 1$

b) (1) $\qquad 3x + 2y = 7$

(2) $\qquad 7x - y = -12$

(2) × 2 $\qquad 14x - 2y = -24$ (3)

(1) + (3) $\qquad 17x = -17 \Rightarrow x = -1$

$x = -1$ in (1) $-3 + 2y = 7$

$\Rightarrow 2y = 10 \Rightarrow y = 5$

So the solution is $x = -1$, $y = 5$

c) (1) $\qquad 4x + 3y = -4$

(2) $\qquad 6x - 4y = 11$

(1) × 3 $\qquad 12x + 9y = -12$ (3)

(2) × 2 $\qquad 12x - 8y = 22$ (4)

(3) − (4) $\qquad 17y = -34 \Rightarrow y = -2$

$y = -2$ in (2) $6x + 8 = 11 \Rightarrow 6x = 3 \Rightarrow x = \frac{1}{2}$

So the solution is $x = \frac{1}{2}$, $y = -2$

d) (1) $\qquad 7x - 6y = 4$

(2) $\qquad 11x + 9y = -6$

(1) × 3 $\qquad 21x - 18y = 12$ (3)

(2) × 2 $\qquad 22x + 18y = -12$ (4)

(3) + (4) $\qquad 43x = 0 \Rightarrow x = 0$

$x = 0$ in (2) $0 + 9y = -6 \Rightarrow y = -\frac{6}{9} = -\frac{2}{3}$

So the solution is $x = 0$, $y = -\frac{2}{3}$

e) Rearrange (1) $6x + 2y = 8$

Rearrange (2) $4x + 3y = -3$

(1) × 2 $\qquad 12x + 4y = 16$ (3)

(2) × 3 $\qquad 12x + 9y = -9$ (4)

(3) − (4) $\qquad -5y = 25 \Rightarrow y = -5$

$y = -5$ in (2) $4x - 15 = -3$

$\Rightarrow 4x = 12 \Rightarrow x = 3$

So the solution is $x = 3$, $y = -5$

f) Rearrange (1) $2x + 18y = 21$

Rearrange (2) $-3x - 14y = 14$

(1) × 3 $\qquad 6x + 54y = 63$ (3)

(2) × 2 $\qquad -6x - 28y = 28$ (4)

(3) + (4) $\qquad 26y = 91 \Rightarrow y = \frac{7}{2}$

$y = \frac{7}{2}$ in (1) $2x + 63 = 21$

$\Rightarrow 2x = -42 \Rightarrow x = -21$

So the solution is $x = -21$, $y = \frac{7}{2}$

g) (1) $\qquad 2x + 16y = 10$

Rearrange (2) $3x + 64y = 5$

(1) × 4 $\qquad 8x + 64y = 40$ (3)

(2) − (3) $\qquad -5x = -35 \Rightarrow x = 7$

$x = 7$ in (1) $14 + 16y = 10$

$\Rightarrow 16y = -4 \Rightarrow y = -\frac{1}{4}$

So the solution is $x = 7$, $y = -\frac{1}{4}$

Q2 **a)** (1) $\qquad y = 2x - 3$

(2) $\qquad y = \frac{1}{2}x + 3$

(2) × 4 $\qquad 4y = 2x + 12$ (3)

(1) − (3) $\qquad -3y = -15 \Rightarrow y = 5$

$y = 5$ in (1) $5 = 2x - 3 \Rightarrow 8 = 2x \Rightarrow x = 4$

So they intersect at (4, 5)

b) (1) $\qquad y = -\frac{2}{3}x + 7$

(2) $\qquad y = \frac{1}{2}x + \frac{21}{2}$

(1) × 3 $\qquad 3y = -2x + 21$ (3)

(2) × 4 $\qquad 4y = 2x + 42$ (4)

(3) + (4) $\qquad 7y = 63 \Rightarrow y = 9$

$y = 9$ in (1) $9 = -\frac{2}{3}x + 7$

$\Rightarrow 2 = -\frac{2}{3}x \Rightarrow x = -3$

So they intersect at (−3, 9)

c) Rearrange (1) $x + 2y = -5$

Rearrange (2) $3x - 5y = 7$

(1) × 3 $\qquad 3x + 6y = -15$ (3)

(2) − (3) $\qquad -11y = 22 \Rightarrow y = -2$

$y = -2$ in (1) $x - 4 = -5 \Rightarrow x = -1$

So they intersect at (−1, −2)

d) (1) $\qquad 2x - 3y = 7$

(2) $\qquad 5x - \frac{15}{2}y = 9$

(1) × 5 $\qquad 10x - 15y = 35$ (3)

(2) × 2 $\qquad 10x - 15y = 18$ (4)

(3) − (4) $\quad 0 = 17$

This is not possible — so these lines do not intersect.

The lines are actually parallel.

e) Rearrange (1) $8x + 3y = 10$

Rearrange (2) $6x + 9y = 3$

(1) × 3 $\qquad 24x + 9y = 30$ (3)

(2) − (3) $\qquad -18x = -27 \Rightarrow x = \frac{3}{2}$

$x = \frac{3}{2}$ in (2) $9 + 9y = 3$

$\Rightarrow 9y = -6 \Rightarrow y = -\frac{2}{3}$

So they intersect at $(\frac{3}{2}, -\frac{2}{3})$

f) (1) $\qquad 7x - 5y = 15$

Rearrange (2) $\quad 2x - 3y = 9$

(1) $\times 2 \qquad 14x - 10y = 30 \quad$ (3)

(2) $\times 7 \qquad 14x - 21y = 63 \quad$ (4)

(3) $-$ (4) $\qquad 11y = -33 \Rightarrow y = -3$

$y = -3$ in (2) $\quad 2x + 9 = 9$

$\qquad\qquad\qquad \Rightarrow 2x = 0 \Rightarrow x = 0$

So they intersect at $(0, -3)$

Exercise 2.2 — Simultaneous equations — if one is quadratic

Q1 a) (1) $\qquad y = 4x + 3$

(2) $\qquad 2y - 3x = 1$

Sub (1) in (2) $\quad 2(4x + 3) - 3x = 1$

$\Rightarrow 8x + 6 - 3x = 1 \Rightarrow 5x = -5 \Rightarrow x = -1$

$x = -1$ in (1) $\quad y = 4 \times -1 + 3 = -1$

So the solution is $x = -1, y = -1$

b) (1) $\qquad 5x + 2y = 16$

Rearrange (2) $\quad x = 2y - 4$

Sub (2) in (1) $\qquad 5(2y - 4) + 2y = 16$

$\Rightarrow 12y - 20 = 16 \Rightarrow 12y = 36 \Rightarrow y = 3$

$y = 3$ in (2) $\quad x = 2 \times 3 - 4 = 2$

So the solution is $x = 2, y = 3$

Q2 a) (1) $\qquad y = 2x + 5$

(2) $\qquad y = x^2 - x + 1$

Sub (1) in (2) $\quad 2x + 5 = x^2 - x + 1$

$\Rightarrow 0 = x^2 - 3x - 4 \Rightarrow (x - 4)(x + 1) = 0$

$\Rightarrow x = 4$ or $x = -1$

When $x = 4$, $y = 8 + 5 = 13$, and

when $x = -1$, $y = -2 + 5 = 3$

So $x = 4, y = 13 \quad$ or $\quad x = -1, y = 3$

b) (1) $\qquad y = 2x^2 - 3$

(2) $\qquad y = 3x + 2$

Sub (2) in (1) $\quad 3x + 2 = 2x^2 - 3$

$\Rightarrow 2x^2 - 3x - 5 = 0 \Rightarrow (2x - 5)(x + 1) = 0$

$\Rightarrow x = \dfrac{5}{2}$ or $x = -1$

When $x = \dfrac{5}{2}$, $y = \dfrac{15}{2} + 2 = \dfrac{19}{2}$, and

when $x = -1$, $y = -3 + 2 = -1$

So $x = \dfrac{5}{2}, y = \dfrac{19}{2} \quad$ or $\quad x = -1, y = -1$

c) (1) $\qquad 2x^2 - xy = 6$

Rearrange (2) $\quad y = 3x - 7$

Sub (2) in (1) $\qquad 2x^2 - x(3x - 7) = 6$

$\Rightarrow 2x^2 - 3x^2 + 7x - 6 = 0$

$\Rightarrow -x^2 + 7x - 6 = 0 \Rightarrow x^2 - 7x + 6 = 0$

$\Rightarrow (x - 6)(x - 1) = 0$

$\Rightarrow x = 6$ or $x = 1$

When $x = 6$, $y = 18 - 7 = 11$, and

when $x = 1$, $y = 3 - 7 = -4$

So $x = 6, y = 11 \quad$ or $\quad x = 1, y = -4$

d) (1) $\qquad xy = 6$

Rearrange (2) $\quad 2y + 4 = x$

Sub (2) in (1) $\qquad y(2y + 4) = 6 \Rightarrow 2y^2 + 4y = 6$

$\Rightarrow 2y^2 + 4y - 6 = 0$

$\Rightarrow y^2 + 2y - 3 = 0 \Rightarrow (y + 3)(y - 1) = 0$

$\Rightarrow y = -3$ or $y = 1$

When $y = -3$, $x = -6 + 4 = -2$, and

when $y = 1$, $x = 2 + 4 = 6$

So $x = -2, y = -3 \quad$ or $\quad x = 6, y = 1$

e) (1) $\qquad y = x^2 - 2x - 3$

Rearrange (2) $\quad y = -x - 8$

Sub (2) in (1) $\qquad -x - 8 = x^2 - 2x - 3$

$\Rightarrow 0 = x^2 - x + 5$

$b^2 - 4ac = 1 - 20 = -19 < 0 \Rightarrow$ no real roots

So there are no solutions for the simultaneous equations.

f) (1) $\qquad y = 2x^2 - 3x + 5$

Rearrange (2) $\quad 5x - 3 = y$

Sub (2) in (1) $\qquad 5x - 3 = 2x^2 - 3x + 5$

$\Rightarrow 0 = 2x^2 - 8x + 8$

$\Rightarrow x^2 - 4x + 4 = 0$

$\Rightarrow (x - 2)^2 = 0 \Rightarrow x = 2$

When $x = 2$, $y = 10 - 3 = 7$, so $x = 2, y = 7$

There is only one solution here.

g) (1) $\qquad 2x^2 + 3y^2 = 77$

Rearrange (2) $\quad x = -3y + 14$

Sub (2) in (1) $\qquad 2(-3y + 14)^2 + 3y^2 = 77$

$\Rightarrow 2(9y^2 - 84y + 196) + 3y^2 = 77$

$\Rightarrow 21y^2 - 168y + 315 = 0 \Rightarrow y^2 - 8y + 15 = 0$

$\Rightarrow (y - 3)(y - 5) = 0 \Rightarrow y = 3$ or $y = 5$

When $y = 3$, $x = -9 + 14 = 5$, and

when $y = 5$, $x = -15 + 14 = -1$

So $x = 5, y = 3 \quad$ or $\quad x = -1, y = 5$

Q3 a) (1) $\qquad y = \dfrac{1}{2}x^2 + 4x - 8$

(2) $\qquad y = \dfrac{3}{2}x + 4$

Sub (2) in (1) $\quad \dfrac{3}{2}x + 4 = \dfrac{1}{2}x^2 + 4x - 8$

$\Rightarrow 3x + 8 = x^2 + 8x - 16$

$\Rightarrow 0 = x^2 + 5x - 24 \Rightarrow (x + 8)(x - 3) = 0$

$\Rightarrow x = -8$ or $x = 3$

When $x = -8$, $y = -12 + 4 = -8$, and

when $x = 3$, $y = \dfrac{9}{2} + 4 = \dfrac{17}{2}$

So they intersect at $(-8, -8)$ and $(3, \dfrac{17}{2})$

b) (1) $\qquad y = 2x^2 + x - 6$

Rearrange (2) $\quad 5x + 10 = y$

Sub (2) in (1) $\qquad 5x + 10 = 2x^2 + x - 6$

$\Rightarrow 0 = 2x^2 - 4x - 16 \Rightarrow x^2 - 2x - 8 = 0$

$\Rightarrow (x - 4)(x + 2) = 0 \Rightarrow x = 4$ or $x = -2$

When $x = 4$, $y = 20 + 10 = 30$, and

when $x = -2$, $y = -10 + 10 = 0$

So they intersect at $(4, 30)$ and $(-2, 0)$

c) (1) $\qquad x^2 + y^2 = 50$

Rearrange (2) $\quad x = -2y + 5$

Sub (2) in (1) $\qquad (-2y + 5)^2 + y^2 = 50$

$\Rightarrow 4y^2 - 20y + 25 + y^2 - 50 = 0$

$\Rightarrow 5y^2 - 20y - 25 = 0 \Rightarrow y^2 - 4y - 5 = 0$

$\Rightarrow (y - 5)(y + 1) = 0 \Rightarrow y = 5$ or $y = -1$

When $y = 5$, $x = -10 + 5 = -5$, and
when $y = -1$, $x = 2 + 5 = 7$

So they intersect at $(-5, 5)$ and $(7, -1)$

d) (1) $\qquad 2x^2 - y + 3x + 1 = 0$

Rearrange (2) $\quad y = x + 5$

Sub (2) in (1) $\qquad 2x^2 - (x + 5) + 3x + 1 = 0$

$\Rightarrow 2x^2 + 2x - 4 = 0 \Rightarrow x^2 + x - 2 = 0$

$\Rightarrow (x + 2)(x - 1) = 0 \Rightarrow x = -2$ or $x = 1$

When $x = -2$, $y = -2 + 5 = 3$, and
when $x = 1$, $y = 1 + 5 = 6$

So they intersect at $(-2, 3)$ and $(1, 6)$

Q4 a) (1) $\qquad x^2 + y^2 = 10$

Rearrange (2) $\quad x = 3y - 10$

Sub (2) in (1) $\qquad (3y - 10)^2 + y^2 = 10$

$\Rightarrow 9y^2 - 60y + 100 + y^2 - 10 = 0$

$\Rightarrow 10y^2 - 60y + 90 = 0 \Rightarrow y^2 - 6y + 9 = 0$

$\Rightarrow (y - 3)^2 = 0 \Rightarrow y = 3$

When $y = 3$, $x = 9 - 10 = -1$

So $x = -1$, $y = 3$.

b) $x^2 + y^2 = 10$ is a circle and $x - 3y + 10 = 0$ is a straight line. Part a) tells us that they intersect at a single point, so the line must actually be a tangent to the circle.

Q5 a) (1) $\qquad y = x^2 + 6x - 7$

(2) $\qquad y = 2x - 3$

Sub (2) in (1) $\quad 2x - 3 = x^2 + 6x - 7$

$\Rightarrow x^2 + 4x - 4 = 0$

So $b^2 - 4ac = 16 + 16 = 32 > 0$

So they will intersect at two points.

b) (1) $\qquad 3x^2 + 4y^2 = 7$

Rearrange (2) $\quad x = -\frac{4}{3}y + \frac{7}{3}$

Sub (2) in (1) $\quad 3(-\frac{4}{3}y + \frac{7}{3})^2 + 4y^2 = 7$

$\Rightarrow 3(\frac{16}{9}y^2 - \frac{56}{9}y + \frac{49}{9}) + 4y^2 = 7$

$\Rightarrow \frac{16}{3}y^2 - \frac{56}{3}y + \frac{49}{3} + 4y^2 - 7 = 0$

$\Rightarrow 16y^2 - 56y + 49 + 12y^2 - 21 = 0$

$\Rightarrow 28y^2 - 56y + 28 = 0$

$\Rightarrow y^2 - 2y + 1 = 0$

Now $b^2 - 4ac = 4 - 4 = 0$

So they will intersect only once — (2) is a tangent to (1).

c) (1) $\qquad xy + 2x - y = 8$

Rearrange (2) $\quad x = -y + 1$

Sub (2) in (1) $\quad (-y + 1)y + 2(-y + 1) - y = 8$

$\Rightarrow -y^2 + y - 2y + 2 - y = 8$

$\Rightarrow -y^2 - 2y - 6 = 0$

$\Rightarrow y^2 + 2y + 6 = 0$

So $b^2 - 4ac = 4 - 24 = -20 < 0$

So the graphs will not intersect.

Review Exercise — Chapter 3

Q1 a) $7x - 4 > 2x - 42 \Rightarrow 5x > -38 \Rightarrow x > -\frac{38}{5}$

b) $12y - 3 \leq 4y + 4 \Rightarrow 8y \leq 7 \Rightarrow y \leq \frac{7}{8}$

c) $9y - 4 \geq 17y + 2 \Rightarrow -8y \geq 6 \Rightarrow y \leq -\frac{3}{4}$

d) $x + 6 < 5x - 4 \Rightarrow -4x < -10 \Rightarrow x > \frac{5}{2}$

e) $4x - 2 > x - 14 \Rightarrow 3x > -12 \Rightarrow x > -4$

f) $7 - x \leq 4 - 2x \Rightarrow x \leq -3$

Q2 a) $3x^2 - 5x - 2 = 0 \Rightarrow (3x + 1)(x - 2) = 0$

$\Rightarrow x = -\frac{1}{3}$ or $x = 2$

$3x^2 - 5x - 2 \leq 0 \Rightarrow -\frac{1}{3} \leq x \leq 2$

b) $x^2 + 2x + 7 = 4x + 9 \Rightarrow x^2 - 2x - 2 = 0$

$\Rightarrow x = \frac{2 \pm \sqrt{4 - (-8)}}{2} = \frac{2 \pm \sqrt{12}}{2} = \frac{2 \pm 2\sqrt{3}}{2}$

$\Rightarrow x = 1 \pm \sqrt{3}$

$x^2 - 2x - 2 > 0$

$\Rightarrow x < 1 - \sqrt{3}$ or $x > 1 + \sqrt{3}$

c) $3x^2 + 7x + 4 = 2(x^2 + x - 1) \Rightarrow x^2 + 5x + 6 = 0$

$\Rightarrow (x + 3)(x + 2) = 0 \Rightarrow x = -3$ or $x = -2$

$x^2 + 5x + 6 \geq 0 \Rightarrow x \leq -3$ or $x \geq -2$

d) $x^2 + 3x - 1 = x + 2 \Rightarrow x^2 + 2x - 3 = 0$

$\Rightarrow (x + 3)(x - 1) = 0 \Rightarrow x = -3$ or $x = 1$

$x^2 + 3x - 1 \geq x + 2 \Rightarrow x \leq -3$ or $x \geq 1$

e) $2x^2 = x + 1 \Rightarrow 2x^2 - x - 1 = 0$

$\Rightarrow (2x + 1)(x - 1) = 0 \Rightarrow x = -\frac{1}{2}$ or $x = 1$

$2x^2 > x + 1 \Rightarrow x < -\frac{1}{2}$ or $x > 1$

f) $3x^2 - 12 = x^2 - 2x \Rightarrow 2x^2 + 2x - 12 = 0$

$\Rightarrow x^2 + x - 6 = 0 \Rightarrow (x - 2)(x + 3) = 0$

$\Rightarrow x = 2$ or $x = -3$

$3x^2 - 12 < x^2 - 2x \Rightarrow -3 < x < 2$

Q3 a) (1) $\qquad 3x - 4y = 7$

(2) $\qquad -2x + 7y = -22$

(1) $\times 2 \quad 6x - 8y = 14 \quad$ (3)

(2) $\times 3 \quad -6x + 21y = -66 \quad$ (4)

(3) + (4) $\quad 13y = -52 \Rightarrow y = -4$

$y = -4$ in (1) $\quad 3x + 16 = 7 \Rightarrow x = -3$

So the solution is $x = -3$, $y = -4$

b) (1) $\qquad 2x - 3y = \frac{11}{12}$

(2) $\qquad x + y = -\frac{7}{12}$

(2) $\times 2 \quad 2x + 2y = -\frac{14}{12}$ $\qquad$ (3)

(1) $- (3) \quad -5y = \frac{25}{12} \Rightarrow y = -\frac{5}{12}$

$y = -\frac{5}{12}$ in (2) $\Rightarrow x - \frac{5}{12} = -\frac{7}{12} \Rightarrow x = -\frac{1}{6}$

So the solution is $x = -\frac{1}{6}, \; y = -\frac{5}{12}$

Q4 a) (1) $y = 3x - 4$

(2) $y = 7x - 5$

Sub (2) in (1) $\;7x - 5 = 3x - 4 \Rightarrow x = \frac{1}{4}$

when $x = \frac{1}{4}, y = 3\left(\frac{1}{4}\right) - 4 = -\frac{13}{4}$

So they intersect at $\left(\frac{1}{4}, -\frac{13}{4}\right)$

b) (1) $y = 13 - 2x$

(2) $7x - y - 23 = 0$

Sub (1) in (2) $7x - (13 - 2x) - 23 = 0$

$\Rightarrow x = 4$

when $x = 4, y = 13 - 2(4) = 5$

So they intersect at (4, 5)

c) (1) $2x - 3y + 4 = 0$

Rearrange (2) $\;x = 2y - 1$

Sub (2) in (1) $\quad 2(2y - 1) - 3y + 4 = 0$

$\Rightarrow y = -2$

when $y = -2, x = 2(-2) - 1 = -5$

So they intersect at (–5, –2)

Q5 a) (1) $y = x^2 - 7x + 4$

Rearrange (2) $\quad y = 2x - 10 \, (3)$

Sub (3) in (1) $x^2 - 9x + 14 = 0$

$\Rightarrow (x - 2)(x - 7) = 0 \Rightarrow x = 2$ or $x = 7$

when $x = 2, y = 2(2) - 10 = -6$

when $x = 7, y = 2(7) - 10 = 4$

The line and the curve meet at the points (2, –6) and (7, 4).

b) (1) $y = 30 - 6x + 2x^2$

(2) $y = 2(x + 11)$

Sub (2) in (1) $2x^2 - 8x + 8 = 0$

$\Rightarrow x^2 - 4x + 4 = 0$

$\Rightarrow (x - 2)^2 = 0 \Rightarrow x = 2$

when $x = 2, y = 2(2 + 11) = 26$

The line is a tangent to the parabola at the point (2, 26).

c) (1) $2x^2 + 2y^2 - 3 = 0$

(2) $y = x + 4$

Sub (2) in (1) to get $2x^2 + 2(x + 4)^2 - 3 = 0$

$\Rightarrow 4x^2 + 16x + 29 = 0$

$b^2 - 4ac = 16^2 - (4 \times 4 \times 29)$

$= 16^2 - (16 \times 29) < 0$

The equations have no solution and so the line and the curve never meet.

Q6 (1) $y = x^2 - 2x - 3$

(2) $y = 3x + 11$

Sub (2) in (1) to get $x^2 - 5x - 14 = 0$

Subbing into $b^2 - 4ac$ gives $b^2 - 4ac = 81 > 0$

There will be two points of intersection as the discriminant is greater than zero.

Exam-Style Questions — Chapter 3

Q1 a) $3x + 2 \le x + 6$

$\qquad 2x \le 4 \qquad$ *[1 mark]*

$\qquad x \le 2 \qquad$ *[1 mark]*

b) $\qquad 20 - x - x^2 > 0$

$(4 - x)(5 + x) > 0$ *[1 mark]*

The graph crosses the x-axis at $x = 4$ and $x = -5$ *[1 mark]*. The coefficient of x^2 is negative so the graph is n-shaped *[1 mark]*. So $20 - x - x^2 > 0$ when $-5 < x < 4$ *[1 mark]*.

c) From above, x will satisfy both inequalities when $-5 < x \le 2$ *[1 mark]*.
For this bit, all you need to do is use your answers to parts a) and b) and work out which values of x fit in them both.

Q2 a) $3 \le 2p + 5 \le 15$
This inequality has 3 parts. Subtract 5 from each part to give: $-2 \le 2p \le 10$ *[1 mark]*.
Now divide each part by 2 to give: $-1 \le p \le 5$ *[1 mark for –1 ≤ p and 1 mark for p ≤ 5]*.

b) $q^2 - 9 > 0$

$(q + 3)(q - 3) > 0$ *[1 mark]*

The function is 0 at $q = -3$ and $q = 3$ *[1 mark]*. The coefficient of q^2 is positive so the graph is u-shaped. So $q^2 - 9 > 0$ when $q < -3$ or $q > 3$ *[1 mark for each correct inequality]*.
Use D.O.T.S. (Difference of Two Squares) to factorise the quadratic — remember that $a^2 - b^2 = (a + b)(a - b)$.

Q3 a) $(3x + 2)(x - 5)$ *[1 mark]*

b) $(3x + 2)(x - 5) \le 0$
The function is 0 at $x = -\frac{2}{3}$ and $x = 5$ *[1 mark]*.
The coefficient of x^2 is positive so the graph is u-shaped, meaning the function is less than or equal to 0 between these x-values.
i.e. $3x^2 - 13x - 10 \le 0$ when $-\frac{2}{3} \le x \le 5$ *[2 marks, 1 for $-\frac{2}{3} \le x$ and 1 for $x \le 5$]*.

Q4 a) (1) $\qquad 2x + 3y = 5$

(2) $\qquad 5x + 4y = 2$

(1) $\times 4 \qquad 8x + 12y = 20$

(2) $\times 3 \qquad 15x + 12y = 6$ *[1 mark]*

Subtract: $\quad -7x = 14 \Rightarrow x = -2$ *[1 mark]*

$x = -2$ in (1) $-4 + 3y = 5$

$\Rightarrow 3y = 9 \Rightarrow y = 3$

So the solution is $x = -2, y = 3$ *[1 mark]*

b) Rearrange (1) $5x + y = 6$

Rearrange (2) $7x + 2y = 6$ *[1 mark]*

(1) × 2 $10x + 2y = 12$ (3)   *[1 mark]*

(2) − (3) $-3x = -6 \Rightarrow x = 2$ *[1 mark]*

$x = 2$ in (1) $10 + y = 6 \Rightarrow y = -4$

So the solution is $x = 2$, $y = -4$ *[1 mark]*

For this question, you could have eliminated x first to find y, or used the substitution method instead.

Q5 a) (1) $x^2 + y^2 = 13$

Rearrange (2) $x = 5y - 13$

Sub (2) in (1) $(5y - 13)^2 + y^2 = 13$ *[1 mark]*

$\Rightarrow 25y^2 - 130y + 169 + y^2 - 13 = 0$ *[1 mark]*

$\Rightarrow 26y^2 - 130y + 156 = 0$

$\Rightarrow y^2 - 5y + 6 = 0$ *[1 mark]*

b) $(y - 2)(y - 3) = 0$ *[1 mark]*

$\Rightarrow y = 2$ or $y = 3$ *[1 mark]*

When $y = 2$, $x = 10 - 13 = -3$, and when $y = 3$, $x = 15 - 13 = 2$

So $x = -3$, $y = 2$ *[1 mark]*

or $x = 2$, $y = 3$ *[1 mark]*

Q6 First, take the linear equation and rearrange it to get x on its own: $x = 6 - y$ *[1 mark]*. Now substitute the equation for x into the quadratic equation:

$(6 - y)^2 + 2y^2 = 36$ *[1 mark]*

$36 - 12y + y^2 + 2y^2 = 36$

$3y^2 - 12y = 0$

$y^2 - 4y = 0$

$y(y - 4) = 0$ *[1 mark]*

so $y = 0$ and $y = 4$. *[1 mark]*.

Now you've got the y-values, put them back into the equation for x ($x = 6 - y$) to find the x-values.

When $y = 0$, $x = 6 - y = 6 - 0 = 6$.

When $y = 4$, $x = 6 - y = 6 - 4 = 2$.

So the line and the curve intersect at (6, 0) *[1 mark]* and (2, 4) *[1 mark]*.

You could have substituted y = 6 − x into the quadratic instead and solved it that way.

Q7 a) At points of intersection,

$-2x + 4 = -x^2 + 3$ *[1 mark]*

$x^2 - 2x + 1 = 0$

$(x - 1)^2 = 0$ *[1 mark]*

so $x = 1$ *[1 mark]*. When $x = 1$, $y = -2x + 4 = 2$, so there is one point of intersection at (1, 2) *[1 mark]*.

b)

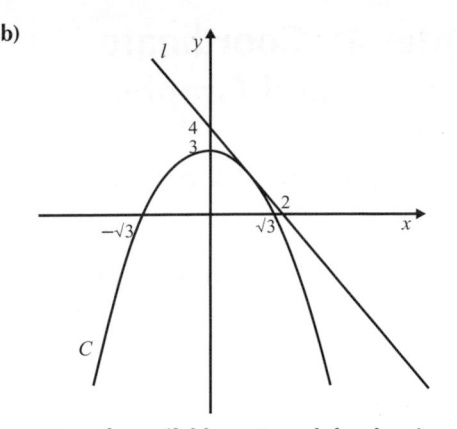

[5 marks available — 1 mark for drawing n-shaped curve, 1 mark for x-axis intercepts at ±√3, 1 mark for maximum point of curve and y-axis intercept at (0, 3). 1 mark for line crossing the y-axis at (0, 4) and the x-axis at (2, 0). 1 mark for line and curve touching in one place.]

Q8 a)

[5 marks available — 1 mark for drawing u-shaped curve, 1 mark for x-axis intercepts at −2 and 4 , 1 mark for y-axis intercept at (0, −8). 1 mark for line crossing the y-axis at (0, −3) and the x-axis at (3/2, 0). 1 mark for line and curve intersecting in two places.]

b) At points of intersection,

$2x - 3 = (x + 2)(x - 4)$

$2x - 3 = x^2 - 2x - 8$ *[1 mark]*

$0 = x^2 - 4x - 5$ *[1 mark]*

c) $x^2 - 4x - 5 = 0$

$(x - 5)(x + 1) = 0$ *[1 mark]*

so $x = 5$, $x = -1$ *[1 mark]*.

When $x = 5$, $y = (2 \times 5) - 3 = 7$ and when $x = -1$, $y = (2 \times -1) - 3 = -5$, so the points of intersection are (5, 7) *[1 mark]* and (−1, −5) *[1 mark]*.

Chapter 4: Coordinate Geometry and Graphs

1. The Equation of a Straight Line

Exercise 1.1

— $y - y_1 = m(x - x_1)$ and $y = mx + c$

Q1 a) gradient = –4, y-intercept = (0, 11)

   b) gradient = –1, y-intercept = (0, 4)

   c) gradient = 1.7, y-intercept = (0, –2.3)

Q2 a) $y = -3x + 2$

   b) $y = 5x - 3$

   c) $y = \frac{1}{2}x + 6$

   d) $y = 0.8x + 1.2$

Q3 a) $c = 8$

   $(x_1, y_1) = (-4, 0), (x_2, y_2) = (0, 8)$

   $m = \frac{8 - 0}{0 - (-4)} = \frac{8}{4} = 2$

   $\Rightarrow y = 2x + 8$

   b) $c = -5$

   $(x_1, y_1) = (-2, 11), (x_2, y_2) = (0, -5)$

   $m = \frac{-5 - 11}{0 - (-2)} = \frac{-16}{2} = -8$

   $\Rightarrow y = -8x - 5$

   c) $c = -1$

   $(x_1, y_1) = (0, -1), (x_2, y_2) = (2, 0)$

   $m = \frac{0 - (-1)}{2 - 0} = \frac{1}{2}$

   $\Rightarrow y = \frac{1}{2}x - 1$

Q4 a) $(x_1, y_1) = (4, 1), (x_2, y_2) = (0, -3)$

   $m = \frac{-3 - 1}{0 - 4} = \frac{-4}{-4} = 1$

   (i) $y - 1 = 1(x - 4)$

   $\Rightarrow y - 1 = x - 4$

   (ii) $y = x - 3$

   b) $(x_1, y_1) = (12, -3), (x_2, y_2) = (14, 1)$

   $m = \frac{1 - (-3)}{14 - 12} = \frac{4}{2} = 2$

   (i) $y - (-3) = 2(x - 12)$

   $\Rightarrow y + 3 = 2(x - 12)$

   (ii) $y = 2x - 27$

   c) $(x_1, y_1) = (5, 7), (x_2, y_2) = (-2, 5)$

   $m = \frac{5 - 7}{-2 - 5} = \frac{-2}{-7} = \frac{2}{7}$

   (i) $y - 7 = \frac{2}{7}(x - 5)$

   (ii) $y = \frac{2}{7}x + \frac{39}{7}$

   d) $(x_1, y_1) = (-3, 6), (x_2, y_2) = (4, -2)$

   $m = \frac{-2 - 6}{4 - (-3)} = -\frac{8}{7}$

   (i) $y - 6 = -\frac{8}{7}(x - (-3))$

   $\Rightarrow y - 6 = -\frac{8}{7}(x + 3)$

   (ii) $y = -\frac{8}{7}x + \frac{18}{7}$

Q5 $y = mx + c$

   $\Rightarrow -3 = \frac{1}{4} \times (-4) + c$

   $\Rightarrow -3 = -1 + c \Rightarrow c = -2$

   $\Rightarrow y = \frac{1}{4}x - 2$

Q6 Find the equation of the line first.
   $m = 3$, find c using the point (2, –7) on the line:
   $y = mx + c$

   $\Rightarrow -7 = 3 \times 2 + c$

   $\Rightarrow -7 = 6 + c \Rightarrow c = -13$

   $\Rightarrow y = 3x - 13$

   The points a), c) and e) lie on the line.
   *Sub in the x value from each point — if the resulting value
   for y matches the value of y in the original point, then the
   point lies on that line.*

Exercise 1.2 — $ax + by + c = 0$

Q1 a) $5x - y + 2 = 0$

   b) $3y = -\frac{1}{2}x + 3$

   $\Rightarrow \frac{1}{2}x + 3y - 3 = 0$

   $\Rightarrow x + 6y - 6 = 0$

   c) $2(x - 1) = 4y - 1$

   $\Rightarrow 2x - 2 = 4y - 1$

   $\Rightarrow 2x - 4y - 1 = 0$

   d) $7x - 2y - 9 = 0$

   e) $\frac{1}{2}(4x + 3) = 3(y - 2)$

   $\Rightarrow 2x + \frac{3}{2} = 3y - 6$

   $\Rightarrow 2x - 3y + \frac{15}{2} = 0$

   $\Rightarrow 4x - 6y + 15 = 0$

   f) $3(y - 4) = 4(x - 3)$

   $\Rightarrow 3y - 12 = 4x - 12$

   $\Rightarrow 4x - 3y = 0$

Q2 a) $6x - 2y + 3 = 0$

   $\Rightarrow 2y = 6x + 3$

   $\Rightarrow y = 3x + \frac{3}{2}$

   $m = 3$, y-intercept = $(0, \frac{3}{2})$

b) $-9x + 3y - 12 = 0$

$\Rightarrow 3y = 9x + 12$

$\Rightarrow y = 3x + 4$

$m = 3$, y-intercept $= (0, 4)$

c) $-x - 4y - 2 = 0$

$\Rightarrow -4y = x + 2$

$\Rightarrow y = -\frac{1}{4}x - \frac{1}{2}$

$m = -\frac{1}{4}$, y-intercept $= (0, -\frac{1}{2})$

d) $7x + 8y + 11 = 0$

$\Rightarrow 8y = -7x - 11$

$\Rightarrow y = -\frac{7}{8}x - \frac{11}{8}$

$m = -\frac{7}{8}$, y-intercept $= (0, -\frac{11}{8})$

Q3 a) $(x_1, y_1) = (5, 2)$, $(x_2, y_2) = (3, 4)$

$m = \frac{4-2}{3-5} = \frac{2}{-2} = -1$

$y - y_1 = m(x - x_1)$

$\Rightarrow y - 2 = -1(x - 5) \Rightarrow y - 2 = -x + 5$

$\Rightarrow x + y - 7 = 0$

b) $(x_1, y_1) = (9, -1)$, $(x_2, y_2) = (7, 2)$

$m = \frac{2-(-1)}{7-9} = -\frac{3}{2}$

$y - y_1 = m(x - x_1)$

$\Rightarrow y - (-1) = -\frac{3}{2}(x - 9)$

$\Rightarrow y + 1 = -\frac{3}{2}x + \frac{27}{2}$

$\Rightarrow \frac{3}{2}x + y - \frac{25}{2} = 0$

$\Rightarrow 3x + 2y - 25 = 0$

c) $(x_1, y_1) = (-6, 1)$, $(x_2, y_2) = (4, 0)$

$m = \frac{0-1}{4-(-6)} = -\frac{1}{10}$

$y - y_1 = m(x - x_1)$

$\Rightarrow y - 1 = -\frac{1}{10}(x - (-6))$

$\Rightarrow y - 1 = -\frac{1}{10}x - \frac{6}{10}$

$\Rightarrow \frac{1}{10}x + y - \frac{4}{10} = 0$

$\Rightarrow x + 10y - 4 = 0$

d) $(x_1, y_1) = (-12, 3)$, $(x_2, y_2) = (5, 7)$

$m = \frac{7-3}{5-(-12)} = \frac{4}{17}$

$y - y_1 = m(x - x_1)$

$\Rightarrow y - 3 = \frac{4}{17}(x - (-12))$

$\Rightarrow y - 3 = \frac{4}{17}x + \frac{48}{17}$

$\Rightarrow -\frac{4}{17}x + y - \frac{99}{17} = 0$

$\Rightarrow -4x + 17y - 99 = 0$

$\Rightarrow 4x - 17y + 99 = 0$

Q4 a) $(x_1, y_1) = (0, -5)$, $(x_2, y_2) = (-5, 0)$

$m = \frac{0-(-5)}{-5-0} = -1$

$y - y_1 = m(x - x_1)$

$\Rightarrow y - (-5) = -1(x - 0)$

$\Rightarrow y + 5 = -x$

$\Rightarrow x + y + 5 = 0$

b) $(x_1, y_1) = (0, -2)$, $(x_2, y_2) = (3, 0)$

$m = \frac{0-(-2)}{3-0} = \frac{2}{3}$

$y - y_1 = m(x - x_1)$

$\Rightarrow y - (-2) = \frac{2}{3}(x - 0)$

$\Rightarrow y + 2 = \frac{2}{3}x$

$\Rightarrow -\frac{2}{3}x + y + 2 = 0$

$\Rightarrow 2x - 3y - 6 = 0$

2. Parallel and Perpendicular Lines

Exercise 2.1 — Parallel lines

Q1 a), c) and e) are parallel.

Rearrange each equation so it's in the form $y = mx + c$ and then compare gradients. If a line is parallel to $y = -3x + c$, then it'll have a gradient of -3.

Q2 a) $y = 4x + c$

Sub in $x = 3$ and $y = 2$

$\Rightarrow 2 = 4 \times 3 + c \Rightarrow -10 = c$

So $y = 4x - 10$

$\Rightarrow 4x - y - 10 = 0$

b) First rearrange the given equation:

$4x - 2y - 1 = 0$

$-2y = -4x + 1$

$y = 2x - \frac{1}{2}$

So the equation of the line we want is:

$y = 2x + c$

Sub in $x = -4$, $y = -5 \Rightarrow -5 = 2(-4) + c \Rightarrow c = 3$

So $y = 2x + 3 \Rightarrow 2x - y + 3 = 0$.

Q3 a) no **b)** yes **c)** yes

Q4 a) Find the gradient of the other line first:

Rearrange $2x - 4y + 3 = 0$

$\Rightarrow 4y = 2x + 3 \Rightarrow y = \frac{1}{2}x + \frac{3}{4}$

So gradient, $m = \frac{1}{2}$

$y = \frac{1}{2}x + c$

Sub in $x = 4$ and $y = 3$

$\Rightarrow 3 = \frac{1}{2} \times 4 + c \Rightarrow c = 1$

$\Rightarrow y = \frac{1}{2}x + 1$

b) Rearrange $y = \frac{1}{2}x + 1$

$\Rightarrow \frac{1}{2}x - y + 1 = 0 \Rightarrow x - 2y + 2 = 0$

Exercise 2.2 — Perpendicular lines

Q1 a) $m = -1 \div 2 = -\frac{1}{2} \Rightarrow y = -\frac{1}{2}x + c$

Sub in $(-2, 5)$

$\Rightarrow 5 = \left(-\frac{1}{2}\right) \times (-2) + c \Rightarrow c = 5 - 1 = 4$

$\Rightarrow y = -\frac{1}{2}x + 4$

b) Rearrange $x - 5y - 30 = 0 \Rightarrow y = \frac{1}{5}x - 6$

$m = -1 \div \frac{1}{5} = -5 \Rightarrow y = -5x + c$

Sub in $(5, 2)$

$\Rightarrow 2 = -5 \times 5 + c \Rightarrow c = 2 + 25 = 27$

$\Rightarrow y = -5x + 27$

Q2 a) $m = -1 \div \frac{1}{4} = -4$

$\Rightarrow y = -4x + c$

Sub in $(-1, 2)$

$\Rightarrow 2 = (-4) \times (-1) + c \Rightarrow c = 2 - 4 = -2$

$\Rightarrow y = -4x - 2$

$\Rightarrow 4x + y + 2 = 0$

b) Rearrange to get $y = -\frac{2}{3}x + \frac{1}{3}$

$m = -1 \div -\frac{2}{3} = \frac{3}{2} \Rightarrow y = \frac{3}{2}x + c$

Sub in $(-3, -1)$

$\Rightarrow -1 = \frac{3}{2} \times (-3) + c \Rightarrow c = -1 + \frac{9}{2} = \frac{7}{2}$

$\Rightarrow y = \frac{3}{2}x + \frac{7}{2} \Rightarrow 2y = 3x + 7$

$\Rightarrow 3x - 2y + 7 = 0$

c) Rearrange to get $y = \frac{1}{2}x + \frac{1}{10}$

$m = -1 \div \frac{1}{2} = -2 \Rightarrow y = -2x + c$

Sub in $(6, -5)$

$\Rightarrow -5 = -2 \times 6 + c \Rightarrow c = -5 + 12 = 7$

$\Rightarrow y = -2x + 7 \Rightarrow 2x + y - 7 = 0$

d) $m = -1 \div \frac{3}{2} = -\frac{2}{3} \Rightarrow y = -\frac{2}{3}x + c$

Sub in $(2, 1)$

$\Rightarrow 1 = -\frac{2}{3} \times 2 + c \Rightarrow c = 1 + \frac{4}{3} = \frac{7}{3}$

$\Rightarrow y = -\frac{2}{3}x + \frac{7}{3} \Rightarrow 3y = -2x + 7$

$\Rightarrow 2x + 3y - 7 = 0$

Q3 a) Rearrange $3x + 4y - 1 = 0 \Rightarrow y = -\frac{3}{4}x + \frac{1}{4}$

Multiply the gradients of both lines:

$\frac{4}{3} \times -\frac{3}{4} = -1$

So the lines are perpendicular.

Remember, if you multiply the gradients of two perpendicular lines you get −1.

b) Rearrange $3x + 2y - 3 = 0 \Rightarrow y = -\frac{3}{2}x + \frac{3}{2}$

Multiply the gradients of both lines:

$\frac{3}{2} \times -\frac{3}{2} = -\frac{9}{4}$

So the lines are not perpendicular.

c) Rearrange $4x - y + 3 = 0 \Rightarrow y = 4x + 3$

Rearrange $2x + 8y + 1 = 0 \Rightarrow y = -\frac{1}{4}x - \frac{1}{8}$

Multiply the gradients of both lines:

$4 \times -\frac{1}{4} = -1$

So the lines are perpendicular.

Q4 a) AB: $m = \frac{3-2}{4-0} = \frac{1}{4} \Rightarrow y = \frac{1}{4}x + c$

Sub in $(0, 2) \Rightarrow 2 = 0 + c \Rightarrow c = 2$

$\Rightarrow y = \frac{1}{4}x + 2$

BC: $m = \frac{-1-3}{5-4} = -4 \Rightarrow y = -4x + c$

Sub in $(4, 3) \Rightarrow 3 = -4 \times 4 + c \Rightarrow c = 19$

$\Rightarrow y = -4x + 19$

AC: $m = \frac{-1-2}{5-0} = -\frac{3}{5} \Rightarrow y = -\frac{3}{5}x + c$

Sub in $(0, 2) \Rightarrow 2 = 0 + c \Rightarrow c = 2$

$\Rightarrow y = -\frac{3}{5}x + 2$

b) The triangle is right-angled, as AB is perpendicular to BC:

$m_{AB} \times m_{BC} = \frac{1}{4} \times -4 = -1$

Q5 $3x - 2y = 6$

Rearrange into $y = mx + c$:

$\Rightarrow -2y = -3x + 6$

$\Rightarrow y = \frac{3}{2}x - 3$

So the line we want will have gradient

$m = -1 \div \frac{3}{2} = -\frac{2}{3}$

Now sub in (a, b) to find c:

$y = -\frac{2}{3}x + c$

$b = -\frac{2}{3}a + c$

$c = b + \frac{2}{3}a$

So the equation of line A is $y = -\frac{2}{3}x + \frac{2}{3}a + b$

You could also have given the line in the form $2x + 3y - 2a - 3b = 0$ as the question didn't tell you which form to use.

3. Curve Sketching

Exercise 3.1 — Cubic functions and higher positive powers

Q1 a) $y = -1.5x^4$ will be u-shaped or n-shaped because the power is even and since the coefficient is negative it will be below the x-axis, so it must be graph D.

b) $y = 0.5x^3$ has an odd power and a positive coefficient so it will have a bottom-left to top-right curve. It must be graph B.

c) $y = 2x^6$ has an even power so it'll be u-shaped or n-shaped and it has a positive coefficient so it'll be above the x-axis. It must be graph A.

d) $y = -3x^3$ has an odd power of x and a negative coefficient so it must have a top-left to bottom-right curve. It must be graph C.

Q2 a)

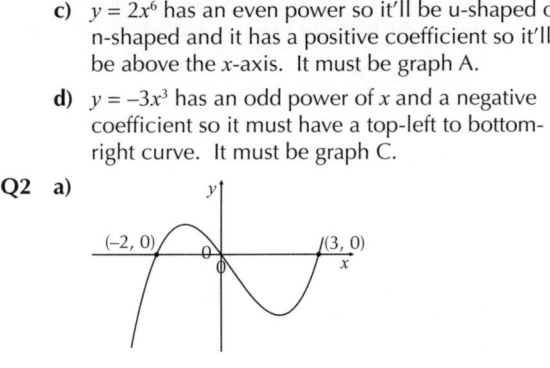

b)

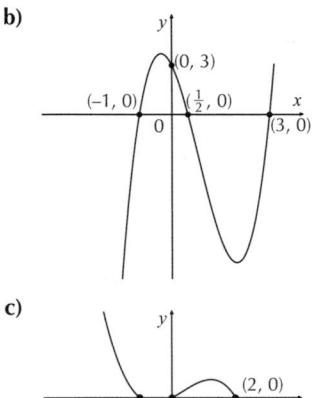

c)

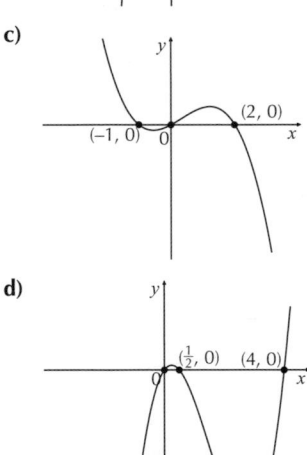

d)

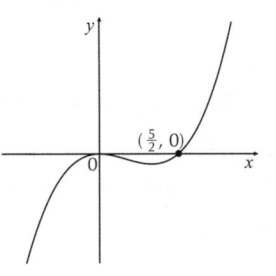

Your graphs don't need to look exactly like these, e.g. you don't need to get the size of the 'dips' right — as long as you've shown the rough shape and intercept points with the axes.

Q3 a)

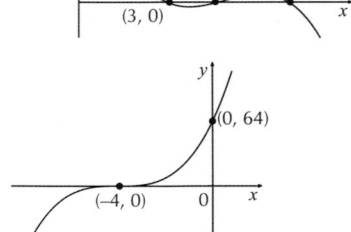

b)

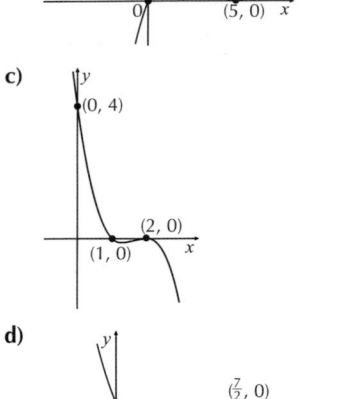

c)

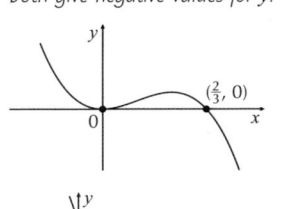

d)

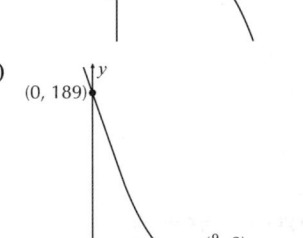

Remember — putting in values for x near the key points can really help understand the shape of the graphs. E.g. for part d) above, pop in $x = 3$ and 4 to check that both give negative values for y.

Q4 a)

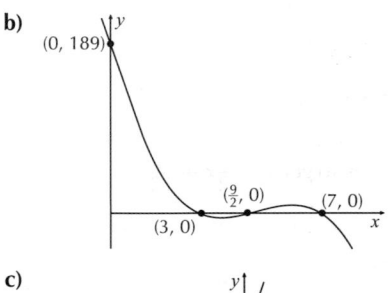

b)

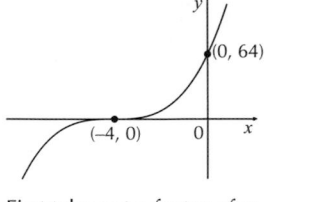

c)

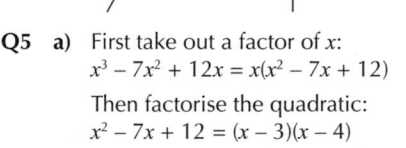

Q5 a) First take out a factor of x:
$x^3 - 7x^2 + 12x = x(x^2 - 7x + 12)$

Then factorise the quadratic:
$x^2 - 7x + 12 = (x - 3)(x - 4)$

So $x^3 - 7x^2 + 12x = x(x - 3)(x - 4)$.

b)

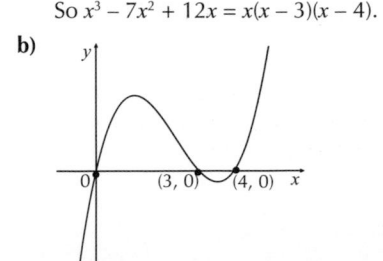

Q6 a) $x^3 - 16x = x(x^2 - 16) = x(x + 4)(x - 4)$

Using this information we can sketch the graph:

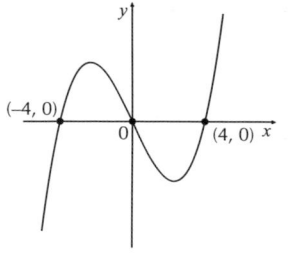

b) $2x^3 - 12x^2 + 18x = 2x(x^2 - 6x + 9)$

$= 2x(x - 3)^2$

Using this information we can sketch the graph:

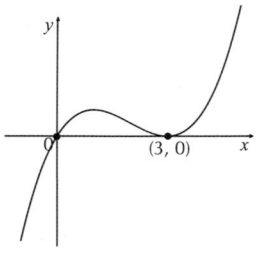

Q7 a)

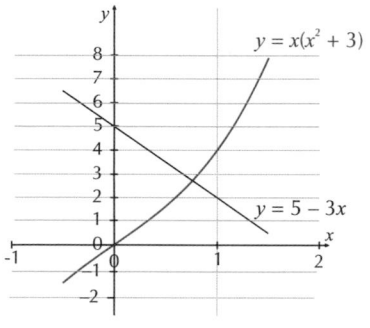

b) The x-coordinates of the points of intersection of the curve and the line are found by setting them equal to each other: $x(x^2 + 3) = 5 - 3x$

Rearranging: $x^3 + 3x = 5 - 3x$
$\Rightarrow x^3 + 3x - 5 + 3x = 0 \Rightarrow x^3 + 6x - 5 = 0$

So the intersection point of the curve and the line is the real solution to $x^3 + 6x - 5 = 0$.

c) Looking at the graph from part a) — particularly at the point where the curve and the line cross, you can estimate the x-value of the real solution to the equation.

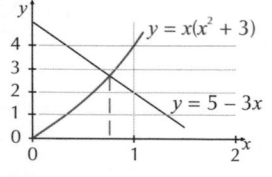

It looks like the solution is at about $x = 0.7$. The exact solution is actually close to 0.76 but anything between 0.6 and 0.9 would be a good answer.

Q8 a) $y = x(x^2 - 3x + 12)$

Look at the discriminant to see if the quadratic has any roots:
$b^2 - 4ac = 9 - 4(12) < 0$, so there are no real roots, which means the only root of the cubic is $x = 0$.

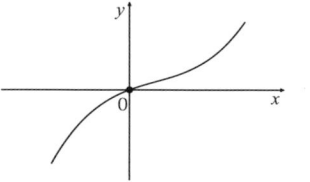

b) The discriminant of the quadratic factor is negative, so it has no real roots — so the cubic has just one root:

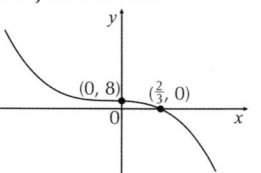

These graphs flatten rather than 'dip' — putting in lots of values for x will help you see this. But don't worry if you didn't get them exactly right. In C2 you'll look at ways of finding the max / min points of graphs which will help you to do sketches like this more accurately.

c) The discriminant of the quadratic factor is negative, so it has no real roots — so the cubic has just one root:

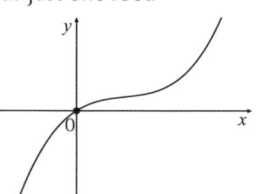

Exercise 3.2 — The reciprocal function and other negative powers

Q1 a) $y = x^{-2} = \frac{1}{x^2}$. $n = 2$ is and even so you'll get a graph with two bits next to each other. $k = 1$ is positive so the graph will all be above the axis so it must be graph D.

b) $y = -3x^{-3} = \frac{-3}{x^3}$. $n = 3$ is odd so you'll get a graph with two bits opposite each other. $k = -3$ is negative so the graph will be in the top-left and bottom-right quadrants so it must be graph A.

c) $y = -\frac{3}{x^4}$. $n = 4$ is even so you'll get a graph with two bits next to each other. $k = -3$ so the graph will all be below the x-axis so it must be graph B.

d) $y = 2x^{-5} = \frac{2}{x^5}$. $n = 5$ is odd so you'll get a graph with two bits opposite each other. $k = 2$ is positive so the graph will be in the bottom-left and top-right quadrants so it must be graph C.

Q2 **a)**

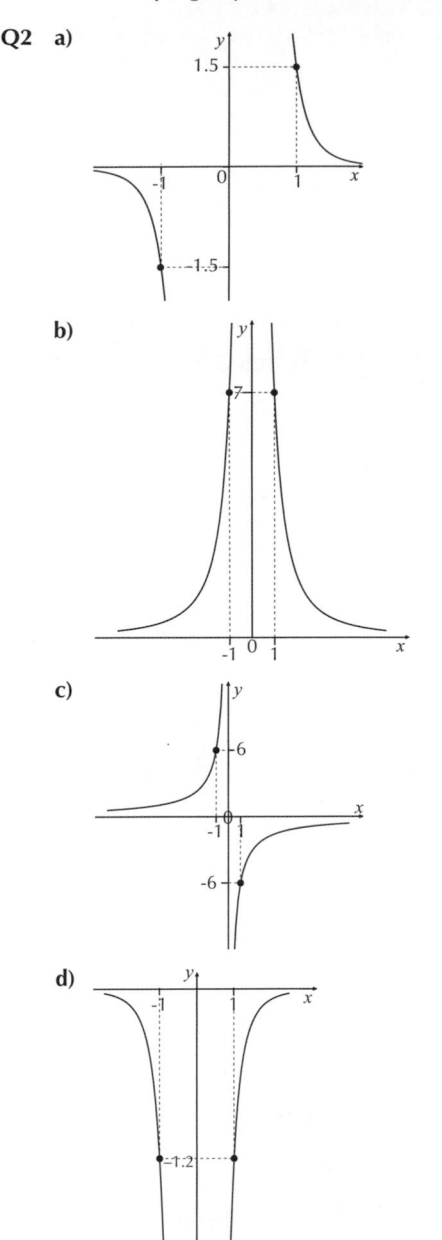

b)

c)

d)

Q3 **a)** $y = -x^3 - 2x^2 = -x^2(x + 2)$

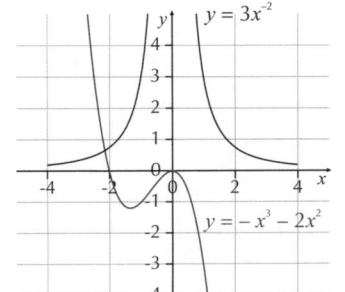

b) The number of real roots of the equation $3x^{-2} = -x^3 - 2x^2$ is just the number of times the two graphs cross. This equation therefore has 1 real root.

Q4 **a)**

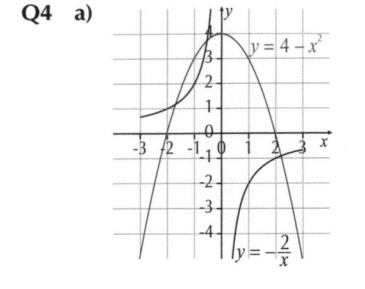

b) The solutions are at the points of intersection on the graph in part a). The actual solutions are $x = -0.54, -1.68$ and 2.21 (to 2 d.p.). Acceptable solutions are: between -0.4 and -0.7, between -1.6 and -1.8 and between 2.1 and 2.3.

4. Transformations

Exercise 4.1 — Translations

Q1 **a)**

b)

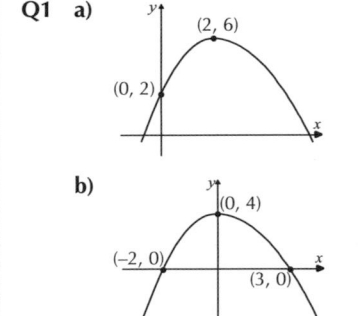

Q2 The graph of $y = g(x - 1)$ is the graph of $y = g(x)$ translated 1 unit to the right so it must be graph B.

Q3 **a)** The asymptotes are at $x = 0$ and $y = 0$.

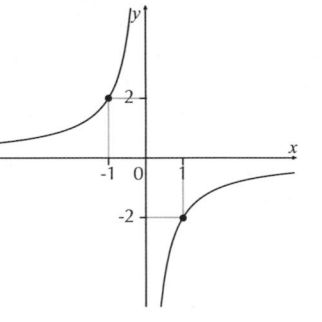

b) The asymptotes are at $x = -3$ and $y = 0$.

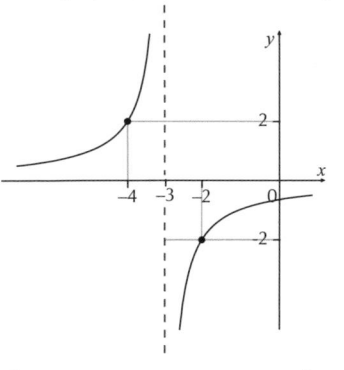

c) The asymptotes are at $x = 0$ and $y = 3$.

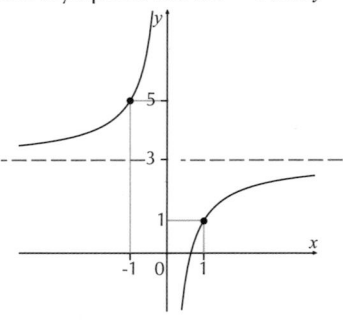

Q4 $y = (x - 2)^2(x - 6) = (x - 2)^2 ((x - 2) - 4)$ so it is the curve $y = x^2(x - 4)$ with x replaced by $x - 2$ so it will be translated 2 units to the right.

Q5 $y = x^3 + 3x + 2 = (x^3 + 3x + 7) - 5$ so the translation will be -5 in the y-direction, i.e. 5 units down.

Q6 The equation will be $y = (x + 1)^2 - 3(x + 1) + 7$
$= x^2 + 2x + 1 - 3x - 3 + 7 = x^2 - x + 5$.

Q7 **a) and b)**

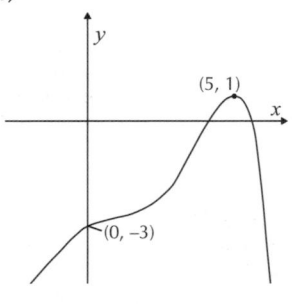

Q8 **a)**

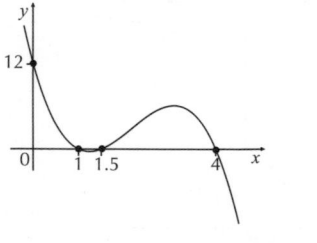

b) The equation of the translated graph would be
$y = ((x - 2) - 1)(2(x - 2) - 3)(4 - (x - 2))$
$= (x - 3)(2x - 4 - 3)(4 - x + 2)$
$= (x - 3)(2x - 7)(6 - x)$

c)

Exercise 4.2 — Stretches and reflections

Q1 **a)**

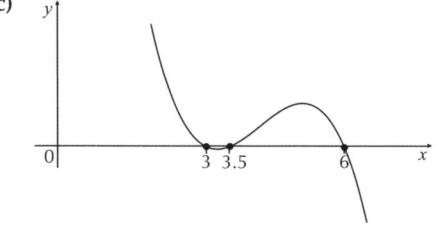

b)

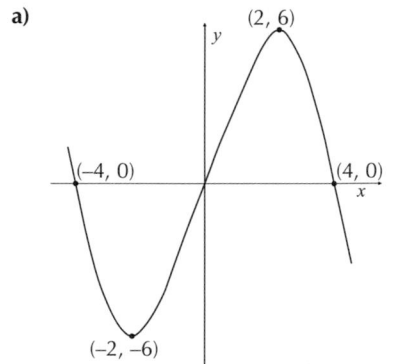

c)

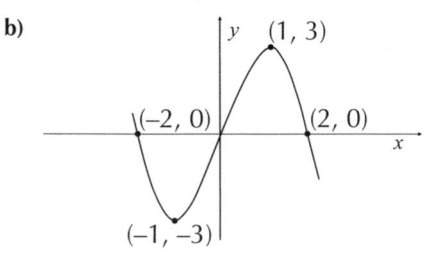

d)

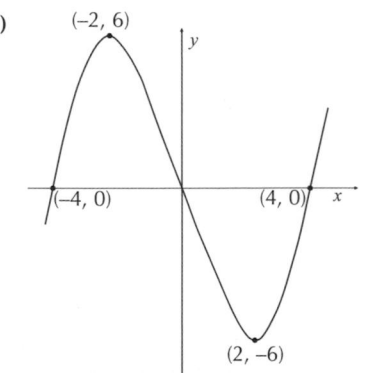

Q2 The graph has been squashed to half its width, so it's a horizontal stretch of scale factor $\frac{1}{2}$, so it must be b).

Q3 The graph has been reflected in the x-axis and stretched vertically by a factor of 3 so it must be b).

Q4 **a)** $f(x) = x^3 - x = x(x^2 - 1) = x(x + 1)(x - 1)$

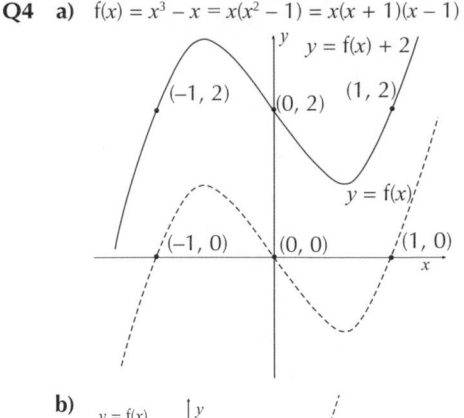

b)

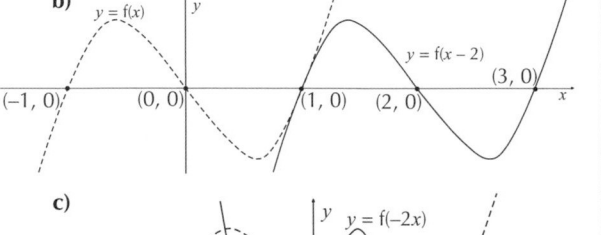

c)

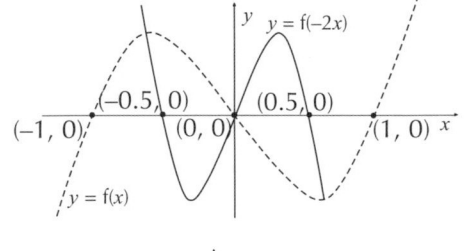

d)

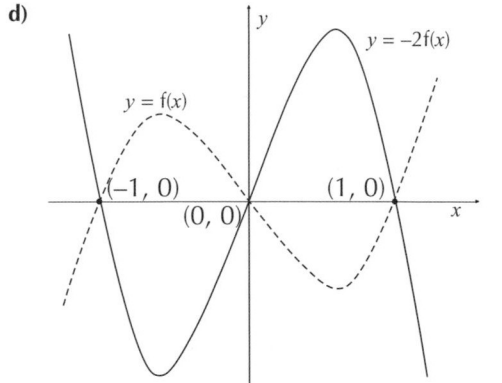

Q5 $3x^3 + 6x + 12 = 3(x^3 + 2x + 4)$ so the whole function has been multiplied by 3. This means the transformation is a stretch vertically by a scale factor of 3.

Q6 $4x^2 - 2x + 4 = (-2x)^2 + (-2x) + 4$ so x has been replaced with $-2x$. The transformation is therefore a reflection in the y-axis followed by a horizontal stretch by a scale factor of $\frac{1}{2}$ (i.e. a squash).

Q7 **a)** $f(x) = x^2 - 6x - 7 = (x - 3)^2 - 16$, so the turning point (i.e. minimum point) is at $(3, -16)$.
Solving $(x - 3)^2 - 16 = 0$ gives $x = -1$ or 7.

So the graph is:

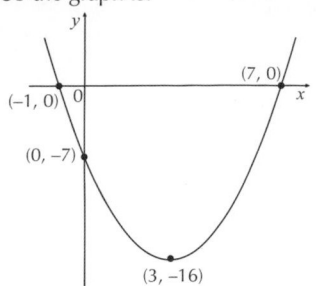

b) $y = -2f(x) = -2(x^2 - 6x - 7)$

c)

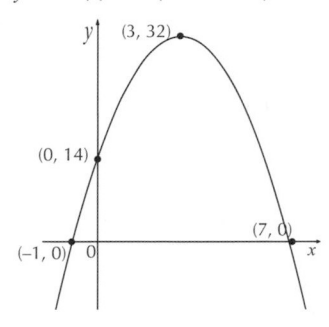

Review Exercise — Chapter 4

Q1 **a)** **(i)** $y + 1 = 3(x - 2)$
    (ii) $y = 3x - 7$
    (iii) $3x - y - 7 = 0$

    b) **(i)** $y + \frac{1}{3} = \frac{1}{5}x$
    (ii) $y = \frac{1}{5}x - \frac{1}{3}$
    (iii) $3x - 15y - 5 = 0$

Q2 **a)** $y = \frac{3}{2}x - 4$ **b)** $y = -\frac{1}{2}x + 4$

Q3 The equation of the required line is $y = \frac{3}{2}x + \frac{15}{2}$.

Q4 **a)**

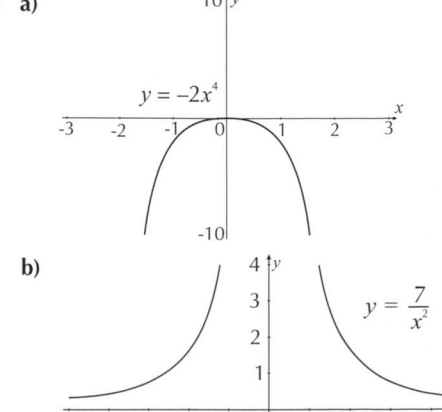

b)

c)

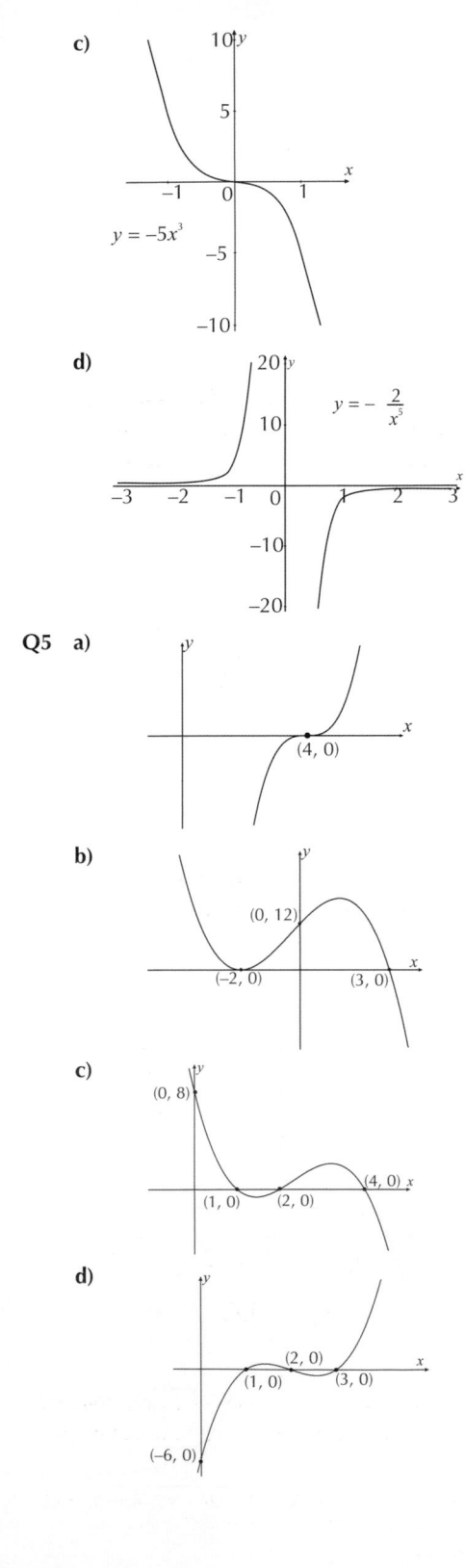

$y = -5x^3$

d)

$y = -\dfrac{2}{x^5}$

Q5 a)

(4, 0)

b)

(0, 12)
(-2, 0)   (3, 0)

c)

(0, 8)
(1, 0)   (2, 0)   (4, 0)

d)

(2, 0)
(1, 0)   (3, 0)
(-6, 0)

Q6 a)

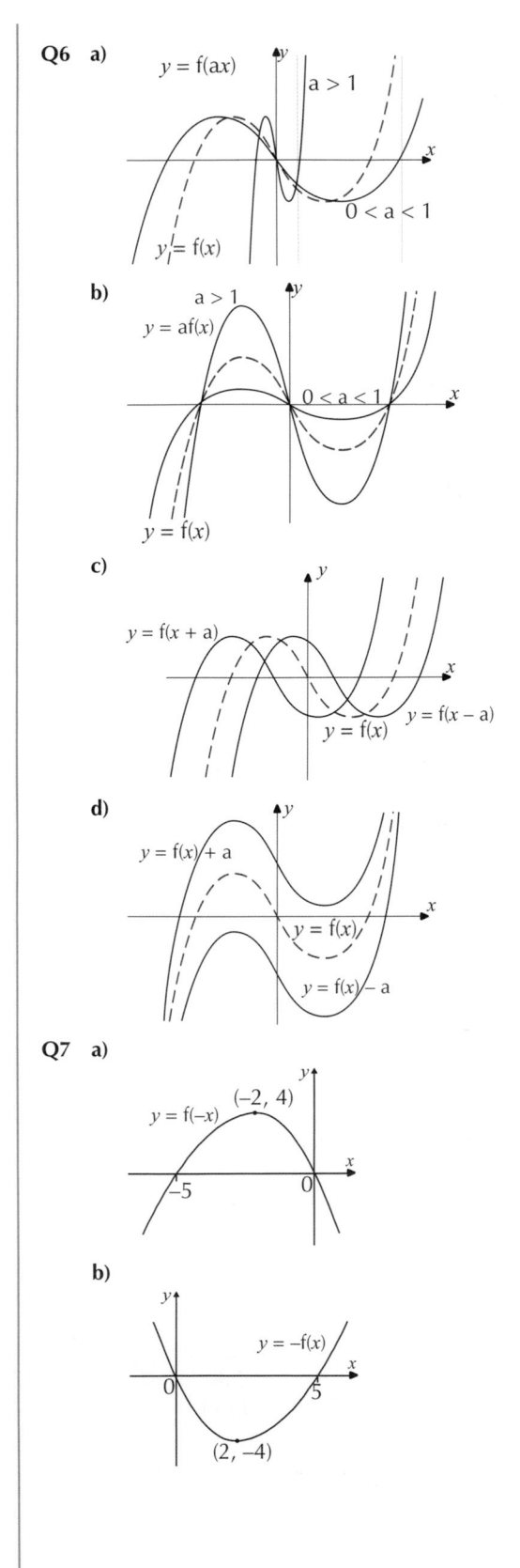

$y = f(ax)$ $a > 1$
$y = f(x)$ $0 < a < 1$

b)

$a > 1$
$y = af(x)$ $0 < a < 1$
$y = f(x)$

c)

$y = f(x + a)$ $y = f(x - a)$
$y = f(x)$

d)

$y = f(x) + a$ $y = f(x)$ $y = f(x) - a$

Q7 a)

$y = f(-x)$ (-2, 4)
-5   0

b)

$y = -f(x)$
0   5
(2, -4)

c)

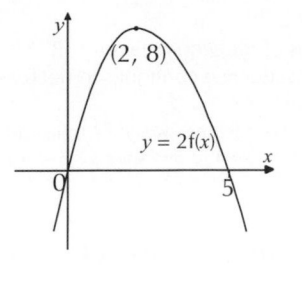

d)

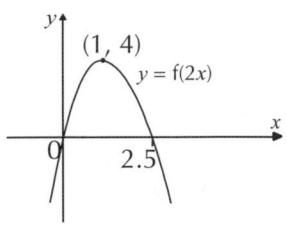

Exam-Style Questions — Chapter 4

Q1 a) Rearrange into $y = mx + c$ form and read off m:

$3y = 15 - 4x$

$y = -\frac{4}{3}x + 5$ **[1 mark]**

so the gradient of the line PQ is $-\frac{4}{3}$ **[1 mark]**.

b) Gradient of line $= -1 \div -\frac{4}{3} = \frac{3}{4}$ **[1 mark]**

So $y = \frac{3}{4}x + c$.

Now use the x- and y- values of R to find C:

$1 = \frac{3}{4}(3) + c$

$1 = \frac{9}{4} + c$

$\Rightarrow c = -\frac{5}{4}$ **[1 mark]**

so the equation is $y = \frac{3}{4}x - \frac{5}{4}$ **[1 mark]**

Q2 When the brackets are multiplied out, the first term is $2x^3$, so the graph is a positive cubic graph.

$y = 0$ when $x = 2$ or $x = -\frac{1}{2}$, so the graph touches the x-axis at $(2, 0)$ and crosses it at $(-\frac{1}{2}, 0)$.

When $x = 0$, $y = (1)(-2)^2 = 4$.

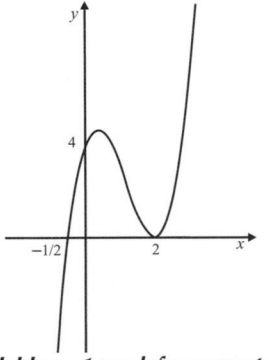

[4 marks available — 1 mark for correct shape, 1 mark for x-axis intercept at -1/2, 1 mark for graph touching the x-axis at 2 and 1 mark for correct y-axis intercept at 4.]

Q3 a)

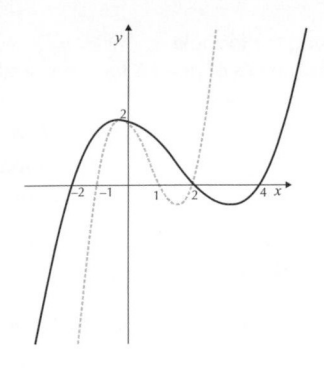

[3 marks available — 1 mark for horizontal stretch, 1 mark for x-axis intercepts at -2, 2 and 4, 1 mark for correct y-axis intercept at 2.]

b)

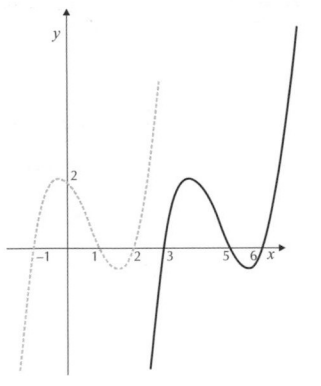

[2 marks available — 1 mark for horizontal translation to the right, 1 mark for x-axis intercepts at 3, 5 and 6]

Q4 a)

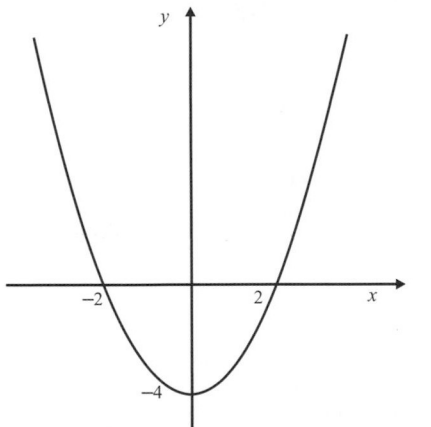

[2 marks available — 1 mark for x-axis intercepts at -2 and 2, 1 mark for correct y-axis intercept (0, -4)]

b) The curve is reflected in the x-axis *[1 mark]*, and stretched vertically by a scale factor of 2 *[1 mark]*.

c) $y = f(x) + 2$ *[1 mark]*

Q5 **a)** Using the formula $y - y_1 = m(x - x_1)$, with the coordinates of point S for the x- and y- values and $m = -2$,

$$y - (-3) = -2(x - 7) \quad \textbf{[1 mark]}$$
$$y + 3 = -2x + 14 \quad \textbf{[1 mark]}$$
$$y = -2x + 11 \quad \textbf{[1 mark]}$$

b) Putting $x = 5$ into $y = -2x + 11$ gives $y = 1$ **[1 mark]**, so T does lie on the line.

Q6 **a)** Gradient of $LK = \frac{8-6}{5-2} = \frac{2}{3}$ **[1 mark]**

so gradient of $l_1 = -1 \div \frac{2}{3} = -\frac{3}{2}$ **[1 mark]**.

Now, putting this gradient and the x- and y-coordinates of L into the formula $y - y_1 = m(x - x_1)$ gives:

$$y - 6 = -\frac{3}{2}(x - 2)$$
$$y = -\frac{3}{2}x + 3 + 6$$
$$y = -\frac{3}{2}x + 9 \quad \textbf{[1 mark]}$$
$$\Rightarrow 3x + 2y - 18 = 0 \quad \textbf{[1 mark]}$$

b) Putting $x = 0$ into $y = -\frac{3}{2}x + 9$ gives $y = 9$ **[1 mark]**,

so M = (0, 9) **[1 mark]**.

c) Putting $y = 0$ into $3x + 2y - 18 = 0$ gives $x = 6$ **[1 mark]**, so N = (6, 0) **[1 mark]**.

Chapter 5:
Sequences and Series

1. Sequences
Exercise 1.1 — n^{th} term

Q1 20th term = $3(20) - 5 = 55$

Q2 4th term = $4(4 + 2) = 24$

Q3 1st term = $(1 - 1)(1 + 1) = 0$
2nd term = $(2 - 1)(2 + 1) = 3$
Using the same method, 3rd, 4th and 5th terms
= 8, 15, 24

Q4 $29 = 4k - 3$
$k = 8$

Q5 Form equations for the 2nd and 5th terms:
$15 = a(2^2) + b$
$99 = a(5^2) + b$
Solve the equations simultaneously to get $a = 4$,
$b = -1$

Q6 Form equations for the first 3 terms:
$9 = (1^2)e + f + g$
$20 = (2^2)e + 2f + g$
$37 = (3^2)e + 3f + g$
Solve the equations simultaneously to get $e = 3$,
$f = 2$, $g = 4$.
To solve simultaneous equations with 3 unknowns, you use a similar method to when there are 2 unknowns — it just takes a few more steps.

Q7 $49 = (n - 1)^2$, $n = 8$

Q8 This first 8 terms of the sequence are: 13, 11, 9, 7, 5, 3, 1, -1,... The sequence continues to decrease. So 7 terms are positive.
A different way to solve this one would be to use an inequality — set $15 - 2n > 0$ and solve for n (taking the integer value of n).

Exercise 1.2 — Recurrence relations

Q1 $u_1 = 10$
$u_2 = 3u_1 = 3(10) = 30$
$u_3 = 3u_2 = 3(30) = 90$
$u_4 = 3u_3 = 3(90) = 270$
$u_5 = 3u_4 = 3(270) = 810$

Q2 $u_1 = 2$
$u_2 = u_1^2 = 2^2 = 4$
$u_3 = u_2^2 = 4^2 = 16$
$u_4 = u_3^2 = 16^2 = 256$

For Q3, 4, 5, you can use any letter in place of u.

Q3 Each term is the previous term doubled. The first term is 3.
$u_{n+1} = 2u_n, u_1 = 3$

Q4 **a)** Each term is 4 more than the previous term. The first term is 12.
$u_{n+1} = u_n + 4, u_1 = 12$

b) Work out the number of 'jumps' of 4 needed to get from 28 to 100:
$100 - 28 = 72$, $72 \div 4 = 18$
Add on the first 5 terms given in the question:
$18 + 5 = 23$ terms
You could have written an nth term expression and used it to find the position of 100 in the sequence (it's the last term). The nth term expression would be $4n + 8$.

Q5 $u_{n+1} = 11 - u_n$ or $u_{n+1} = 28 \div u_n$, with $u_1 = 7$.
This one is tricky. It's the sort you suddenly go "aah" with.

Q6 $u_1 = 4$
$u_2 = 3(4) - 1 = 11$
$u_3 = 3(11) - 1 = 32$
$u_4 = 3(32) - 1 = 95$, so $k = 4$

Q7 $x_1 = 9$
$x_2 = (9 + 1) \div 2 = 5$
Keep substituting the result into the formula until...
$x_6 = (\frac{3}{2} + 1) \div 2 = \frac{5}{4}$, so $r = 6$

Q8 $u_1 = 7$
$u_2 = 7 + 1 = 8$
$u_3 = 8 + 2 = 10$
$u_4 = 10 + 3 = 13$
$u_5 = 13 + 4 = 17$

Q9 Form an equation for getting the 2nd term from the 1st term, and an equation for getting the 3rd term from the 2nd term:

$7 = 6a + b$

$8.5 = 7a + b$

Solve the equations simultaneously to get $a = 1.5$, $b = -2$

Q10 First 5 terms:

$u_1 = 8$

$u_2 = \frac{1}{2}(8) = 4$

$u_3 = \frac{1}{2}(4) = 2$

$u_4 = \frac{1}{2}(2) = 1$

$u_5 = \frac{1}{2}(1) = \frac{1}{2}$

The terms are all powers of 2:

$8 = 2^3$, $4 = 2^2$, $2 = 2^1$, $1 = 2^0$, $\frac{1}{2} = 2^{-1}$

so $u_n = 2^{(4-n)}$ or $u_n = 16 \div 2^n$

Exercise 1.3 — Arithmetic sequences

Q1 $a = 7$, $d = 5$

n^{th} term $= a + (n - 1)d$

$\qquad = 7 + (n - 1)5$

$\qquad = 5n + 2$

10th term $= 5(10) + 2$

$\qquad = 52$

Q2 **a)** $a = 6$, $d = 3$,

so n^{th} term $= 6 + (n - 1)3 = 3n + 3$

b) $a = 4$, $d = 5$, n^{th} term $= 5n - 1$

c) $a = 12$, $d = -4$, n^{th} term $= -4n + 16$

d) $a = 1.5$, $d = 2$, n^{th} term $= 2n - 0.5$

Q3 $a = 60$, $d = 3$

n^{th} term $= a + (n - 1)d$

$\qquad = 60 + (n - 1)3$

$\qquad = 3n + 57$

12th term $= 3(12) + 57$

$\qquad = 93$

So she'll earn **£93** in her 12th week.

With wordy problems, don't forget to check what the units should be and include them.

Q4 $a = 40$, $d = 5$

n^{th} term $= a + (n - 1)d$

$\qquad = 40 + (n - 1)5$

$\qquad = 5n + 35$

$80 = 5n + 35$

$n = (80 - 35) \div 5$

$\qquad = 9$

So he'll sell 80 sandwiches on the **9th** day.

Q5 Form equations for 4th and 10th terms:

n^{th} term $= a + (n - 1)d$

$19 = a + (4 - 1)d \qquad 19 = a + 3d$

$43 = a + (10 - 1)d \qquad 43 = a + 9d$

Solving the simultaneous equations: $a = 7$, $d = 4$.

Q6 Form equations for 7th and 11th terms:

n^{th} term $= a + (n - 1)d$

$8 = a + (7 - 1)d \qquad 8 = a + 6d$

$10 = a + (11 - 1)d \qquad 10 = a + 10d$

Solving the simultaneous equations: $a = 5$, $d = 0.5$

So $u_3 = 5 + 2(0.5) = 6$

Q7 Form equations for 3rd and 7th terms:

n^{th} term $= a + (n - 1)d$

$15 = a + (3 - 1)d \qquad 15 = a + 2d$

$27 = a + (7 - 1)d \qquad 27 = a + 6d$

Solving the simultaneous equations: $a = 9$, $d = 3$.

Now write an equation for the kth term:

$66 = 9 + (k - 1)3 = 6 + 3k$

And solve to find k:

$k = 20$

Q8 $a = 300\,000$, $d = -30\,000$

n^{th} term $= a + (n - 1)d$

$\qquad = 300\,000 - 30\,000(n - 1)$

$\qquad = 330\,000 - 30\,000n$

$330\,000 - 30\,000n < 50\,000$

$n > 280\,000 \div 30\,000 = 9.33...$

You want the smallest integer value of n that satisfies the inequality, so round up. Sales will have fallen below £50 000 after 10 months.

$n = 9$ doesn't satisfy the inequality.

2. Series

Exercise 2.1 — Arithmetic series

Q1 $a = 8$, $d = 3$

n^{th} term $= a + (n - 1)d$

$\qquad = 8 + (n - 1)3$

$\qquad = 3n + 5$

10th term $= 3(10) + 5 = 35$

$S_n = \frac{n}{2}[2a + (n - 1)d]$

$S_{10} = \frac{10}{2}[2(8) + 9(3)]$

$S_{10} = 215$

Alternatively, you could have used the $S_n = n\dfrac{(a + l)}{2}$ formula here. You'd worked out the last term earlier in the question.

Q2 Form equations for 2nd and 5th terms:

n^{th} term $= a + (n - 1)d$

$16 = a + d$

$10 = a + 4d$

Solving the simultaneous equations: $a = 18$, $d = -2$.

$$S_n = \frac{n}{2}[2a + (n-1)d]$$

$$S_8 = \frac{8}{2}[2(18) + 7(-2)]$$

$$S_8 = 88$$

Q3 $a = 12$, $d = 6$

n^{th} term $= a + (n-1)d$

$$= 12 + (n-1)6$$

$$= 6n + 6$$

$$u_{100} = 6(100) + 6 = 606$$

$$S_n = n\frac{(a+l)}{2}$$

$$S_{100} = 100\left(\frac{12+606}{2}\right)$$

$$S_{100} = 30\,900$$

Q4 $a = 5(1) - 2 = 3$

$l = 5(12) - 2 = 58$

$$S_n = n\frac{(a+l)}{2}$$

$$S_{12} = 12\left(\frac{3+58}{2}\right)$$

$$S_{12} = 366$$

Q5 $a = 20 - 2(1) = 18$

$l = 20 - 2(9) = 2$

$$S_n = n\frac{(a+l)}{2}$$

$$S_9 = 9\left(\frac{18+2}{2}\right)$$

$$S_9 = 90$$

Q6 $a = 6000$

$d = 2000$

$n = 12$ (12 months in the year)

$$S_n = \frac{n}{2}[2a + (n-1)d]$$

$$S_{12} = \frac{12}{2}[2(6000) + 11(2000)]$$

$$S_{12} = 204\,000$$

204 000 copies will be sold.

Q7 $a = 3$

$d = 2$

$$S_n = \frac{n}{2}[2a + (n-1)d]$$

$$960 = \frac{n}{2}[2(3) + 2(n-1)]$$

$$960 = n^2 + 2n$$

$$n^2 + 2n - 960 = 0$$

You're expecting a whole number for n, so you should be able to factorise the quadratic — you need two numbers that are 2 apart and multiply to give 960.

$(n + 32)(n - 30) = 0$

Ignore the negative solution since n needs to be positive, so $n = 30$.

Q8 $a = 5(1) + 2 = 7$

$l = 5k + 2$

$$S_n = n\frac{(a+l)}{2}$$

$$553 = k\left(\frac{7 + 5k + 2}{2}\right)$$

$$1106 = 5k^5 + 9k$$

$$5k^5 + 9k - 1106 = 0$$

Factorising gives:

$(5k + 79)(k - 14) = 0$

Now we can ignore the negative solution, so $k = 14$.

This one looked very tricky to factorise, but you can cheat a little here — you know you're trying to get to $k = 14$, so one of the brackets is going to be $(k - 14)$...

Q9 The first thing to do use the fact that it's an arithmetic progression to write down some equations — remember, there's a common difference, d, between each term.

$x + 11 + d = 4x + 4 \implies -3x + d = -7$

$x + 11 + 2d = 9x + 5 \implies -8x + 2d = -6$

You've now got a pair of simultaneous equations in d and x. Solving these gives $x = -4$, $d = -19$

So the first term is $a = -4 + 11 = 7$.

Now you can put $a = 7$, $d = -19$ and $n = 11$ into the formula for S_n:

$$S_n = \frac{n}{2}[2a + (n-1)d]$$

$$S_{11} = \frac{11}{2}[2(7) + 10(-19)]$$

$$S_{11} = \frac{11}{2} \times -176$$

$$S_{11} = -968$$

Exercise 2.2
— Sum of the first n natural numbers

Q1 **a)** $S_n = \frac{1}{2}n(n+1)$

$$S_{10} = \frac{1}{2} \times 10 \times 11$$

$$S_{10} = 55$$

b) $S_{2000} = \frac{1}{2} \times 2000 \times 2001$

$$S_{2000} = 2\,001\,000$$

Q2 $S_{32} = \frac{1}{2} \times 32 \times 33$

$$S_{32} = 528$$

Q3 $\displaystyle\sum_{n=11}^{20} n = \sum_{n=1}^{20} n - \sum_{n=1}^{10} n$

$$S_{10} = \frac{1}{2} \times 10 \times 11$$

$$S_{10} = 55$$

$$S_{20} = \frac{1}{2} \times 20 \times 21$$

$$S_{20} = 210$$

$$\sum_{n=11}^{20} n = 210 - 55 = 155$$

Q4 Frazer's series is the natural numbers up to 31.

$S_n = \frac{1}{2}n(n + 1)$

$S_{31} = \frac{1}{2} \times 31 \times 32$

$S_{31} = 496$

Q5 $66 = \frac{1}{2}n(n + 1)$

$132 = n^2 + n$

$0 = n^2 + n - 132$

$(n + 12)(n - 11) = 0$

$n = -12$ or 11 — so ignoring the negative answer, the sum of the first 11 terms is 66, so $n = 11$.

Q6 $S_n = \frac{1}{2}n(n + 1)$

$120 = \frac{1}{2}k(k + 1)$

$240 = k^2 + k$

$0 = k^2 + k - 240$

$(k + 16)(k - 15) = 0$

Ignoring the negative solution gives $k = 15$.

Q7 Subtract the sum of the first 15 natural numbers from the sum of the first 35:

$S_{35} = \frac{1}{2} \times 35 \times 36 = 630$

$S_{15} = \frac{1}{2} \times 15 \times 16 = 120$

So the sum of the series is $630 - 120 = 510$.

Q8 $S_n = \frac{1}{2}n(n + 1)$

$\frac{1}{2}n(n + 1) > 1\,000\,000$

$n^2 + n > 2\,000\,000$

$n^2 + n - 2\,000\,000 > 0$

Put the quadratic equal to zero and solve using the quadratic formula to get $n = 1413.7...$ or $-1414.7...$ It's a u-shaped quadratic, so the quadratic is positive when $n > 1413.7$ (ignoring the negative solution). So you need 1414 natural numbers to exceed 1 000 000.

Q9 Laura's series is the natural numbers. You need to find how many are needed to exceed 1000 (£10 in pence).

$S_n = \frac{1}{2}n(n + 1)$

$\frac{1}{2}(n^2 + n) > 1000$

$n^2 + n > 2000$

$n^2 + n - 2000 > 0$

Putting the quadratic equal to zero and solving using the quadratic formula gives $n = 44.2$ (ignoring the negative solution), which by looking at the shape of the quadratic graph gives $n > 44.2$ as the solution to the inequality. So on the 45th day she'll have over £10.

Review Exercise — Chapter 5

Q1 a) n^{th} term $= 4n - 2$

b) n^{th} term $= 0.5n - 0.3$

c) n^{th} term $= -3n + 24$

d) n^{th} term $= -6n + 82$

Q2 10th term $= (10 - 1) \div (10 + 2) = 0.75$

Q3 8th term $= 8^2 - 3 = 61$

Q4 $64 = r^3, r = 4$

Q5 $44 = k^2 + 3k + 4$

$k^2 + 3k - 40 = 0$

$(k + 8)(k - 5) = 0$

Ignoring the negative solution, $k = 5$.

It's the only positive solution — you can't have the -8th term.

Q6 Substituting $n = 1, 2, 3, 4, 5$ in the formula $(-1)^n n$ generates the first 5 terms: $-1, 2, -3, 4, -5$

Q7 Form equations for the 3rd and 7th terms:

$18 = a(3^2) + 3b \Rightarrow 6 = 3a + b$

$70 = a(7^2) + 7b \Rightarrow 10 = 7a + b$

Solving the simultaneous equations: $a = 1, b = 3$.

Q8 $a_{k+1} = a_k + 5, \ a_1 = 32$

Q9 a) $u_1 = 7, u_2 = 7 + 3 = 10, u_3 = 10 + 3 = 13,$
$u_4 = 13 + 3 = 16, u_5 = 16 + 3 = 19$

b) $u_1 = 2, u_2 = 6 \div 2 = 3, u_3 = 6 \div 3 = 2,$
$u_4 = 6 \div 2 = 3, u_5 = 6 \div 3 = 2$

Q10 a) Each term is the square root of the term before:
$a_{k+1} = \sqrt{a_k}, \ a_1 = 65\,536$

b) Each term is equal to the previous term minus double the previous term's position.
$a_{k+1} = a_k - 2k, \ a_1 = 40$

c) Each term (from the third onwards) is equal to the sum of the previous two terms.
$u_{n+2} = u_n + u_{n+1}, \ u_1 = 1, u_2 = 1$

This one is a bit different. You have to state two consecutive terms to establish the relation. Oh, and you can use a variety of letters for variables in recurrence relations, so I used some different ones here.

Q11 $u_1 = 5$
$u_2 = 7$
$u_3 = u_2 - u_1 = 7 - 5 = 2$
$u_4 = u_3 - u_2 = 2 - 7 = -5$
$u_5 = u_4 - u_3 = -5 - 2 = -7$
and so on...

The first 10 terms are 5, 7, 2, −5, −7, −2, 5, 7, 2, −5. The sequence is cyclic/repeats every 6 terms.

Q12 Form an equation for getting the 2nd term from the 1st term, and an equation for getting the 3rd term from the 2nd term:

$8 = 2a + b$

$26 = 8a + b$

Solving the equations simultaneously: $a = 3, b = 2$

Q13 Form an equation for getting the 2nd term from the 1st term, and solve to find k.
$11 = 4k + 3 \Rightarrow k = 2$

$u_3 = 2u_2 + 3 = 2(11) + 3 = 25$
$u_4 = 2u_3 + 3 = 2(25) + 3 = 53$

Q14 $u_1 = 8$, $u_2 = 18 - 8 = 10$, $u_3 = 18 - 10 = 8$,
$u_4 = 18 - 8 = 10$, $u_5 = 18 - 10 = 8$
$u_n = 9 + (-1)^n$

This is a tricky one. You need a way of alternating between −1 and +1, and putting −1 to alternating odd and even powers does this.

Q15 $l = a + (n - 1)d$
$19 = -2 + (29 - 1)d$
$21 = 28d \Rightarrow d = 0.75$

Q16 Work in millions to make the calculations easier:
$a = 3$, $d = -0.2$
You need to find the 10th term:
10th term $= 3 + 9(-0.2) = 1.2$

So the film makes £1.2 million pounds in the 10th week of release.

Q17 Form equations for the 7th and 11th terms:
$8 = a + (7 - 1)d \Rightarrow 8 = a + 6d$
$10 = a + (11 - 1)d \Rightarrow 10 = a + 10d$

Solve the equations gives $a = 5$, $d = 0.5$
3rd term $= 5 + (3 - 1)0.5 = 6$

Q18 $a = £300$, $d = £15$
n^{th} term $= 300 + 15(n - 1) = 285 + 15n$

$285 + 15n > 500$
$15n > 215$
$3n > 43$
$n > 14.333...$
The shop will take over £500 on the 15th day.

Q19 Form equations for the 3rd and 7th terms:
$15 = a + (3 - 1)d \Rightarrow 15 = a + 2d$
$27 = a + (7 - 1)d \Rightarrow 27 = a + 6d$

Solving the equations gives $a = 9$, $d = 3$

Now form an equation for the kth term and solve:
$66 = 9 + (k - 1)3 \Rightarrow k = 20$

Q20 We've previously used simultaneous equations to solve this type. Here's a different method:

First, work out d:
We know that the 7th term is 36 and the 10th is 30.
So the difference in 3 'moves' is −6 i.e. $d = -2$.

The nth term expression must contain $-2n$, and when $n = 10$, the nth term $= 30$, so the expression for the nth term must be $-2n + 50$.

$a = 48$ (when $n = 1$) and $l = 40$ (when $n = 5$)

Now find the sum of the series:
$S_n = n\dfrac{(a + l)}{2}$
$S_5 = 5\left(\dfrac{48 + 40}{2}\right)$
$S_5 = 220$

Q21 $a = 30$ mins, $d = 10$ mins
n^{th} term $= 30 + (n - 1)10$
$\qquad\quad = 10n + 20$

12th term $= 10(12) + 20 = 140$ mins

So in the last week, he'll have to do 140 mins or 2 hours 20 mins.

$S_n = n\dfrac{(a + l)}{2}$
$S_{12} = 12\left(\dfrac{30 + 140}{2}\right)$
$S_{12} = 1020$ mins
Total time running is $1020 \div 60 = 17$ hours.

Q22 $a = 3(1) - 1 = 2$
$l = 3(20) - 1 = 59$
$S_n = n\dfrac{(a + l)}{2}$
$S_{20} = 20\left(\dfrac{2 + 59}{2}\right)$
$S_{20} = 610$

Q23 **a)** $S_n = \frac{1}{2}n(n + 1)$

$S_{24} = \frac{1}{2} \times 24 \times 25$
$S_{24} = 300$

b) $\displaystyle\sum_{n=13}^{24} n = \sum_{n=1}^{24} n - \sum_{n=1}^{12} n$

$\displaystyle\sum_{n=1}^{24} n = 300$

$\displaystyle\sum_{n=1}^{12} n = \frac{1}{2}n(n + 1) = \frac{1}{2} \times 12 \times 13 = 78$

$\displaystyle\sum_{n=13}^{24} n = 300 - 78 = 222$

Q24 The series is the natural numbers up to $13 \times 5 = 65$.
$S_n = \frac{1}{2}n(n + 1)$
$S_{65} = \frac{1}{2} \times 65 \times 66$
$S_{65} = 2145$
He will have put 2145 stones on the wall.

Q25 $S_n = \frac{1}{2}n(n + 1)$

$630 = \frac{1}{2}k(k + 1)$
$1260 = k^2 + k$
$0 = k^2 + k - 1260$
$(k + 36)(k - 35) = 0$
So $k = 35$ (ignoring negative solution)

Exam-Style Questions — Chapter 5

Q1 a) $h_2 = h_{1+1} = 2 \times 5 + 2 = 12$ *[1 mark]*

$h_3 = h_{2+1} = 2 \times 12 + 2 = 26$ *[1 mark]*

$h_4 = 2h_3 + 2 = 54$ *[1 mark]*

b) $\sum_{r=3}^{6} h_r = h_3 + h_4 + h_5 + h_6$

$h_5 = 2h_4 + 2 = 110$ *[1 mark]*

$h_6 = 2(110) + 2 = 222$ *[1 mark]*

so $\sum_{r=3}^{6} h_r = 26 + 54 + 110 + 222$

$= 412$ *[1 mark]*

Q2 Use the nth term formula: $a_n = a_1 + (n-1)d$:

$a_7 = a + (7-1)d = a + 6d$ *[1 mark]*

You know that $a_7 = 580$ so

$a + 6d = 580$ *[1 mark]*

And you know that $S_{15} = 9525$, so using the series sum formula:

$S_{15} = \frac{15}{2}[2a + (15-1)d] = 9525$ *[1 mark]*

$\Rightarrow \frac{15}{2}(2a + 14d) = 9525,$

i.e. $15a + 105d = 9525$

then you can divide everything by 15 to give:

$a + 7d = 635$ *[1 mark]*

then solve them simultaneously:

$(a + 7d) - (a + 6d)$

$= d = 635 - 580$ *[1 mark]*

$d = 55$ *[1 mark]*

and finally use this value of d to find a:

$a + (6 \times 55) = 580$

$a = 580 - 330$

$= 250$ *[1 mark]*

A lot of steps were needed for that one, but don't panic if the question seems complicated. If you're stuck, write down all the sequence and series formulas — then see what formulas you can fill in using the info in the question.

Q3 a) $a_{31} = 22 + (31-1)(-1.1)$ *[1 mark]*

$= 22 + 30(-1.1)$

$= 22 - 33 = -11$ *[1 mark]*

b) $a_k = 0$

$a_1 + (k-1)d = 0$

$22 + (k-1) \times -1.1 = 0$ *[1 mark]*

$k - 1 = \frac{-22}{-1.1} = \frac{220}{11} = 20$

$k = 20 + 1 = 21$ *[1 mark]*

c) We want to find the first value of n for which $S_n < 0$. Using the formula for sum of a series:

$S_n = \frac{n}{2}[2 \times 22 + (n-1)(-1.1)] < 0$ *[1 mark]*

$S_n = \frac{n}{2}(44 - 1.1n + 1.1) < 0$

$\frac{n}{2}(45.1 - 1.1n) < 0$ *[1 mark]*

Consider $\frac{n}{2}(45.1 - 1.1n) = 0$

$\Rightarrow \frac{n}{2} = 0$ or $45.1 - 1.1n = 0$

$\Rightarrow n = 0$ or $n = \frac{45.1}{1.1} = 41$

The coefficient of n^2 is negative so graph is n-shaped.

Need to find negative part, so $n < 0$ or $n > 41$. Since n cannot be negative then $n > 41$. Now we just want the first (i.e. lowest) value of n for which this is true, which is $n = 42$. *[1 mark]*

Q4 a) $a = 6$

$d = 8$ *[1 mark]*

$a_n = 6 + 8(n-1)$ *[1 mark]*

$= 8n - 2$ *[1 mark]*

b) $S_{10} = \frac{10}{2}[2 \times 6 + (10-1)8]$ *[1 mark]*

$= 5 \times (12 + 72)$ *[1 mark]*

$= 420$ *[1 mark]*

c) First find an expression for S_k:

$S_k = \frac{k}{2}[2 \times 6 + 8(k-1)]$

$= \frac{k}{2} \times (12 + 8k - 8)$

$= \frac{k}{2}(8k + 4)$ *[1 mark]*

$= \frac{8k^2 + 4k}{2} = 4k^2 + 2k$ *[1 mark]*

Then, you know that the total sum will be less than 2450, because he hadn't yet reached that limit by day k, so:

$4k^2 + 2k < 2450$

$\Rightarrow 2k^2 + k < 1225$

$\Rightarrow 2k^2 + k - 1225 < 0$

$\Rightarrow (2k - 49)(k + 25) < 0$ *[1 mark]*

d) Since $(2k - 49)(k + 25) < 0$,
consider $(2k - 49)(k + 25) = 0$
$2k - 49 = 0$ or $k + 25 = 0$
$k = 24.5$ or $k = -25$ *[1 mark]*
Coefficient of k^2 is positive so graph is u-shaped.
Need negative part, so $-25 < k < 24.5$.
k will be the largest whole number that satisfies the inequality, i.e. $k = 24$. *[1 mark]*

Keep an eye on what you're being asked to find. Values in a sequence can be any number but the term positions are always whole numbers. So if you calculate a position and get a decimal number... something's not right.

Chapter 6: Differentiation

1. The Gradient of a Curve
Exercise 1.1
— Differentiating from first principles

Q1 The gradient of the straight line joining points
(x_1, y_1) and (x_2, y_2) is given by $\frac{y_2 - y_1}{x_2 - x_1}$.

a) (i) When $x = 1$, $y = 1$ and when $x = 2$, $y = 8$ so
the gradient is $\frac{8 - 1}{2 - 1} = \frac{7}{1} = 7$.

(ii) When $x = 1$, $y = 1$ and when
$x = 1.5$, $y = 3.375$ so the gradient is
$\frac{3.375 - 1}{1.5 - 1} = \frac{2.375}{0.5} = 4.75$.

(iii) When $x = 1$, $y = 1$ and when
$x = 1.1$, $y = 1.331$ so the gradient is
$\frac{1.331 - 1}{1.1 - 1} = \frac{0.331}{0.1} = 3.31$.

b) The gradients of the straight lines in part a) move
closer to 3 as the value of x moves closer to 1.

Q2 a) $\frac{dy}{dx} = \lim_{h \to 0}\left[\frac{(x+h) - x}{(x+h) - x}\right] = \lim_{h \to 0}[1] = 1$

b) $f'(x) = \lim_{h \to 0}\left[\frac{(x+h)^3 - x^3}{(x+h) - x}\right]$

$= \lim_{h \to 0}\left[\frac{(x+h)^2(x+h) - x^3}{(x+h) - x}\right]$

$= \lim_{h \to 0}\left[\frac{(x^2 + 2xh + h^2)(x+h) - x^3}{(x+h) - x}\right]$

$= \lim_{h \to 0}\left[\frac{x^3 + 3x^2h + 3xh^2 + h^3 - x^3}{(x+h) - x}\right]$

$= \lim_{h \to 0}\left[\frac{3x^2h + 3xh^2 + h^3}{h}\right]$

$= \lim_{h \to 0}[3x^2 + 3xh + h^2] = 3x^2$

c) $f'(x) = \lim_{h \to 0}\left[\frac{2(x+h) - 2x}{(x+h) - x}\right] = \lim_{h \to 0}\left[\frac{2x + 2h - 2x}{h}\right]$

$= \lim_{h \to 0}\left[\frac{2h}{h}\right] = \lim_{h \to 0}[2] = 2$

2. Differentiating $y = f(x)$
Exercise 2.1 — Differentiating x^n

Q1 a) $\frac{dy}{dx} = 6x^5$ **b)** $\frac{dy}{dx} = 3x^2$

c) $\frac{dy}{dx} = -2x^{-3} = -\frac{2}{x^3}$ **d)** $\frac{dy}{dx} = 6x$

e) $\frac{dy}{dx} = 7$ **f)** $\frac{dy}{dx} = 0$

g) $\frac{dy}{dx} = \frac{3}{2}x^{-\frac{1}{2}} = \frac{3}{2\sqrt{x}}$ **h)** $\frac{dy}{dx} = -2x^{-2}$

Q2 a) $f'(x) = 5x^4$ **b)** $f'(x) = 7x^6$

c) $f'(x) = -4x^{-5}$ **d)** $f'(x) = 12x^2$

e) $f'(x) = 4x^{-\frac{1}{2}} = \frac{4}{\sqrt{x}}$ **f)** $f'(x) = x^{-\frac{2}{3}} = \frac{1}{\sqrt[3]{x^2}}$

g) $f'(x) = 0$ **h)** $f'(x) = -8x^{-3}$

Q3 a) $\frac{dy}{dx} = 4x \Rightarrow$ At $x = 4$, $\frac{dy}{dx} = 16$

b) $\frac{dy}{dx} = -x^{-2} = -\frac{1}{x^2} \Rightarrow$ At $x = 2$, $\frac{dy}{dx} = -\frac{1}{4}$

c) $\frac{dy}{dx} = -20x^4 \Rightarrow$ At $x = 1$, $\frac{dy}{dx} = -20$

d) $f'(x) = x^{-\frac{1}{2}} = \frac{1}{\sqrt{x}} \Rightarrow f'(9) = \frac{1}{3}$

e) $f'(x) = 4x^3 \Rightarrow f'(-2) = -32$

f) $f(x) = -250$, $-250 = -2x^3$
$\Rightarrow 125 = x^3 \Rightarrow x = 5$
$f'(x) = -6x^2 \Rightarrow f'(5) = -150$

Exercise 2.2 — Differentiating functions

Q1 a) $\frac{dy}{dx} = 12x^2 - 2x$

b) $\frac{dy}{dx} = 1 + (-x^{-2}) = 1 - \frac{1}{x^2}$

c) $\frac{dy}{dx} = 6x + \frac{1}{2}x^{-\frac{1}{2}} = 6x + \frac{1}{2\sqrt{x}}$

d) $f'(x) = -10x^4 + 4 - (-2x^{-3}) = -10x^4 + 4 + \frac{2}{x^3}$

e) $f'(x) = \frac{3}{2}x^{\frac{1}{2}} - 1 = \frac{3}{2}\sqrt{x} - 1$

f) $f'(x) = 5 - 2(-3x^{-4}) + \frac{1}{3}x^{-\frac{2}{3}} = 5 + \frac{6}{x^4} + \frac{1}{3\sqrt[3]{x^2}}$

Q2 a) $\frac{d}{dx}(x(x^6 - 1)) = \frac{d}{dx}(x^7 - x) = 7x^6 - 1$

b) $\frac{d}{dx}((x - 3)(x + 4)) = \frac{d}{dx}(x^2 - 3x + 4x - 12)$

$= \frac{d}{dx}(x^2 + x - 12)$

$= 2x + 1$

c) $\frac{d}{dx}(x(x - 1)(x - 2)) = \frac{d}{dx}(x(x^2 - x - 2x + 2))$

$= \frac{d}{dx}(x(x^2 - 3x + 2))$

$= \frac{d}{dx}(x^3 - 3x^2 + 2x)$

$= 3x^2 - 3(2x) + 2$

$= 3x^2 - 6x + 2$

d) $\frac{d}{dx}((x - 3)(x + 4)(x - 1))$

$= \frac{d}{dx}((x - 3)(x^2 + 3x - 4))$

$= \frac{d}{dx}(x^3 + 3x^2 - 4x - 3x^2 - 9x + 12)$

$= \frac{d}{dx}(x^3 - 13x + 12)$

$= 3x^2 - 13$

e) $\frac{d}{dx}(x^2(x-4)(3-x^3))$

$$= \frac{d}{dx}(x^2(3x-x^4-12+4x^3))$$
$$= \frac{d}{dx}(3x^3-x^6-12x^2+4x^5)$$
$$= 9x^2-6x^5-24x+20x^4$$

f) $\frac{d}{dx}((x-3)^2(x^2-2))$

$$= \frac{d}{dx}((x^2-3x-3x+9)(x^2-2))$$
$$= \frac{d}{dx}((x^2-6x+9)(x^2-2))$$
$$= \frac{d}{dx}((x^4-6x^3+9x^2)+(-2x^2+12x-18))$$
$$= \frac{d}{dx}(x^4-6x^3+7x^2+12x-18)$$
$$= 4x^3-18x^2+14x+12$$

Q3 a) $\frac{dy}{dx} = 4x^3-2x$. At $x=3$, $\frac{dy}{dx} = 102$.

b) $\frac{dy}{dx} = 10x^4+(-x^{-2}) = 10x^4 - \frac{1}{x^2}$.

At $x=-2$, $\frac{dy}{dx} = 159\frac{3}{4}$.

c) $y = x(x-1)(x-2) = x(x^2-3x+2)$

$$= x^3-3x^2+2x$$

$\frac{dy}{dx} = 3x^2-6x+2$. At $x=-3$, $\frac{dy}{dx} = 47$.

d) $y = 5(x^2-1)(3-x) = 5(-x^3+3x^2+x-3)$

$$= -5x^3+15x^2+5x-15$$

$\frac{dy}{dx} = -15x^2+30x+5$. At $x=0$, $\frac{dy}{dx} = 5$.

e) $y = \sqrt{x}(x-1) = x^{\frac{1}{2}}(x-1) = x^{\frac{3}{2}} - x^{\frac{1}{2}}$

$\frac{dy}{dx} = \frac{3}{2}x^{\frac{1}{2}} - \frac{1}{2}x^{-\frac{1}{2}} = \frac{3}{2}\sqrt{x} - \frac{1}{2\sqrt{x}}$.

At $x=4$, $\frac{dy}{dx} = 2\frac{3}{4}$.

f) $f(x) = x^3(x^2-5) = x^5-5x^3$

$f'(x) = 5x^4-15x^2$. $f'(-1) = -10$

g) $f(x) = \frac{1}{x^2}(x^3-x) = x-x^{-1}$

$f'(x) = 1+x^{-2} = 1+\frac{1}{x^2}$. $f'(5) = \frac{26}{25}$.

h) $f(x) = \frac{3x^3+18x^2+24x}{x+4}$

$$= \frac{3x(x+4)(x+2)}{x+4} = 3x(x+2) = 3x^2+6x$$

$f'(x) = 6x+6$. $f'(-2) = -6$.

Q4 a) $y = (x+3)(x+4) = x^2+7x+12$

$\frac{dy}{dx} = 2x+7$. If $2x+7=3 \Rightarrow 2x=-4 \Rightarrow x=-2$.

So $y = (-2+3)(-2+4) = 2$.

Coordinates are $(-2, 2)$.

b) $y = (x+3)(x-5) = x^2-2x-15$

$\frac{dy}{dx} = 2x-2$. If $2x-2=2 \Rightarrow 2x=4 \Rightarrow x=2$

So $y = (2+3)(2-5) = -15$.

Coordinates are $(2, -15)$.

c) $\frac{dy}{dx} = 2x+8$. If $2x+8=4 \Rightarrow 2x=-4 \Rightarrow x=-2$

So $y = (-2)^2+8(-2) = -12$.

Coordinates are $(-2, -12)$.

d) $y = \frac{x^3-3x^2+2x}{x-1} = \frac{x(x-1)(x-2)}{x-1} = x^2-2x$

$\frac{dy}{dx} = 2x-2$. If $2x-2=-6 \Rightarrow 2x=-4 \Rightarrow x=-2$

So $y = (-2)^2-2(-2) = 8$. Coordinates are $(-2, 8)$.

Q5 a) $\frac{dy}{dx} = 2x-2$. If $2x-2=0 \Rightarrow 2x=2 \Rightarrow x=1$.

So $y = (1)^2-2(1) = -1$. Coordinates are $(1, -1)$.

b) $\frac{dy}{dx} = 6x+4$. If $6x+4=0 \Rightarrow 6x=-4$

$\Rightarrow x = -\frac{4}{6} = -\frac{2}{3}$.

So $y = 3(-\frac{2}{3})^2+4(-\frac{2}{3}) = -\frac{4}{3}$.

Coordinates are $(-\frac{2}{3}, -\frac{4}{3})$.

c) $\frac{dy}{dx} = 10x-3$. If $10x-3=0 \Rightarrow 10x=3$

$\Rightarrow x = \frac{3}{10} \Rightarrow y = 5(\frac{3}{10})^2-3(\frac{3}{10}) = -\frac{9}{20}$.

Coordinates are $(\frac{3}{10}, -\frac{9}{20})$.

d) $\frac{dy}{dx} = 9-9x^2$. If $9-9x^2=0 \Rightarrow 9=9x^2 \Rightarrow 1=x^2$

$\Rightarrow x=1$ or -1

$\Rightarrow y = 9(1)-3(1)^3 = 6$ or $y = 9(-1)-3(-1)^3 = -6$.

Coordinates of points are $(1, 6)$ and $(-1, -6)$.

e) $\frac{dy}{dx} = 6x^2-2x$. If $6x^2-2x=0 \Rightarrow 2x(3x-1)=0$

$\Rightarrow 2x=0$ or $3x-1=0 \Rightarrow x=0$ or $x=\frac{1}{3}$

So $y = 2(0)^3-(0)^2 = 0$ or $y = 2(\frac{1}{3})^3-(\frac{1}{3})^2 = -\frac{1}{27}$.

So points are $(0, 0)$ and $(\frac{1}{3}, -\frac{1}{27})$.

f) $\frac{dy}{dx} = 6x^2+6x-12$. If $6x^2+6x-12=0$

$\Rightarrow 6(x^2+x-2)=0 \Rightarrow x^2+x-2=0$

$\Rightarrow (x+2)(x-1)=0 \Rightarrow x=-2$ or $x=1$.

So $y = 2(-2)^3+3(-2)^2-12(-2) = 20$ or

$y = 2(1)^3+3(1)^2-12(1) = -7$.

So the points are $(-2, 20)$ and $(1, -7)$.

Q6 a) $y = \frac{x^2-3x-4}{x+1} = \frac{(x-4)(x+1)}{x+1} = x-4$

$\Rightarrow \frac{dy}{dx} = 1$

b) $f(x) = \frac{x^4-9}{x^2+3} = \frac{(x^2+3)(x^2-3)}{x^2+3} = x^2-3$

$\Rightarrow f'(x) = 2x$

c) $f(x) = \frac{x^5-16x^3}{x+4} = \frac{x^3(x+4)(x-4)}{x+4} = x^3(x-4)$

$= x^4-4x^3 \Rightarrow f'(x) = 4x^3-12x^2$

d) $y = \frac{1}{x}(x-3)(x-4) = \frac{1}{x}(x^2 - 3x - 4x + 12)$

$\qquad = \frac{1}{x}(x^2 - 7x + 12)$

$\qquad = x - 7 + \frac{12}{x} = x - 7 + 12x^{-1}$

$\qquad \Rightarrow \frac{dy}{dx} = 1 - 12x^{-2} = 1 - \frac{12}{x^2}$

e) $y = \sqrt{x}(x^3 - \sqrt{x}) = x^{\frac{1}{2}}(x^3 - x^{\frac{1}{2}}) = x^{\frac{7}{2}} - x$

$\qquad \Rightarrow \frac{dy}{dx} = \frac{7}{2}x^{\frac{5}{2}} - 1 = \frac{7}{2}\sqrt{x^5} - 1$

f) $f(x) = \frac{3 - \sqrt{x}}{\sqrt{x}} = \frac{3 - x^{\frac{1}{2}}}{x^{\frac{1}{2}}} = x^{-\frac{1}{2}}(3 - x^{\frac{1}{2}})$

$\qquad = 3x^{-\frac{1}{2}} - x^0 = 3x^{-\frac{1}{2}} - 1$

$\qquad f'(x) = 3\left(-\frac{1}{2}x^{-\frac{3}{2}}\right) = -\frac{3}{2}x^{-\frac{3}{2}} = -\frac{3}{2\sqrt{x^3}}$

g) $f(x) = \frac{x + 5\sqrt{x}}{\sqrt{x}} = \frac{x + 5x^{\frac{1}{2}}}{x^{\frac{1}{2}}} = x^{-\frac{1}{2}}(x + 5x^{\frac{1}{2}})$

$\qquad = x^{\frac{1}{2}} + 5x^0 = x^{\frac{1}{2}} + 5$

$\qquad f'(x) = \frac{1}{2}x^{-\frac{1}{2}} = \frac{1}{2\sqrt{x}}$

h) Factorising the numerator:

$\qquad f(x) = \frac{x - 3\sqrt{x} + 2}{\sqrt{x} - 1} = \frac{(\sqrt{x} - 2)(\sqrt{x} - 1)}{\sqrt{x} - 1}$

$\qquad = \sqrt{x} - 2 = x^{\frac{1}{2}} - 2$

$\qquad f'(x) = \frac{1}{2}x^{-\frac{1}{2}} = \frac{1}{2\sqrt{x}}$

Exercise 2.3
— Finding tangents and normals

Q1 a) $\frac{dy}{dx} = 9 - 4x$. At $(1, 7)$, $\frac{dy}{dx} = 5$

$\qquad \Rightarrow$ tangent has a gradient of 5 and has an equation of the form $y = 5x + c$.
Using the point $(1, 7)$, $7 = 5 + c$
$\Rightarrow c = 2$. So the tangent's equation is $y = 5x + 2$.

b) $\frac{dy}{dx} = 3x^2 - 2$. At $(2, 7)$, $\frac{dy}{dx} = 10$

$\qquad \Rightarrow$ tangent has a gradient of 10 and has an equation of the form $y = 10x + c$.
Using the point $(2, 7)$, $7 = 20 + c \Rightarrow c = -13$.
So the tangent's equation is $y = 10x - 13$.

c) $y = (x + 2)(2x - 3) = 2x^2 + x - 6$

$\qquad \frac{dy}{dx} = 4x + 1$. At $(2, 4)$, $\frac{dy}{dx} = 9$

$\qquad \Rightarrow$ tangent has a gradient of 9 and has an equation of the form $y = 9x + c$.
Using the point $(2, 4)$, $4 = 18 + c \Rightarrow c = -14$.
So the tangent's equation is $y = 9x - 14$.

d) $y = x(x - 1)^2 = x(x^2 - 2x + 1) = x^3 - 2x^2 + x$

$\qquad \frac{dy}{dx} = 3x^2 - 4x + 1$. At $(-1, -4)$, $\frac{dy}{dx} = 8$

$\qquad \Rightarrow$ tangent has a gradient of 8 and has an equation of the form $y = 8x + c$.
Using the point $(-1, -4)$, $-4 = -8 + c \Rightarrow c = 4$.
So the tangent's equation is $y = 8x + 4$.

e) $y = x^2(x + 3) - 10 = x^3 + 3x^2 - 10$

$\qquad \frac{dy}{dx} = 3x^2 + 6x$. At $(2, 10)$, $\frac{dy}{dx} = 24$

$\qquad \Rightarrow$ tangent has a gradient of 24 and has an equation of the form $y = 24x + c$.
Using the point $(2, 10)$, $10 = 48 + c \Rightarrow c = -38$.
So the tangent's equation is $y = 24x - 38$.

f) $y = x(2x^2 - 2x - 12) = 2x^3 - 2x^2 - 12x$

$\qquad \frac{dy}{dx} = 6x^2 - 4x - 12$. At $(-1, 8)$, $\frac{dy}{dx} = -2$

$\qquad \Rightarrow$ tangent has a gradient of -2 and has an equation of the form $y = -2x + c$.
Using the point $(-1, 8)$, $8 = 2 + c \Rightarrow c = 6$.
So the tangent's equation is $y = -2x + 6$.

Q2 a) $y = x^{-1} + x + 3$

$\qquad \frac{dy}{dx} = -x^{-2} + 1$. At $(2, 5\frac{1}{2})$, $\frac{dy}{dx} = \frac{3}{4}$

$\qquad \Rightarrow$ tangent has a gradient of $\frac{3}{4}$ and has an equation of the form $y = \frac{3}{4}x + c$.
Using the point $(2, 5\frac{1}{2})$, $5\frac{1}{2} = 1\frac{1}{2} + c \Rightarrow c = 4$.
So the tangent's equation is $y = \frac{3}{4}x + 4$
$\Rightarrow 4y = 3x + 16 \Rightarrow 3x - 4y + 16 = 0$.

b) $y = 4x^2 - 3x^{\frac{1}{2}}$

$\qquad \frac{dy}{dx} = 8x - 3\left(\frac{1}{2}x^{-\frac{1}{2}}\right) = 8x - \frac{3}{2}x^{-\frac{1}{2}}$.

At $(1, 1)$, $\frac{dy}{dx} = 6\frac{1}{2}$

$\qquad \Rightarrow$ tangent has a gradient of $6\frac{1}{2}$ and has an equation of the form $y = 6\frac{1}{2}x + c$.
Using the point $(1, 1)$, $1 = 6\frac{1}{2} + c \Rightarrow c = -5\frac{1}{2}$.
So the tangent's equation is $y = 6\frac{1}{2}x - 5\frac{1}{2}$
$\Rightarrow 2y = 13x - 11 \Rightarrow 13x - 2y - 11 = 0$.

c) $y = 3x^{-1} + 2x^{\frac{1}{2}}$

$\qquad \frac{dy}{dx} = 3(-x^{-2}) + 2\left(\frac{1}{2}x^{-\frac{1}{2}}\right) = -3x^{-2} + x^{-\frac{1}{2}}$.

At $(4, 4\frac{3}{4})$, $\frac{dy}{dx} = \frac{5}{16}$

$\qquad \Rightarrow$ tangent has a gradient of $\frac{5}{16}$ and has an equation of the form $y = \frac{5}{16}x + c$.
Using the point $(4, 4\frac{3}{4})$, $4\frac{3}{4} = \frac{5}{4} + c \Rightarrow c = 3\frac{1}{2}$.
So the tangent's equation is $y = \frac{5}{16}x + 3\frac{1}{2}$
$\Rightarrow 16y = 5x + 56 \Rightarrow 5x - 16y + 56 = 0$.

d) $y = x^{-1} + 4x^{-2}$

$\frac{dy}{dx} = -x^{-2} + 4(-2x^{-3}) = -x^{-2} - 8x^{-3}$.

At $(2, 1\frac{1}{2})$, $\frac{dy}{dx} = -\frac{5}{4}$

$\Rightarrow$ tangent has a gradient of $-\frac{5}{4}$ and has an equation of the form $y = -\frac{5}{4}x + c$.

Using the point $(2, 1\frac{1}{2})$, $1\frac{1}{2} = -\frac{5}{2} + c \Rightarrow c = 4$.

So the tangent's equation is $y = -\frac{5}{4}x + 4$

$\Rightarrow 4y = -5x + 16 \Rightarrow 5x + 4y - 16 = 0$.

e) $y = \frac{1}{3}x^2 - 4x^{\frac{1}{2}} - \frac{1}{3}$

$\frac{dy}{dx} = \frac{1}{3}(2x) - 4(\frac{1}{2}x^{-\frac{1}{2}}) = \frac{2}{3}x - 2x^{-\frac{1}{2}}$.

At $(4, -3)$, $\frac{dy}{dx} = \frac{5}{3}$

$\Rightarrow$ tangent has a gradient of $\frac{5}{3}$ and has an equation of the form $y = \frac{5}{3}x + c$.

Using the point $(4, -3)$, $-3 = \frac{20}{3} + c \Rightarrow c = -\frac{29}{3}$.

So the tangent's equation is $y = \frac{5}{3}x - \frac{29}{3}$

$\Rightarrow 3y = 5x - 29 \Rightarrow 5x - 3y - 29 = 0$.

f) $y = x - 2x^{-1} + 3x^{-2}$

$\frac{dy}{dx} = 1 + 2x^{-2} - 6x^{-3}$. At $(-3, -2)$, $\frac{dy}{dx} = \frac{13}{9}$

$\Rightarrow$ tangent has a gradient of $\frac{13}{9}$ and has an equation of the form $y = \frac{13}{9}x + c$.

Using the point $(-3, -2)$, $-2 = -\frac{13}{3} + c \Rightarrow c = \frac{7}{3}$.

So the tangent's equation is $y = \frac{13}{9}x + \frac{7}{3}$

$\Rightarrow 9y = 13x + 21 \Rightarrow 13x - 9y + 21 = 0$.

Q3 **a)** $\frac{dy}{dx} = 6x - 4$. At $(2, 6)$, $\frac{dy}{dx} = 8$.

So the normal has a gradient of $-\frac{1}{8}$ and an equation of the form $y = -\frac{1}{8}x + c$.

Don't forget — the gradient of the normal to a curve at a point is $-\dfrac{1}{Gradient\ of\ the\ curve}$.

Using the point $(2, 6)$, $6 = -\frac{1}{4} + c \Rightarrow c = 6\frac{1}{4}$.

So the normal's equation is $y = -\frac{1}{8}x + 6\frac{1}{4}$

$\Rightarrow 8y = -x + 50 \Rightarrow x + 8y - 50 = 0$.

b) $y = x^3 + 4x^2 - 5x$

$\frac{dy}{dx} = 3x^2 + 8x - 5$. At $(-1, 8)$, $\frac{dy}{dx} = -10$.

So the normal has a gradient of $\frac{1}{10}$ and an equation of the form $y = \frac{1}{10}x + c$.

Using the point $(-1, 8)$, $8 = -\frac{1}{10} + c \Rightarrow c = \frac{81}{10}$

So the normal's equation is $y = \frac{1}{10}x + \frac{81}{10}$

$\Rightarrow 10y = x + 81 \Rightarrow x - 10y + 81 = 0$.

c) $y = x(x^2 - 3x + 2) = x^3 - 3x^2 + 2x$

$\frac{dy}{dx} = 3x^2 - 6x + 2$. At $(3, 6)$, $\frac{dy}{dx} = 11$.

So the normal has a gradient of $-\frac{1}{11}$ and an equation of the form $y = -\frac{1}{11}x + c$.

Using the point $(3, 6)$, $6 = -\frac{3}{11} + c \Rightarrow c = \frac{69}{11}$.

So the normal's equation is $y = -\frac{1}{11}x + \frac{69}{11}$

$\Rightarrow 11y = -x + 69 \Rightarrow x + 11y - 69 = 0$.

d) $y = x(x^2 + x - 12) - 10 = x^3 + x^2 - 12x - 10$

$\frac{dy}{dx} = 3x^2 + 2x - 12$. At $(-2, 10)$, $\frac{dy}{dx} = -4$.

So the normal has a gradient of $\frac{1}{4}$ and an equation of the form $y = \frac{1}{4}x + c$.

Using the point $(-2, 10)$, $10 = -\frac{1}{2} + c \Rightarrow c = \frac{21}{2}$.

So the normal's equation is $y = \frac{1}{4}x + \frac{21}{2}$

$\Rightarrow 4y = x + 42 \Rightarrow x - 4y + 42 = 0$.

e) $y = \frac{(x + 2)(x^2 - 7x)}{x + 2} = x^2 - 7x$

$\frac{dy}{dx} = 2x - 7$. At $(5, -10)$, $\frac{dy}{dx} = 3$.

So the normal has a gradient of $-\frac{1}{3}$ and an equation of the form $y = -\frac{1}{3}x + c$.

Using the point $(5, -10)$, $-10 = -\frac{5}{3} + c$

$\Rightarrow c = -\frac{25}{3}$.

So the normal's equation is $y = -\frac{1}{3}x - \frac{25}{3}$

$\Rightarrow 3y = -x - 25 \Rightarrow x + 3y + 25 = 0$.

Q4 **a)** $y = \frac{2x^5 - 2x^4}{3x^3} = \frac{2}{3}x^2 - \frac{2}{3}x$

Remember — if the numerator is a single term, split the equation up into separate terms.

$\frac{dy}{dx} = \frac{2}{3}(2x) - \frac{2}{3} = \frac{4}{3}x - \frac{2}{3}$

At $(-2, 4)$, $\frac{dy}{dx} = -\frac{10}{3}$.

So the normal has a gradient of $\frac{3}{10}$ and an equation of the form $y = \frac{3}{10}x + c$.

Using the point $(-2, 4)$, $4 = -\frac{6}{10} + c$

$\Rightarrow c = \frac{23}{5}$. So the normal's equation is

$y = \frac{3}{10}x + \frac{23}{5} \Rightarrow 10y = 3x + 46$

$\Rightarrow 3x - 10y + 46 = 0$.

b) $y = \frac{5x^2 - 2x + 3}{x^2} = 5 - \frac{2}{x} + \frac{3}{x^2}$

$\frac{dy}{dx} = -2(-x^{-2}) + 3(-2x^{-3}) = \frac{2}{x^2} - \frac{6}{x^3}$

At $(2, 4\frac{3}{4})$, $\frac{dy}{dx} = -\frac{1}{4}$.

So the normal has a gradient of 4 and an equation of the form $y = 4x + c$.

Using the point $(2, 4\frac{3}{4})$, $4\frac{3}{4} = 8 + c \Rightarrow c = -\frac{13}{4}$.

So the normal's equation is

$y = 4x - \frac{13}{4} \Rightarrow 4y = 16x - 13 \Rightarrow 16x - 4y - 13 = 0$.

c) $y = 3xx^{-\frac{1}{2}} - x^2 x^{-\frac{3}{2}} = 3x^{\frac{1}{2}} - x^{\frac{3}{2}}$

$\frac{dy}{dx} = 3(\frac{1}{2}x^{-\frac{1}{2}}) - \frac{3}{2}x^{\frac{1}{2}} = \frac{3}{2\sqrt{x}} - \frac{3}{2}\sqrt{x}$

At $(4, -2)$, $\frac{dy}{dx} = -\frac{9}{4}$.

So the normal has a gradient of $\frac{4}{9}$ and an equation of the form $y = \frac{4}{9}x + c$.

Using the point $(4, -2)$, $-2 = \frac{16}{9} + c \Rightarrow c = -\frac{34}{9}$.

So the normal's equation is

$y = \frac{4}{9}x - \frac{34}{9} \Rightarrow 9y = 4x - 34$

$\Rightarrow 4x - 9y - 34 = 0$.

d) $y = \frac{1}{x} - \frac{3}{x^2} - \frac{4}{x^3} + \frac{7}{4} = x^{-1} - 3x^{-2} - 4x^{-3} + \frac{7}{4}$

$\frac{dy}{dx} = -x^{-2} - 3(-2x^{-3}) - 4(-3x^{-4})$

$= -x^{-2} + 6x^{-3} + 12x^{-4}$

At $(-2, 1)$, $\frac{dy}{dx} = -\frac{1}{4}$.

So the normal has a gradient of 4 and an equation of the form $y = 4x + c$.

Using the point $(-2, 1)$, $1 = -8 + c \Rightarrow c = 9$.

So the normal's equation is $y = 4x + 9$.

e) $y = \frac{x^3 - 5x^2 - 4x}{x^{\frac{3}{2}}} = x^{\frac{3}{2}} - 5x^{\frac{1}{2}} - 4x^{-\frac{1}{2}}$

$\frac{dy}{dx} = \frac{3}{2}x^{\frac{1}{2}} - 5(\frac{1}{2}x^{-\frac{1}{2}}) - 4(-\frac{1}{2}x^{-\frac{3}{2}})$

$= \frac{3}{2}\sqrt{x} - \frac{5}{2\sqrt{x}} + \frac{2}{x\sqrt{x}}$

At $(4, -4)$, $\frac{dy}{dx} = 2$.

So the normal has a gradient of $-\frac{1}{2}$ and an equation of the form $y = -\frac{1}{2}x + c$.

Using the point $(4, -4)$, $-4 = -2 + c \Rightarrow c = -2$.

So the normal's equation is $y = -\frac{1}{2}x - 2$

$\Rightarrow 2y = -x - 4 \Rightarrow x + 2y + 4 = 0$.

Q5 a) $f'(x) = 3x^2 - 6x$. If $f'(x) = 9$, $3x^2 - 6x = 9$

$\Rightarrow 3x^2 - 6x - 9 = 0 \Rightarrow x^2 - 2x - 3 = 0$

$\Rightarrow (x - 3)(x + 1) = 0 \Rightarrow x = 3$ or $x = -1$. So $x = 3$ since $x > 0$. So $y = f(3) = 3^3 - 3(3)^2 + 3 = 3$.

The coordinates are $(3, 3)$.

b) The gradient of the tangent at $(3, 3)$ is 9 from part a). So the equation is of the form $y = 9x + c$. You know the tangent goes through $(3, 3)$ so use this point: $3 = 27 + c \Rightarrow c = -24$.

So the equation is $y = 9x - 24$.

c) The gradient of the normal is $-\frac{1}{9}$ so the equation has the form $y = -\frac{1}{9}x + c$. Again, use the point $(3, 3)$, so $3 = -\frac{1}{3} + c \Rightarrow c = \frac{10}{3}$.

So the equation is $y = -\frac{1}{9}x + \frac{10}{3} \Rightarrow 9y = -x + 30$

$\Rightarrow x + 9y - 30 = 0$

Q6 a) Putting $x = -2$ into the equation gives:

$y = \frac{x^3 + x^2 + x + 5}{x^2}$

$= \frac{(-2)^3 + (-2)^2 + (-2) + 5}{(-2)^2}$

$= \frac{-8 + 4 - 2 + 5}{4} = -\frac{1}{4}$

so $(2, -\frac{1}{4})$ is a point on the curve.

b) $y = \frac{x^3 + x^2 + x + 5}{x^2} = x + 1 + \frac{1}{x} + \frac{5}{x^2}$

$\frac{dy}{dx} = 1 + 0 + (-x^{-2}) + 5(-2x^{-3})$

$= 1 - \frac{1}{x^2} - \frac{10}{x^3}$

At $(-2, -\frac{1}{4})$, $\frac{dy}{dx} = 2$. So the gradient of the tangent at this point is 2 and it has equation $y = 2x + c$. Using the point $(-2, -\frac{1}{4})$,

$-\frac{1}{4} = -4 + c \Rightarrow c = \frac{15}{4}$.

So the equation of the tangent is $y = 2x + \frac{15}{4}$

$\Rightarrow 4y = 8x + 15 \Rightarrow 8x - 4y + 15 = 0$.

c) The gradient of the normal at $(-2, -\frac{1}{4})$ is $-\frac{1}{2}$ and so it has equation $y = -\frac{1}{2}x + c$. Using the point $(-2, -\frac{1}{4})$, $-\frac{1}{4} = 1 + c \Rightarrow c = -\frac{5}{4}$. So the equation of the normal is $y = -\frac{1}{2}x - \frac{5}{4} \Rightarrow 4y = -2x - 5 \Rightarrow 2x + 4y + 5 = 0$.

3. Second Order Derivatives
Exercise 3.1
— Finding second order derivatives

Q1 a) $\frac{dy}{dx} = 3x^2$ and $\frac{d^2y}{dx^2} = 6x$.

b) $\frac{dy}{dx} = 5x^4$ and $\frac{d^2y}{dx^2} = 20x^3$.

c) $\frac{dy}{dx} = 4x^3$ and $\frac{d^2y}{dx^2} = 12x^2$.

d) $\frac{dy}{dx} = 1$ and $\frac{d^2y}{dx^2} = 0$.

e) $y = x^{-1}$, so $\frac{dy}{dx} = -x^{-2} = -\frac{1}{x^2}$

and $\frac{d^2y}{dx^2} = 2x^{-3} = \frac{2}{x^3}$.

f) $y = x^{\frac{1}{2}}$, so $\frac{dy}{dx} = \frac{1}{2}x^{-\frac{1}{2}} = \frac{1}{2\sqrt{x}}$

and $\frac{d^2y}{dx^2} = -\frac{1}{4}x^{-\frac{3}{2}} = -\frac{1}{4(\sqrt{x})^3}$.

g) $y = x^{-2}$, so $\frac{dy}{dx} = -2x^{-3} = -\frac{2}{x^3}$

and $\frac{d^2y}{dx^2} = 6x^{-4} = \frac{6}{x^4}$.

h) $y = x\sqrt{x} = x^1 x^{\frac{1}{2}} = x^{1+\frac{1}{2}} = x^{\frac{3}{2}}$,

so $\frac{dy}{dx} = \frac{3}{2}x^{\frac{1}{2}} = \frac{3}{2}\sqrt{x}$ and $\frac{d^2y}{dx^2} = \frac{3}{4}x^{-\frac{1}{2}} = \frac{3}{4\sqrt{x}}$.

Q2 a) $f(x) = x(4x^2 - x) = 4x^3 - x^2$
$f'(x) = 12x^2 - 2x$
$f''(x) = 24x - 2$

b) $f(x) = (x^2 - 3)(x - 4) = x^3 - 4x^2 - 3x + 12$
$f'(x) = 3x^2 - 8x - 3$
$f''(x) = 6x - 8$

c) $f(x) = \dfrac{4x^5 + 12x^3 - 40x}{4(x^2 + 5)} = \dfrac{4x(x^4 + 3x^2 - 10)}{4(x^2 + 5)}$
$= \dfrac{4x(x^2 + 5)(x^2 - 2)}{4(x^2 + 5)} = x(x^2 - 2) = x^3 - 2x$
$f'(x) = 3x^2 - 2$
$f''(x) = 6x$

d) $f(x) = 3x^{\frac{1}{2}} + xx^{\frac{1}{2}} = 3x^{\frac{1}{2}} + x^{\frac{3}{2}}$
$f'(x) = \frac{3}{2}x^{-\frac{1}{2}} + \frac{3}{2}x^{\frac{1}{2}} = \frac{3}{2\sqrt{x}} + \frac{3}{2}\sqrt{x}$
$f''(x) = \frac{3}{2}(-\frac{1}{2}x^{-\frac{3}{2}}) + \frac{3}{2}(\frac{1}{2}x^{-\frac{1}{2}}) = -\frac{3}{4}x^{-\frac{3}{2}} + \frac{3}{4}x^{-\frac{1}{2}}$
$= -\dfrac{3}{4(\sqrt{x})^3} + \dfrac{3}{4\sqrt{x}} \left(= -\dfrac{3}{4x\sqrt{x}} + \dfrac{3}{4\sqrt{x}} \right)$

e) $f(x) = \frac{1}{x}(3x^4 - 2x^3) = 3x^3 - 2x^2$
$f'(x) = 9x^2 - 4x$
$f''(x) = 18x - 4$

f) $f(x) = \dfrac{x^2 - xx^{\frac{1}{2}} + 7x}{x^{\frac{1}{2}}} = x^2x^{-\frac{1}{2}} - xx^{\frac{1}{2}}x^{-\frac{1}{2}} + 7xx^{-\frac{1}{2}}$
$= x^{\frac{3}{2}} - x + 7x^{\frac{1}{2}}$
$f'(x) = \frac{3}{2}x^{\frac{1}{2}} - 1 + 7(\frac{1}{2}x^{-\frac{1}{2}}) = \frac{3}{2}\sqrt{x} - 1 + \dfrac{7}{2\sqrt{x}}$
$f''(x) = \frac{3}{2}(\frac{1}{2}x^{-\frac{1}{2}}) + \frac{7}{2}(-\frac{1}{2}x^{-\frac{3}{2}}) = \dfrac{3}{4\sqrt{x}} - \dfrac{7}{4(\sqrt{x})^3}$

Q3 a) $f'(x) = 3x^2 - 2x$ and so $f''(x) = 6x - 2$.
$f''(3) = 16$.

b) $y = xx^{\frac{1}{2}} - x^{-1} = x^{\frac{3}{2}} - x^{-1}$ so $\dfrac{dy}{dx} = \frac{3}{2}x^{\frac{1}{2}} + x^{-2}$
so $\dfrac{d^2y}{dx^2} = \frac{3}{2}(\frac{1}{2}x^{-\frac{1}{2}}) - 2x^{-3} = \dfrac{3}{4\sqrt{x}} - \dfrac{2}{x^3}$
so at $x = 4$, $\dfrac{d^2y}{dx^2} = \dfrac{11}{32}$.

c) $f(x) = x^2(x^3 - 4x^2 - 5x) = x^5 - 4x^4 - 5x^3$
so $f'(x) = 5x^4 - 16x^3 - 15x^2$ and
$f''(x) = 20x^3 - 48x^2 - 30x$.
$f''(-1) = -38$.

d) $y = \dfrac{x^3(x + 6)(x - 2)}{(x + 6)} = x^3(x - 2) = x^4 - 2x^3$
so $\dfrac{dy}{dx} = 4x^3 - 6x^2$, $\dfrac{d^2y}{dx^2} = 12x^2 - 12x$.
At $x = 5$, $\dfrac{d^2y}{dx^2} = 240$.

e) $f(x) = \dfrac{9x^2 + 3x}{3\sqrt{x}} = 3x^{\frac{3}{2}} + x^{\frac{1}{2}}$ so
$f'(x) = 3(\frac{3}{2}x^{\frac{1}{2}}) + \frac{1}{2}x^{-\frac{1}{2}} = \frac{9}{2}\sqrt{x} + \dfrac{1}{2\sqrt{x}}$ and so
$f''(x) = \frac{9}{2}(\frac{1}{2}x^{-\frac{1}{2}}) + \frac{1}{2}(-\frac{1}{2}x^{-\frac{3}{2}}) = \dfrac{9}{4\sqrt{x}} - \dfrac{1}{4(\sqrt{x})^3}$.
$f''(1) = 2$.

f) $y = (x^{-2} + x^{-1})(5 - x)$
$= 5x^{-2} - x^{-2}x + 5x^{-1} - xx^{-1}$
$= 5x^{-2} - x^{-1} + 5x^{-1} - 1 = 5x^{-2} + 4x^{-1} - 1$
$\dfrac{dy}{dx} = 5(-2x^{-3}) + 4(-x^{-2}) = -10x^{-3} - 4x^{-2}$
so $\dfrac{d^2y}{dx^2} = 30x^{-4} + 8x^{-3} = \dfrac{30}{x^4} + \dfrac{8}{x^3}$.
At $x = -3$, $\dfrac{d^2y}{dx^2} = \dfrac{2}{27}$.

Q4 a) $\dfrac{dx}{dt} = 6t - 7$.

b) **(i)** $t = 2 \Rightarrow \dfrac{dx}{dt} = 12 - 7 = 5$ ms⁻¹
(ii) $t = 5 \Rightarrow \dfrac{dx}{dt} = 30 - 7 = 23$ ms⁻¹

c) If $\dfrac{dx}{dt} = 17 \Rightarrow 6t - 7 = 17 \Rightarrow 6t = 24 \Rightarrow t = 4$ s.

d) $\dfrac{d^2x}{dt^2} = 6$ ms⁻²

Q5 a) $\dfrac{dx}{dt} = 6t^2 - 8t$

b) If $\dfrac{dx}{dt} = 30$ then $6t^2 - 8t = 30 \Rightarrow 6t^2 - 8t - 30 = 0$
$\Rightarrow 3t^2 - 4t - 15 = 0 \Rightarrow (3t + 5)(t - 3) = 0$
$\Rightarrow t = 3$ or $t = -\frac{5}{3}$. But $t > 0$ so $t = 3$.
If $t = 3$, $x = 2t^3 - 4t^2 = 18$.
So $t = 3$ s and $x = 18$ m.

c) $\dfrac{d^2x}{dt^2} = 12t - 8$.

d) $t = 5 \Rightarrow \dfrac{d^2x}{dt^2} = 52$ ms⁻²

e) If $\dfrac{d^2x}{dt^2} = 16 \Rightarrow 12t - 8 = 16 \Rightarrow 12t = 24 \Rightarrow t = 2$.
$\dfrac{dx}{dt} = 6t^2 - 8t = 8$ ms⁻¹.

Review Exercise — Chapter 6

Q1 a) $\dfrac{dy}{dx} = \lim_{h \to 0}\left[\dfrac{f(x + h) - f(x)}{(x + h) - x}\right]$
$= \lim_{h \to 0}\left[\dfrac{(x + h + 1) - (x + 1)}{(x + h) - x}\right]$
$= \lim_{h \to 0}\left[\dfrac{x + h + 1 - x - 1}{x + h - x}\right]$
$= \lim_{h \to 0}\left[\dfrac{h}{h}\right] = \lim_{h \to 0}[1] = 1$

b) $\dfrac{dy}{dx} = \lim_{h \to 0}\left[\dfrac{f(x + h) - f(x)}{(x + h) - x}\right]$
$= \lim_{h \to 0}\left[\dfrac{4(x + h)^2 - 4x^2}{(x + h) - x}\right]$
$= \lim_{h \to 0}\left[\dfrac{4x^2 + 8xh + 4h^2 - 4x^2}{x + h - x}\right]$
$= \lim_{h \to 0}\left[\dfrac{8xh + 4h^2}{h}\right] = \lim_{h \to 0}[8x + 4h] = 8x$

c) $\dfrac{dy}{dx} = \lim\limits_{h \to 0}\left[\dfrac{\frac{3}{(x+h)} - \frac{3}{x}}{(x+h) - x}\right]$

$= \lim\limits_{h \to 0}\left[\dfrac{\frac{3x}{x(x+h)} - \frac{3(x+h)}{x(x+h)}}{h}\right]$

$= \lim\limits_{h \to 0}\left[\dfrac{\left(\frac{-3h}{x(x+h)}\right)}{h}\right] = \lim\limits_{h \to 0}\left[\dfrac{-3}{x(x+h)}\right] = -\dfrac{3}{x^2}$

Q2 $\dfrac{d}{dx}(x^n) = nx^{n-1}$

Q3 a) $\dfrac{dy}{dx} = 2x$ **b)** $\dfrac{dy}{dx} = 4x^3 + \dfrac{1}{2\sqrt{x}}$

c) $\dfrac{dy}{dx} = -\dfrac{14}{x^3} + \dfrac{3}{2\sqrt{x^3}} + 36x^2$

Q4 They're the same.

Q5 The gradient of the normal to the curve at a point is $-\dfrac{1}{\text{Gradient of the curve}}$

Q6 a) $\dfrac{dy}{dx} = 4x = 8$

b) $\dfrac{dy}{dx} = 8x - 1 = 15$

c) $\dfrac{dy}{dx} = 3x^2 - 14x = -16$

Q7 a) When $t = 0$, $v = 3(0)^2 + 4 = 4$ ml.

b) Differentiate $v = 3t^2 + 4$ to give: $\dfrac{dv}{dt} = 6t$ so, when $t = 4$, $\dfrac{dv}{dt} = 24$ ml/s.

Q8 The tangent and normal must go through (16, 6).
Differentiate to find $\dfrac{dy}{dx} = \dfrac{3}{2}\sqrt{x} - 3$, so gradient at (16, 6) is 3.

Therefore tangent can be written $y_T = 3x + c_T$; putting $x = 16$ and $y = 6$ gives $6 = 3 \times 16 + c_T$, so $c_T = -42$, and the equation of the tangent is $y = 3x - 42$.
The gradient of the normal must be $-\frac{1}{3}$, so the equation of the normal is $y_N = -\frac{1}{3}x + c_N$
Substituting in the coordinates of the point (16, 6) gives $6 = -\dfrac{16}{3} + c_N \Rightarrow c_N = \dfrac{34}{3}$; so the normal is
$y = -\frac{1}{3}x + \dfrac{34}{3} = \frac{1}{3}(34 - x) \Rightarrow x + 3y - 34 = 0$.

Q9 The tangent must go through (1, 7).
Differentiate to find $\dfrac{dy}{dx} = 3x^2 - \dfrac{4}{x^2} + \dfrac{1}{\sqrt{x}}$, so gradient at (1, 7) is 0.
Therefore tangent can be written $y = c$; putting $x = 1$ and $y = 7$ gives $7 = c$, so $c = 7$, and the equation of the tangent is $y = 7$.

Q10 On the first curve, when $x = 4$,
$y = \dfrac{(4)^3}{3} - 2(4)^2 - 4(4) + \dfrac{86}{3}$
$= \dfrac{64}{3} - 32 - 16 + \dfrac{86}{3} = \dfrac{150}{3} - 48 = 2$
On the second curve, when $x = 4$, $y = \sqrt{4} = 2$.
For both curves, when $x = 4$, $y = 2$, so they meet at (4, 2).
Differentiating the first curve gives $\dfrac{dy}{dx} = x^2 - 4x - 4$, which at $x = 4$ is equal to -4.
Differentiating the other curve gives $\dfrac{dy}{dx} = \dfrac{1}{2\sqrt{x}}$, and so the gradient at (4, 2) is $\frac{1}{4}$. If you multiply these two gradients together you get -1, so the two curves are perpendicular at (4, 2).

Q11 a) C and L intersect when $x^2 - 6 = 3 \Rightarrow x^2 = 9 \Rightarrow x = \pm 3$. If $x = 3$, $y = 3$. If $x = -3$, $y = 3$. So the points are $A = (3, 3)$ and $B = (-3, 3)$.

b) For C, $\dfrac{dy}{dx} = 2x$.
At point A, $\dfrac{dy}{dx} = 6$. At point B, $\dfrac{dy}{dx} = -6$

c) At A, the gradient of the normal is $-\frac{1}{6}$. The normal has an equation of the form $y = -\frac{1}{6}x + c$.
Letting $x = 3$ and $y = 3$, $3 = -\frac{1}{2} + c$, so $c = \frac{7}{2}$.
So the normal at A is given by $y = -\frac{1}{6}x + \frac{7}{2}$
At B, the gradient of the normal is $\frac{1}{6}$. The normal has an equation of the form $y = \frac{1}{6}x + c$.
Letting $x = -3$ and $y = 3$, $3 = -\frac{1}{2} + c$, so $c = \frac{7}{2}$.
So the normal at B is given by $y = \frac{1}{6}x + \frac{7}{2}$.

d) From part c), you know that both tangents cross the y-axis at the same point ($y = \frac{7}{2}$). So $D = (0, \frac{7}{2})$.

Q12 a) The gradient of the line L is 0 for any x since the line is horizontal.

b) The gradient of C is given by $\dfrac{dy}{dx} = 3x^2 - 4x$. If $\dfrac{dy}{dx} = 0$, then $3x^2 - 4x = 0$, so $x(3x - 4) = 0$:
So $x = 0$, which is not possible since $x > 0$, or $3x = 4$ so $x = \frac{4}{3}$. $y = x^3 - 2x^2 + 1 = -\dfrac{5}{27}$.
So the point is $(\frac{4}{3}, -\frac{5}{27})$.

c) The tangent at this point will have gradient 0, so it will be a horizontal line, and it goes through $(\frac{4}{3}, -\frac{5}{27})$, so the tangent line will be $y = -\dfrac{5}{27}$.

You could also have worked this out in the usual way. However when the gradient is 0, you can work out the equation easily from the point that it goes through.

Q13 $\frac{dy}{dx} = \frac{3}{2}x^{\frac{1}{2}}$. At $x = 16$, $\frac{dy}{dx} = \frac{3}{2}\sqrt{16} = \frac{12}{2} = 6$.

For the tangent, the gradient is 6 and it has equation $y = 6x + c$. At $x = 16$, $y = 65$, so $65 = 96 + c \Rightarrow c = -31$. So the equation of the tangent is $y = 6x - 31$.

For the normal, the gradient is $-\frac{1}{6}$ and it has equation $y = -\frac{1}{6}x + c$. At $x = 16$, $y = 65$ so $65 = -\frac{16}{6} + c \Rightarrow c = \frac{203}{3}$. So the equation of the normal is $y = -\frac{1}{6}x + \frac{203}{3} \Rightarrow 6y = -x + 406$ $\Rightarrow x + 6y - 406 = 0$.

Q14 a) $\frac{dx}{dt} = 3t^2 - 8$.

b) If $\frac{dx}{dt} = 19$, then $3t^2 - 8 = 19 \Rightarrow 3t^2 = 27 \Rightarrow t^2 = 9$ $\Rightarrow t = \pm 3$. But t must be non–negative so $t = 3$ s. When $t = 3$ $x = t^3 - 8t = 3$. So $t = 3$ s and $x = 3$ m.

c) $\frac{d^2x}{dt^2} = 6t$

d) If $t = 2$, then $\frac{d^2x}{dt^2} = 12$ ms^{-2}.

e) $\frac{d^2x}{dt^2} = 18 \Rightarrow 6t = 18 \Rightarrow t = 3$ s. The speed when $t = 3$ is $\frac{dx}{dt} = 3t^2 - 8 = 19$ ms^{-1}.

Q15 a) $f'(x) = 3x^2 - 3$. Gradient $= f'(-1) = 0$.

b) $2f''(x) - 3f'(x) + f(x)$
$$= 2(6x) - 3(3x^2 - 3) + (x^3 - 3x)$$
$$= 12x - 9x^2 + 9 + x^3 - 3x$$
$$= x^3 - 9x^2 + 9x + 9$$
$$= x^3 + 9(1 + x - x^2)$$

Q16 $f''(x) + 2f'(x) - 4f(x) = (12x^2) + 2(4x^3) - 4(x^4)$
$$= 12x^2 + 8x^3 - 4x^4$$

Exam-Style Questions — Chapter 6

Q1 a) $f(x) = 2\sqrt{x} + \frac{1}{x} = 2x^{\frac{1}{2}} + x^{-1}$

Differentiate to get :
$$f'(x) = 2(\frac{1}{2}x^{-\frac{1}{2}}) - x^{-2} = \frac{1}{\sqrt{x}} - \frac{1}{x^2}$$
[3 marks available — 1 mark for simplifying the expression and 1 mark for differentiating each term.]

b) $g(x) = \frac{(x + 2)(x + 1)}{\sqrt{x}} = \frac{x^2 + 3x + 2}{x^{\frac{1}{2}}}$
$$= x^{\frac{3}{2}} + 3x^{\frac{1}{2}} + 2x^{-\frac{1}{2}}$$

Differentiate to get:
$$g'(x) = \frac{3}{2}x^{\frac{1}{2}} + 3(\frac{1}{2}x^{-\frac{1}{2}}) + 2(-\frac{1}{2}x^{-\frac{3}{2}})$$
$$= \frac{3}{2}\sqrt{x} + \frac{3}{2\sqrt{x}} - \frac{1}{(\sqrt{x})^3}$$
[4 marks available — 1 mark for simplifying the expression, 3 marks for differentiating each term.]

Q2 a) Rewrite all the terms as powers of x:
$$y = x^7 + \frac{2}{x^3} = x^7 + 2x^{-3} \text{ [1 mark]}$$
and then differentiate each term:
$$\frac{dy}{dx} = 7x^6 + (-3)2x^{-4}$$
$$= 7x^6 - \frac{6}{x^4} \text{ [1 mark]}$$

b) This is a second-order derivative — just differentiate the answer for part a):
$$\frac{d^2y}{dx^2} = \frac{d}{dx}(7x^6 - 6x^{-4}) \text{ [1 mark]}$$
$$= 7(6x^5) - 6(-4x^{-5})$$
$$= 42x^5 + \frac{24}{x^5} \text{ [1 mark]}$$

Q3 a) $\frac{dy}{dx} = 6x^2 - 8x - 4$

[2 marks for all 3 terms correct or 1 mark for 2 terms.]

b) To find the gradient, put $x = 2$ into the answer to part (a): $6(2^2) - 8(2) - 4 = 24 - 16 - 4 = 4$ *[1 mark]*.

c) The gradient of the normal is $-1 \div$ the gradient of the tangent $= -1 \div 4 = -\frac{1}{4}$ *[1 mark]*.

At $x = 2$, the y-value is $2(2^3) - 4(2^2) - 4(2) + 12$ $= 16 - 16 - 8 + 12 = 4$ *[1 mark]*. Putting these values into the formula $y - y_1 = m(x - x_1)$ gives:
$$y - 4 = -\frac{1}{4}(x - 2)$$
$$y = -\frac{1}{4}x + \frac{1}{2} + 4$$
$$y = -\frac{1}{4}x + 4\frac{1}{2} \text{ [1 mark]}.$$

You could have left your answer in the form $y - y_1 = m(x - x_1)$ as the question didn't ask for a specific form.

Q4 Rewrite the expression in powers of x, so it becomes $x^{-\frac{1}{2}} + x^{-1}$ *[1 mark]*. Then differentiate to get $\frac{dy}{dx} = -\frac{1}{2}x^{-\frac{3}{2}} - x^{-2}$ *[1 mark for each correct term]*.
Putting $x = 4$ into the derivative gives:
$$-\frac{1}{2}4^{-\frac{3}{2}} - 4^{-2} = -\frac{1}{2}(\sqrt{4})^{-3} - \frac{1}{4^2}$$
$$= -\frac{1}{2} \cdot \frac{1}{2^3} - \frac{1}{16} = -\frac{1}{2} \cdot \frac{1}{8} - \frac{1}{16}$$
$$= -\frac{1}{16} - \frac{1}{16} = -\frac{1}{8}$$
[1 method mark, 1 answer mark]

Q5 a) Rewrite the expression in powers of x:
$$\frac{x^2 + 3x^{\frac{3}{2}}}{x^{\frac{1}{2}}} \text{ [1 mark]}$$

Then divide the top of the fraction by the bottom:
$$\frac{x^2}{x^{\frac{1}{2}}} + \frac{3x^{\frac{3}{2}}}{x^{\frac{1}{2}}} = x^{\frac{3}{2}} + 3x$$

So $p = \frac{3}{2}$ *[1 mark]* and $q = 1$ *[1 mark]*.

b) Use answer to part a) to rewrite equation:

$y = 3x^3 + 5 + x^{\frac{3}{2}} + 3x$ *[1 mark]*.
Then differentiate each term to give:
$\frac{dy}{dx} = 9x^2 + \frac{3}{2}x^{\frac{1}{2}} + 3$

[1 mark for each correct term].

Q6 a) Rewrite all the terms as powers of x:
$f(x) = \frac{1}{4}x^4 + 7 + 3x^{-\frac{3}{2}}$ *[1 mark]*
and then differentiate each term:
$f'(x) = \frac{1}{4}(4x^3) + 3(-\frac{3}{2}x^{-\frac{5}{2}})$
$= x^3 - \frac{9}{2(\sqrt{x})^5}$ *[2 marks]*

b) This is a second-order derivative
— just differentiate the answer for part a):
$\frac{d^2y}{dx^2} = \frac{d}{dx}\left(x^3 - \frac{9}{2(\sqrt{x})^5}\right)$ *[1 mark]*
$= \frac{d}{dx}\left(x^3 - \frac{9}{2}x^{-\frac{5}{2}}\right)$
$= 3x^2 - \frac{9}{2}(-\frac{5}{2}x^{-\frac{7}{2}})$
$= 3x^2 + \frac{45}{4(\sqrt{x})^7}$ *[2 marks]*

Q7 a) $\frac{dy}{dx} = m(3x^2) - 2x + 8$
$= 3mx^2 - 2x + 8$

[1 method mark, 1 answer mark]

b) Rearranging the equation of the line parallel to the normal gives the equation: $y = 3 - 4x$, so it has a gradient of -4 *[1 mark]*. The normal also has gradient -4 because it is parallel to this line *[1 mark]*.
The gradient of the tangent is $-1 \div$ the gradient of the normal $= -1 \div -4 = \frac{1}{4}$, so the gradient of the curve at P is also $\frac{1}{4}$ *[1 mark]*.

c) (i) So you know that when $x = 5$, the gradient
$3mx^2 - 2x + 8 = \frac{1}{4}$. *[1 mark]*
Now find the value of m:

$m(3 \times 5^2) - (2 \times 5) + 8 = \frac{1}{4}$ *[1 mark]*
$75m - 2 = \frac{1}{4}$
$m = \frac{9}{4} \times \frac{1}{75} = \frac{9}{300} = \frac{3}{100} = 0.03$ *[1 mark]*

(ii) When $x = 5$, then:
$y = (\frac{3}{100} \times 5^3) - (5^2) + (8 \times 5) + 2$

[1 mark]

$= \frac{375}{100} - 25 + 40 + 2$
$= 3.75 + 17$
$= 20.75$ *[1 mark]*

Q8 a) $f'(x) = 3 + 4x^3$ *[1 mark]*

b) If $f'(x) = 111$, then $3 + 4x^3 = 111$ *[1 mark]*,
so $4x^3 = 108$, so $x^3 = \frac{108}{4} = 27$ so $x = 3$ *[1 mark]*.

Q9 a) Rearrange $2x - y = 6$ into an expression for y:
$y = 2x - 6$. *[1 mark]*.
Now find W in terms of x:
$W = x^2(2x - 6)^2 = x^2(4x^2 - 24x + 36)$
$= 4x^4 - 24x^3 + 36x^2$ *[1 mark]*

b) (i) $\frac{dW}{dx} = 16x^3 - 72x^2 + 72x$

[2 marks for all three terms, or 1 mark for two]

$= 8(2x^3 - 9x^2 + 9x)$ *[1 mark]*
So $k = 8$ *[1 mark]*

(ii) At $x = 1$,
$\frac{dW}{dx} = 8(2(1)^3 - 9(1)^2 + 9(1)) = 8(2 - 9 + 9)$
$= 16$ *[1 mark]*.

c) $\frac{d^2W}{dx^2} = 48x^2 - 144x + 72$ *[1 mark]*

So for $x = 1 : \frac{d^2W}{dx^2} = 48 - 144 + 72$
$= -24$ *[1 mark]*

Chapter 7: Integration

1. Integration
Exercise 1.1 — Integrating x^n

Q1 **a)** $y = \int \frac{dy}{dx}\,dx = \int x^7\,dx = \frac{x^8}{8} + C$

b) $y = \int \frac{dy}{dx}\,dx = \int 2x^3\,dx = 2\int x^3\,dx$

$= 2\left(\frac{x^4}{4}\right) + C = \frac{x^4}{2} + C$

c) $y = \int \frac{dy}{dx}\,dx = \int 8x\,dx = 8\int x\,dx$

$= 8\left(\frac{x^2}{2}\right) + C = 4x^2 + C$

d) $y = \int \frac{dy}{dx}\,dx = \int -5x^4\,dx = -5\int x^4\,dx$

$= -5\left(\frac{x^5}{5}\right) + C = -x^5 + C$

e) $y = \int \frac{dy}{dx}\,dx = \int x^{-3}\,dx = \frac{x^{-2}}{-2} + C = -\frac{1}{2x^2} + C$

f) $y = \int \frac{dy}{dx}\,dx = \int 4x^{-4}\,dx = 4\int x^{-4}\,dx$

$= 4\left(\frac{x^{-3}}{-3}\right) + C = \frac{4x^{-3}}{-3} + C = -\frac{4}{3x^3} + C$

g) $y = \int \frac{dy}{dx}\,dx = \int -6x^{-5}\,dx = -6\int x^{-5}\,dx$

$= -6\left(\frac{x^{-4}}{-4}\right) + C = \frac{3x^{-4}}{2} + C = \frac{3}{2x^4} + C$

h) $y = \int \frac{dy}{dx}\,dx = \int -12\,dx = \frac{-12x}{1} + C$

$= -12x + C$

i) $y = \int \frac{dy}{dx}\,dx = \int x^{\frac{1}{2}}\,dx = \frac{x^{\frac{3}{2}}}{\left(\frac{3}{2}\right)} + C = \frac{2x^{\frac{3}{2}}}{3} + C$

Don't forget that dividing by a fraction is the same as multiplying by the flipped fraction.

j) $y = \int \frac{dy}{dx}\,dx = \int x^{\frac{1}{3}}\,dx = \frac{x^{\frac{4}{3}}}{\left(\frac{4}{3}\right)} + C = \frac{3x^{\frac{4}{3}}}{4} + C$

Q2 **a)** $\int x^{\frac{2}{3}}\,dx = \frac{x^{\frac{5}{3}}}{\left(\frac{5}{3}\right)} + C = \frac{3x^{\frac{5}{3}}}{5} + C$

b) $\int 7x^{\frac{4}{3}}\,dx = 7\int x^{\frac{4}{3}}\,dx = 7\left(\frac{x^{\frac{7}{3}}}{\left(\frac{7}{3}\right)}\right) + C = 3x^{\frac{7}{3}} + C$

c) $\int x^{-\frac{1}{2}}\,dx = \frac{x^{\frac{1}{2}}}{\left(\frac{1}{2}\right)} + C = 2x^{\frac{1}{2}} + C$

d) $\int 2x^{-\frac{1}{3}}\,dx = 2\int x^{-\frac{1}{3}}\,dx = 2\frac{x^{\frac{2}{3}}}{\left(\frac{2}{3}\right)} + C = 3x^{\frac{2}{3}} + C$

e) $\int 14x^{0.4}\,dx = 14\int x^{0.4}\,dx = 14\left(\frac{x^{1.4}}{1.4}\right) + C$

$= 10x^{1.4} + C$

f) $\int -1.2x^{-0.6}\,dx = -1.2\int x^{-0.6}\,dx$

$= -1.2\left(\frac{x^{0.4}}{0.4}\right) + C = -3x^{0.4} + C$

g) $\int -2x^{-\frac{5}{4}}\,dx = -2\int x^{-\frac{5}{4}}\,dx = -2\frac{x^{-\frac{1}{4}}}{\left(-\frac{1}{4}\right)} + C$

$= 8x^{-\frac{1}{4}} + C$

h) $\int -\frac{3}{2}x^{-\frac{1}{2}}\,dx = -\frac{3}{2}\int x^{-\frac{1}{2}}\,dx = -\frac{3}{2}\left(\frac{x^{\frac{1}{2}}}{\left(\frac{1}{2}\right)}\right) + C$

$= -3x^{\frac{1}{2}} + C$

i) $\int -\frac{4}{3}x^{-\frac{4}{3}}\,dx = -\frac{4}{3}\int x^{-\frac{4}{3}}\,dx = -\frac{4}{3}\left(\frac{x^{-\frac{1}{3}}}{\left(-\frac{1}{3}\right)}\right) + C$

$= 4x^{-\frac{1}{3}} + C$

Exercise 1.2 — Integrating functions

Q1 **a)** $f(x) = \int f'(x)\,dx = \int (5x + 3x^{-4})\,dx$

$= 5\int x\,dx + 3\int x^{-4}\,dx$

$= 5\left(\frac{x^2}{2}\right) + 3\left(\frac{x^{-3}}{-3}\right) + C$

$= \frac{5x^2}{2} - x^{-3} + C$

b) $f(x) = \int f'(x)\,dx = \int 4x(x^2 - 1)\,dx$

$= \int (4x^3 - 4x)\,dx = 4\int x^3\,dx - 4\int x\,dx$

$= 4\left(\frac{x^4}{4}\right) - 4\left(\frac{x^2}{2}\right) + C = x^4 - 2x^2 + C$

c) $f(x) = \int f'(x)\,dx = \int (x - 3)^2\,dx$

$= \int (x^2 - 6x + 9)\,dx$

$= \int x^2\,dx - 6\int x\,dx + 9\int 1\,dx$

$= \frac{x^3}{3} - 6\left(\frac{x^2}{2}\right) + 9\left(\frac{x^1}{1}\right) + C$

$= \frac{x^3}{3} - 3x^2 + 9x + C$

d) $f(x) = \int f'(x)\,dx = \int x\left(6x + \frac{4}{x^4}\right)\,dx$

$= \int \left(6x^2 + \frac{4}{x^3}\right)\,dx = \int (6x^2 + 4x^{-3})\,dx$

$= 6\int x^2\,dx + 4\int x^{-3}\,dx$

$= 6\left(\frac{x^3}{3}\right) + 4\left(\frac{x^{-2}}{-2}\right) + C$

$= 2x^3 - 2x^{-2} + C = 2x^3 - \frac{2}{x^2} + C$

e) $f(x) = \int f'(x)\,dx = \int \left(x + \frac{2}{x}\right)^2\,dx$

$= \int \left(x^2 + 4 + \frac{4}{x^2}\right)\,dx = \int (x^2 + 4 + 4x^{-2})\,dx$

$= \int x^2\,dx + 4\int 1\,dx + 4\int x^{-2}\,dx$

$= \frac{x^3}{3} + 4\left(\frac{x^1}{1}\right) + 4\left(\frac{x^{-1}}{-1}\right) + C$

$= \frac{x^3}{3} + 4x - \frac{4}{x} + C$

f) $f(x) = \int f'(x)\,dx = \int x\left(3x^{\frac{1}{2}} - \dfrac{2}{x^3}\right)dx$

$\qquad = \int\left(3x^{\frac{3}{2}} - \dfrac{2}{x^3}\right)dx = \int\left(3x^{\frac{3}{2}} - 2x^{-3}\right)dx$

$\qquad = 3\int x^{\frac{3}{2}}\,dx - 2\int x^{-3}\,dx$

$\qquad = 3\left(\dfrac{x^{\frac{5}{2}}}{\left(\frac{5}{2}\right)}\right) - 2\dfrac{x^{\frac{2}{3}}}{\left(\frac{2}{3}\right)} + C$

$\qquad = \frac{6}{5}x^{\frac{5}{2}} - 3x^{\frac{2}{3}} + C$

g) $f(x) = \int f'(x)\,dx = \int\left(6\sqrt{x} - \dfrac{1}{x^2}\right)dx$

$\qquad = 6\int x^{\frac{1}{2}}\,dx - \int x^{-2}\,dx$

$\qquad = 6\left(\dfrac{x^{\frac{3}{2}}}{\left(\frac{3}{2}\right)}\right) - \dfrac{x^{-1}}{-1} + C$

$\qquad = \frac{12}{3}x^{\frac{3}{2}} + \dfrac{1}{x} + C = 4x^{\frac{3}{2}} + \dfrac{1}{x} + C$

h) $f(x) = \int f'(x)\,dx = \int\left(\dfrac{2}{\sqrt{x}} - 7x^2\sqrt{x}\right)dx$

$\qquad = \int\left(2x^{-\frac{1}{2}} - 7x^2x^{\frac{1}{2}}\right)dx = \int\left(2x^{-\frac{1}{2}} - 7x^{\frac{5}{2}}\right)dx$

$\qquad = 2\int x^{-\frac{1}{2}}\,dx - 7\int x^{\frac{5}{2}}\,dx$

$\qquad = 2\left(\dfrac{x^{\frac{1}{2}}}{\left(\frac{1}{2}\right)}\right) - 7\dfrac{x^{\frac{7}{2}}}{\left(\frac{7}{2}\right)} + C$

$\qquad = 4x^{\frac{1}{2}} - 2x^{\frac{7}{2}} + C = 4\sqrt{x} - 2(\sqrt{x})^7 + C$

i) $f(x) = \int f'(x)\,dx = \int\left(5(\sqrt{x})^3 - \dfrac{3x}{\sqrt{x}}\right)dx$

$\qquad = \int\left(5(x^{\frac{1}{2}})^3 - 3xx^{-\frac{1}{2}}\right)dx$

$\qquad = 5\int x^{\frac{3}{2}}\,dx - 3\int x^{\frac{1}{2}}\,dx$

$\qquad = 5\left(\dfrac{x^{\frac{5}{2}}}{\left(\frac{5}{2}\right)}\right) - 3\left(\dfrac{x^{\frac{3}{2}}}{\left(\frac{3}{2}\right)}\right) + C$

$\qquad = 2x^{\frac{5}{2}} - 2x^{\frac{3}{2}} + C = 2(\sqrt{x})^5 - 2(\sqrt{x})^3 + C$

Q2 a) $\int(0.55x^{0.1} - 3x^{-1.5}x)\,dx = \int(0.55x^{0.1} - 3x^{-0.5})\,dx$

$\qquad = 0.55\int x^{0.1}\,dx - 3\int x^{-0.5}\,dx$

$\qquad = 0.55\left(\dfrac{x^{1.1}}{1.1}\right) - 3\left(\dfrac{x^{0.5}}{0.5}\right) + C$

$\qquad = 0.5x^{1.1} - 6x^{0.5} + C$

b) $\int\left(8x^3 - \dfrac{2}{\sqrt{x}} + \dfrac{5}{x^2}\right)dx = \int\left(8x^3 - 2x^{-\frac{1}{2}} + 5x^{-2}\right)dx$

$\qquad = 8\int x^3\,dx - 2\int x^{-\frac{1}{2}}\,dx + 5\int x^{-2}\,dx$

$\qquad = 8\left(\dfrac{x^4}{4}\right) - 2\left(\dfrac{x^{\frac{1}{2}}}{\left(\frac{1}{2}\right)}\right) + 5\left(\dfrac{x^{-1}}{-1}\right) + C$

$\qquad = 2x^4 - 4x^{\frac{1}{2}} - 5x^{-1} + C$

$\qquad = 2x^4 - 4\sqrt{x} - \dfrac{5}{x} + C$

c) $\int\left((\sqrt{x})^5 + \dfrac{1}{2\sqrt{x}}\right)dx = \int\left((x^{\frac{1}{2}})^5 + \dfrac{1}{2}x^{-\frac{1}{2}}\right)dx$

$\qquad = \int x^{\frac{5}{2}}\,dx + \dfrac{1}{2}\int x^{-\frac{1}{2}}\,dx$

$\qquad = \left(\dfrac{x^{\frac{7}{2}}}{\left(\frac{7}{2}\right)}\right) + \dfrac{1}{2}\left(\dfrac{x^{\frac{1}{2}}}{\left(\frac{1}{2}\right)}\right) + C$

$\qquad = \dfrac{2x^{\frac{7}{2}}}{7} + x^{\frac{1}{2}} + C$

$\qquad = \frac{2}{7}(\sqrt{x})^7 + \sqrt{x} + C$

d) $\int\left(\sqrt{x}\left(7x^2 - 1 - \dfrac{2}{x}\right)\right)dx$

$\qquad = \int\left(x^{\frac{1}{2}}(7x^2 - 1 - 2x^{-1})\right)dx$

$\qquad = \int\left(7x^{\frac{5}{2}} - x^{\frac{1}{2}} - 2x^{-\frac{1}{2}}\right)dx$

$\qquad = 7\int x^{\frac{5}{2}}\,dx - \int x^{\frac{1}{2}}\,dx - 2\int x^{-\frac{1}{2}}\,dx$

$\qquad = 7\left(\dfrac{x^{\frac{7}{2}}}{\left(\frac{7}{2}\right)}\right) - \left(\dfrac{x^{\frac{3}{2}}}{\left(\frac{3}{2}\right)}\right) - 2\left(\dfrac{x^{\frac{1}{2}}}{\left(\frac{1}{2}\right)}\right) + C$

$\qquad = 2x^{\frac{7}{2}} - \frac{2}{3}x^{\frac{3}{2}} - 4x^{\frac{1}{2}} + C$

$\qquad = 2(\sqrt{x})^7 - \frac{2}{3}(\sqrt{x})^3 - 4\sqrt{x} + C$

e) $\int(3x - 5\sqrt{x})^2\,dx = \int(9x^2 - 30x\sqrt{x} + 25x)\,dx$

$\qquad = \int\left(9x^2 - 30x^{\frac{3}{2}} + 25x\right)dx$

$\qquad = 9\int x^2\,dx - 30\int x^{\frac{3}{2}}\,dx + 25\int x\,dx$

$\qquad = 9\left(\dfrac{x^3}{3}\right) - 30\left(\dfrac{2}{5}x^{\frac{5}{2}}\right) + 25\left(\dfrac{1}{2}x^2\right) + C$

$\qquad = 3x^3 - 12(\sqrt{x})^5 + \dfrac{25}{2}x^2 + C$

f) $\int\left(\dfrac{2x^3 - \sqrt{x}}{x}\right)dx = \int\left(\dfrac{2x^3}{x} - \dfrac{\sqrt{x}}{x}\right)dx$

$\qquad = \int\left(2x^2 - x^{-\frac{1}{2}}\right)dx$

$\qquad = 2\int x^2\,dx - \int x^{-\frac{1}{2}}\,dx$

$\qquad = 2\left(\dfrac{x^3}{3}\right) - \left(\dfrac{x^{\frac{1}{2}}}{\left(\frac{1}{2}\right)}\right) + C$

$\qquad = \frac{2}{3}x^3 - 2\sqrt{x} + C$

g) $\int\left(\dfrac{10x^2 + 3x + 4}{\sqrt{x}}\right)dx = \int\left(\dfrac{10x^2}{\sqrt{x}} + \dfrac{3x}{\sqrt{x}} + \dfrac{4}{\sqrt{x}}\right)dx$

$\qquad = \int\left(\dfrac{10x^2}{x^{\frac{1}{2}}} + \dfrac{3x}{x^{\frac{1}{2}}} + \dfrac{4}{x^{\frac{1}{2}}}\right)dx$

$\qquad = \int\left(10x^{\frac{3}{2}} + 3x^{\frac{1}{2}} + 4x^{-\frac{1}{2}}\right)dx$

$\qquad = 10\int x^{\frac{3}{2}}\,dx + 3\int x^{\frac{1}{2}}\,dx + 4\int x^{-\frac{1}{2}}\,dx$

$\qquad = 10\left(\dfrac{x^{\frac{5}{2}}}{\left(\frac{5}{2}\right)}\right) + 3\left(\dfrac{x^{\frac{3}{2}}}{\left(\frac{3}{2}\right)}\right) + 4\left(\dfrac{x^{\frac{1}{2}}}{\left(\frac{1}{2}\right)}\right) + C$

$\qquad = 4x^{\frac{5}{2}} + 2x^{\frac{3}{2}} + 8x^{\frac{1}{2}} + C$

$\qquad = 4(\sqrt{x})^5 + 2(\sqrt{x})^3 + 8\sqrt{x} + C$

h) $\int\left(\dfrac{(5x-3)^2}{\sqrt{x}}\right)dx = \int\left(\dfrac{(25x^2-30x+9)}{\sqrt{x}}\right)dx$

$\qquad = \int\left(\dfrac{25x^2}{\sqrt{x}} - \dfrac{30x}{\sqrt{x}} + \dfrac{9}{\sqrt{x}}\right)dx$

$\qquad = \int\left(25x^{\frac{3}{2}} - 30x^{\frac{1}{2}} + 9x^{-\frac{1}{2}}\right)dx$

$\qquad = 25\int x^{\frac{3}{2}}\,dx - 30\int x^{\frac{1}{2}}\,dx + 9\int x^{-\frac{1}{2}}\,dx$

$\qquad = 25\left(\dfrac{x^{\frac{5}{2}}}{\left(\frac{5}{2}\right)}\right) - 30\left(\dfrac{x^{\frac{3}{2}}}{\left(\frac{3}{2}\right)}\right) + 9\left(\dfrac{x^{\frac{1}{2}}}{\left(\frac{1}{2}\right)}\right) + C$

$\qquad = 10x^{\frac{5}{2}} - 20x^{\frac{3}{2}} + 18x^{\frac{1}{2}} + C$

$\qquad = 10(\sqrt{x})^5 - 20(\sqrt{x})^3 + 18\sqrt{x} + C$

i) $\int\left(\sqrt{x}\,(3-\sqrt{x})^2\right)dx = \int\left(\sqrt{x}\,(9 - 6\sqrt{x} + x)\right)dx$

$\qquad = \int\left(9\sqrt{x} - 6\sqrt{x}\sqrt{x} + x\sqrt{x}\right)dx$

$\qquad = \int\left(9x^{\frac{1}{2}} - 6x + x^{\frac{3}{2}}\right)dx$

$\qquad = 9\int x^{\frac{1}{2}}\,dx - 6\int x\,dx + \int x^{\frac{3}{2}}\,dx$

$\qquad = 9\left(\dfrac{x^{\frac{3}{2}}}{\left(\frac{3}{2}\right)}\right) - 6\left(\dfrac{x^2}{2}\right) + \left(\dfrac{x^{\frac{5}{2}}}{\left(\frac{5}{2}\right)}\right) + C$

$\qquad = 6x^{\frac{3}{2}} - 3x^2 + \tfrac{2}{5}x^{\frac{5}{2}} + C$

$\qquad = 6(\sqrt{x})^3 - 3x^2 + \tfrac{2}{5}(\sqrt{x})^5 + C$

j) $\int(x^{\frac{1}{2}}+1)(x^{-\frac{1}{2}}-3)\,dx = \int(1 - 3x^{\frac{1}{2}} + x^{-\frac{1}{2}} - 3)\,dx$

$\qquad = \int(x^{-\frac{1}{2}} - 3x^{\frac{1}{2}} - 2)\,dx$

$\qquad = \int x^{-\frac{1}{2}}\,dx - 3\int x^{\frac{1}{2}}\,dx - 2\int 1\,dx$

$\qquad = \left(\dfrac{x^{\frac{1}{2}}}{\left(\frac{1}{2}\right)}\right) - 3\left(\dfrac{x^{\frac{3}{2}}}{\left(\frac{3}{2}\right)}\right) - 2\left(\dfrac{x^1}{1}\right) + C$

$\qquad = 2x^{\frac{1}{2}} - 2x^{\frac{3}{2}} - 2x + C$

Q3 $y = \int\dfrac{dy}{dx}\,dx = \int\left(1.5x^2 - \dfrac{4}{x^3}\right)dx$

$\qquad = \int(1.5x^2 - 4x^{-3})\,dx = 1.5\int x^2\,dx - 4\int x^{-3}\,dx$

$\qquad = 1.5\left(\dfrac{x^3}{3}\right) - 4\left(\dfrac{x^{-2}}{-2}\right) + C$

$\qquad = \dfrac{x^3}{2} + \dfrac{2}{x^2} + C$

Q4 $f(x) = \int f'(x)\,dx = \int\left(\dfrac{4}{3(x^{\frac{1}{3}})^4} + 5x^{\frac{3}{2}}\right)dx$

$\qquad = \int\left(\dfrac{4}{3x^{\frac{4}{3}}} + 5x^{\frac{3}{2}}\right)dx = \int\left(\tfrac{4}{3}x^{-\frac{4}{3}} + 5x^{\frac{3}{2}}\right)dx$

$\qquad = \tfrac{4}{3}\int x^{-\frac{4}{3}}\,dx + 5\int x^{\frac{3}{2}}\,dx$

$\qquad = \tfrac{4}{3}\left(\dfrac{x^{-\frac{1}{3}}}{\left(-\frac{1}{3}\right)}\right) + 5\dfrac{x^{\frac{5}{2}}}{\left(\frac{5}{2}\right)} + C$

$\qquad = -4x^{-\frac{1}{3}} + 2x^{\frac{5}{2}} + C$

$\qquad \left(= -\dfrac{4}{\sqrt[3]{x}} + 2(\sqrt{x})^5 + C\right)$

Q5 $\int\left(\sqrt{x}\left(\dfrac{3x^3}{2} - \dfrac{1}{x^2}\right)\right)dx = \int\left(\dfrac{3x^3\sqrt{x}}{2} - \dfrac{\sqrt{x}}{x^2}\right)dx$

$\qquad = \int\left(\dfrac{3x^{\frac{7}{2}}}{2} - x^{-\frac{3}{2}}\right)dx$

$\qquad = \tfrac{3}{2}\int x^{\frac{7}{2}}\,dx - \int x^{-\frac{3}{2}}\,dx$

$\qquad = \tfrac{3}{2}\left(\dfrac{x^{\frac{9}{2}}}{\left(\frac{9}{2}\right)}\right) - \left(\dfrac{x^{-\frac{1}{2}}}{\left(-\frac{1}{2}\right)}\right) + C$

$\qquad = \dfrac{x^{\frac{9}{2}}}{3} + 2x^{-\frac{1}{2}} + C$

$\qquad = \dfrac{(\sqrt{x})^9}{3} + \dfrac{2}{\sqrt{x}} + C$

Q6 $\int\left(\dfrac{(\sqrt{x}+3)(\sqrt{x}-1)}{\sqrt{x}}\right)dx = \int\left(\dfrac{x + 2\sqrt{x} - 3}{\sqrt{x}}\right)dx$

$\qquad = \int\left(\dfrac{x}{\sqrt{x}} + \dfrac{2\sqrt{x}}{\sqrt{x}} - \dfrac{3}{\sqrt{x}}\right)dx$

$\qquad = \int\left(x^{\frac{1}{2}} + 2 - 3x^{-\frac{1}{2}}\right)dx$

$\qquad = \int x^{\frac{1}{2}}\,dx + 2\int 1\,dx - 3\int x^{-\frac{1}{2}}\,dx$

$\qquad = \left(\dfrac{x^{\frac{3}{2}}}{\left(\frac{3}{2}\right)}\right) + 2\left(\dfrac{x^1}{1}\right) - 3\left(\dfrac{x^{\frac{1}{2}}}{\left(\frac{1}{2}\right)}\right) + C$

$\qquad = \tfrac{2}{3}x^{\frac{3}{2}} + 2x - 6x^{\frac{1}{2}} + C$

$\qquad = \tfrac{2}{3}(\sqrt{x})^3 + 2x - 6\sqrt{x} + C$

Q7 $\int\left(\sqrt{x}\left(\sqrt{x} - \dfrac{1}{\sqrt{x}}\right)^2\right)dx = \int\left(\sqrt{x}\left(x - 2 + \dfrac{1}{x}\right)\right)dx$

$\qquad = \int\left(x\sqrt{x} - 2\sqrt{x} + \dfrac{\sqrt{x}}{x}\right)dx$

$\qquad = \int\left(x^{\frac{3}{2}} - 2x^{\frac{1}{2}} + x^{-\frac{1}{2}}\right)dx$

$\qquad = \int x^{\frac{3}{2}}\,dx - 2\int x^{\frac{1}{2}}\,dx + \int x^{-\frac{1}{2}}\,dx$

$\qquad = \left(\dfrac{x^{\frac{5}{2}}}{\left(\frac{5}{2}\right)}\right) - 2\left(\dfrac{x^{\frac{3}{2}}}{\left(\frac{3}{2}\right)}\right) + \left(\dfrac{x^{\frac{1}{2}}}{\left(\frac{1}{2}\right)}\right) + C$

$\qquad = \tfrac{2}{5}x^{\frac{5}{2}} - \tfrac{4}{3}x^{\frac{3}{2}} + 2x^{\frac{1}{2}} + C$

$\qquad = \tfrac{2}{5}(\sqrt{x})^5 - \tfrac{4}{3}(\sqrt{x})^3 + 2\sqrt{x} + C$

Exercise 1.3 — Integrating to find equations of curves

Q1 a) $f(x) = \int f'(x)\,dx = \int 4x^3\,dx = 4\int x^3\,dx$

$\qquad = 4\left(\dfrac{x^4}{4}\right) + C = x^4 + C$

At the point $(0, 5)$, $x = 0$ and $f(x) = y = 5$, so
$5 = 0^4 + C$. So $C = 5$ and $f(x) = x^4 + 5$.

b) $f(x) = \int f'(x)\,dx = \int(3x^2 - 4x + 3)\,dx$

$\qquad = 3\int x^2\,dx - 4\int x\,dx + 3\int 1\,dx$

$\qquad = 3\left(\dfrac{x^3}{3}\right) - 4\left(\dfrac{x^2}{2}\right) + 3\left(\dfrac{x^1}{1}\right) + C$

$\qquad = x^3 - 2x^2 + 3x + C$

At the point $(1, -3)$ $x = 1$ and $f(x) = y = -3$, so
$-3 = 1^3 - 2(1^2) + 3(1) + C = 2 + C$. So $C = -5$ and
$f(x) = x^3 - 2x^2 + 3x - 5$.

c) $f(x) = \int f'(x)\,dx = \int 6x(x + 2)\,dx$

$= \int (6x^2 + 12x)\,dx$

$= 6\int x^2\,dx + 12\int x\,dx$

$= 6\left(\frac{x^3}{3}\right) + 12\left(\frac{x^2}{2}\right) + C$

$= 2x^3 + 6x^2 + C$

At the point $(-1, 1)$ $x = -1$ and $f(x) = y = 1$, so
$1 = 2(-1)^3 + 6(-1)^2 + C = 4 + C$. So $C = -3$ and
$f(x) = 2x^3 + 6x^2 - 3$.

d) $f(x) = \int f'(x)\,dx = \int \left(\frac{5}{x^2} + 2x\right)dx$

$= \int (5x^{-2} + 2x)\,dx$

$= 5\int x^{-2}\,dx + 2\int x\,dx$

$= 5\left(\frac{x^{-1}}{-1}\right) + 2\left(\frac{x^2}{2}\right) + C$

$= -\frac{5}{x} + x^2 + C$

At the point $(5, 4)$ $x = 5$ and $f(x) = y = 4$, so
$4 = -\frac{5}{5} + 5^2 + C = 24 + C$. So $C = -20$ and
$f(x) = -\frac{5}{x} + x^2 - 20$.

e) $f(x) = \int f'(x)\,dx = \int 3x^2(x - 4)\,dx$

$= \int (3x^3 - 12x^2)\,dx$

$= 3\int x^3\,dx - 12\int x^2\,dx$

$= 3\left(\frac{x^4}{4}\right) - 12\left(\frac{x^3}{3}\right) + C$

$= \frac{3}{4}x^4 - 4x^3 + C$

At the point $(2, -10)$ $x = 2$ and $f(x) = y = -10$, so
$-10 = \frac{3}{4}(2^4) - 4(2^3) + C = -20 + C$.
So $C = 10$ and $f(x) = \frac{3}{4}x^4 - 4x^3 + 10$.

f) $f(x) = \int f'(x)\,dx = \int (3x + 1)(x - 1)\,dx$

$= \int (3x^2 - 2x - 1)\,dx$

$= 3\int x^2\,dx - 2\int x\,dx - \int 1\,dx$

$= 3\left(\frac{x^3}{3}\right) - 2\left(\frac{x^2}{2}\right) - \left(\frac{x^1}{1}\right) + C$

$= x^3 - x^2 - x + C$

At the point $(3, -3)$ $x = 3$ and $f(x) = y = -3$, so
$-3 = 3^3 - 3^2 - 3 + C = 15 + C$.

So $C = -18$ and $f(x) = x^3 - x^2 - x - 18$.

g) $f(x) = \int f'(x)\,dx = \int x\left(x + \frac{3}{x^3}\right)dx$

$= \int \left(x^2 + \frac{3}{x^2}\right)dx = \int x^2\,dx + 3\int x^{-2}\,dx$

$= \frac{x^3}{3} + 3\left(\frac{x^{-1}}{-1}\right) + C = \frac{x^3}{3} - \frac{3}{x} + C$

At the point $(-3, 5)$ $x = -3$ and $f(x) = y = 5$, so
$5 = \frac{(-3)^3}{3} - \frac{3}{-3} + C = -8 + C$.

So $C = 13$ and $f(x) = \frac{x^3}{3} - \frac{3}{x} + 13$.

h) $f(x) = \int f'(x)\,dx = \int \frac{9x^3 + 2x^{-2}}{x}\,dx$

$= \int \left(\frac{9x^3}{x} + \frac{2x^{-2}}{x}\right)dx = \int (9x^2 + 2x^{-3})\,dx$

$= 9\int x^2\,dx + 2\int x^{-3}\,dx$

$= 9\left(\frac{x^3}{3}\right) + 2\left(\frac{x^{-2}}{-2}\right) + C$

$= 3x^3 - \frac{1}{x^2} + C$

At the point $(-1, 2)$ $x = -1$ and $f(x) = y = 2$, so
$2 = 3(-1)^3 - \frac{1}{(-1)^2} + C = -4 + C$.
So $C = 6$ and $f(x) = 3x^3 - \frac{1}{x^2} + 6$.

Q2 $y = \int \frac{dy}{dx}\,dx = \int (x - 2)(3x - 4)\,dx$

$= \int (3x^2 - 10x + 8)\,dx$

$= 3\int x^2\,dx - 10\int x\,dx + 8\int 1\,dx$

$= 3\left(\frac{x^3}{3}\right) - 10\left(\frac{x^2}{2}\right) + 8\left(\frac{x^1}{1}\right) + C$

$= x^3 - 5x^2 + 8x + C$

At the point $(2, -3)$ $x = 2$ and $y = -3$, so
$-3 = 2^3 - 5(2^2) + 8(2) + C = 4 + C$.

So $C = -7$ and $y = x^3 - 5x^2 + 8x - 7$.

Q3 $y = f(x) = \int f'(x)\,dx = \int \left(\frac{3}{\sqrt{x}} + 2x\right)dx$

$= \int \left(3x^{-\frac{1}{2}} + 2x\right)dx = 3\int x^{-\frac{1}{2}}\,dx + 2\int x\,dx$

$= 3\left(\frac{x^{\frac{1}{2}}}{\left(\frac{1}{2}\right)}\right) + 2\left(\frac{x^2}{2}\right) + C = 6x^{\frac{1}{2}} + x^2 + C$

$= 6\sqrt{x} + x^2 + C$

At the point $(4, 9)$ $x = 4$ and $y = 9$, so
$9 = 6\sqrt{4} + 4^2 + C = 28 + C$.

So $C = -19$ and $y = 6\sqrt{x} + x^2 - 19$.

Q4 $y = \int \frac{dy}{dx}\,dx = \int \left(3\sqrt{x} + \frac{1}{x^2}\right)dx = \int \left(3x^{\frac{1}{2}} + x^{-2}\right)dx$

$= 3\int x^{\frac{1}{2}}\,dx + \int x^{-2}\,dx = 3\left(\frac{x^{\frac{3}{2}}}{\left(\frac{3}{2}\right)}\right) + \left(\frac{x^{-1}}{-1}\right) + C$

$= 2x^{\frac{3}{2}} - \frac{1}{x} + C = 2(\sqrt{x})^3 - \frac{1}{x} + C$

At the point $(1, 7)$ $x = 1$ and $y = 7$, so
$7 = 2((\sqrt{1})^3) - \frac{1}{1} + C = 1 + C$.

So $C = 6$ and $y = 2(\sqrt{x})^3 - \frac{1}{x} + 6$.

Q5 $y = \int \frac{dy}{dt}\, dt = \int (\sqrt{t} - 3)^2\, dt = \int (t - 6\sqrt{t} + 9)\, dt$

$= \int t\, dt - 6 \int t^{\frac{1}{2}}\, dt + 9 \int 1\, dt$

$= \frac{t^2}{2} - 6\left(\frac{t^{\frac{3}{2}}}{\left(\frac{3}{2}\right)}\right) + 9\left(\frac{t^1}{1}\right) + C$

$= \frac{t^2}{2} - 4t^{\frac{3}{2}} + 9t + C = \frac{t^2}{2} - 4(\sqrt{t})^3 + 9t + C$

When $t = 4$, $y = 9$ so

$9 = \frac{4^2}{2} - 4(\sqrt{4})^3 + 9(4) + C = 12 + C$.

So C = –3 and $y = \frac{t^2}{2} - 4(\sqrt{t})^3 + 9t - 3$.

Q6 $f(x) = \int f'(x)\, dx = \int (\sqrt{x}(5x - 1))\, dx$

$= \int (5x\sqrt{x} - \sqrt{x})\, dx = \int (5x^{\frac{3}{2}} - x^{\frac{1}{2}})\, dx$

$= 5 \int x^{\frac{3}{2}}\, dx - \int x^{\frac{1}{2}}\, dx = 5\left(\frac{x^{\frac{5}{2}}}{\left(\frac{5}{2}\right)}\right) - \left(\frac{x^{\frac{3}{2}}}{\left(\frac{3}{2}\right)}\right)$

$= 2x^{\frac{5}{2}} - \frac{2}{3}x^{\frac{3}{2}} + C = 2(\sqrt{x})^5 - \frac{2}{3}(\sqrt{x})^3 + C$

When $x = 1$, $f(x) = y = \frac{1}{3}$ so

$\frac{1}{3} = 2(\sqrt{1})^5 - \frac{2}{3}(\sqrt{1})^3 + C = \frac{4}{3} + C$.

So C = –1 and $f(x) = 2(\sqrt{x})^5 - \frac{2}{3}(\sqrt{x})^3 - 1$.

Q7 $y = f(x) = \int f'(x)\, dx = \int \left(x^2 + \frac{2}{x^{\frac{3}{2}}}\right) dx$

$= \int \left(x^2 + 2x^{-\frac{3}{2}}\right) dx = \int x^2\, dx + 2 \int x^{-\frac{3}{2}}\, dx$

$= \frac{x^3}{3} + 2\left(\frac{x^{-\frac{1}{2}}}{\left(-\frac{1}{2}\right)}\right) + C = \frac{x^3}{3} - \frac{4}{\sqrt{x}} + C$

When $x = 1$, $y = -\frac{5}{3}$ so

$-\frac{5}{3} = \frac{1^3}{3} - \frac{4}{\sqrt{1}} + C = -\frac{11}{3} + C$.

So C = 2 and $y = \frac{x^3}{3} - \frac{4}{\sqrt{x}} + 2$.

Q8 $y = \int \frac{dy}{dx}\, dx = \int \left(\frac{x - 6}{x^3} + 2\right) dx$

$= \int \left(\frac{x}{x^3} - \frac{6}{x^3} + 2\right) dx = \int (x^{-2} - 6x^{-3} + 2)\, dx$

$= \int x^{-2}\, dx - 6 \int x^{-3}\, dx + 2 \int 1\, dx$

$= \left(\frac{x^{-1}}{-1}\right) - 6\left(\frac{x^{-2}}{-2}\right) + 2\left(\frac{x^1}{1}\right) + C$

$= -\frac{1}{x} + \frac{3}{x^2} + 2x + C$

When $x = 3$, $y = -1$ so

$-1 = -\frac{1}{3} + \frac{3}{3^2} + 2(3) + C = 6 + C$.

So C = –7 and $y = -\frac{1}{x} + \frac{3}{x^2} + 2x - 7$.

Review Exercise — Chapter 7

Q1 a) $f(x) = \frac{x^{\frac{1}{2}}}{\left(\frac{1}{2}\right)} + 4x - \frac{5x^4}{4} + C$

and then simplify each term further if possible...

$= 2x^{\frac{1}{2}} + 4x - \frac{5x^4}{4} + C$

b) First rewrite everything in terms of powers of x:

$f'(x) = 2x + 3x^{-2}$

Now you can integrate each term (don't forget to add C):

$f(x) = \frac{2x^2}{2} + \frac{3x^{-1}}{-1} + C$

Then simplify each term:

$f(x) = x^2 - \frac{3}{x} + C$

c) Following the same process as in part b):

$f'(x) = 6x^2 - \frac{1}{3}x^{-\frac{1}{2}}$

$f(x) = \frac{6x^3}{3} + \frac{1}{3}\frac{x^{\frac{1}{2}}}{\left(\frac{1}{2}\right)} + C$

$f(x) = 2x^3 + \frac{2}{3}\sqrt{x} + C$

Q2 Integrating gives $y = 3x^2 - 7x + C$; then substitute $x = 1$ and $y = 0$ to find that C = 4. So the equation of the curve is $y = 3x^2 - 7x + 4$.

Q3 $\int \left(4x^2 + \frac{3}{\sqrt{x}} - 2\right) dx = \int \left(4x^2 + 3x^{-\frac{1}{2}} - 2\right) dx$

$= 4 \int x^2\, dx + 3 \int x^{-\frac{1}{2}}\, dx - 2 \int 1\, dx$

$= 4\left(\frac{x^3}{3}\right) + 3\left(\frac{x^{\frac{1}{2}}}{\left(\frac{1}{2}\right)}\right) - 2\left(\frac{x^1}{1}\right) + C$

$= \frac{4}{3}x^3 + 6x^{\frac{1}{2}} - 2x + C$

$= \frac{4}{3}x^3 + 6\sqrt{x} - 2x + C$

Q4 $\int (3\sqrt{x} + 3)^2\, dx = \int (9x + 18\sqrt{x} + 9)\, dx$

$= \int \left(9x + 18x^{\frac{1}{2}} + 9\right) dx$

$= 9 \int x\, dx + 18 \int x^{\frac{1}{2}}\, dx + 9 \int 1\, dx$

$= 9\left(\frac{x^2}{2}\right) + 18\left(\frac{x^{\frac{3}{2}}}{\left(\frac{3}{2}\right)}\right) + 9\left(\frac{x^1}{1}\right) + C$

$= \frac{9}{2}x^2 + 12x^{\frac{3}{2}} + 9x + C$

$= \frac{9}{2}x^2 + 12(\sqrt{x})^3 + 9x + C$

Q5 a) $y = \int \frac{dy}{dx}\, dx = \int 2(3x - 6.5)\, dx = \int (6x - 13)\, dx$

$= 6 \int x\, dx - 13 \int 1\, dx = 6\left(\frac{x^2}{2}\right) - 13\left(\frac{x^1}{1}\right) + C$

$= 3x^2 - 13x + C$

When $x = 1$, $y = 2$.

So $2 = 3(1^2) - 13(1) + C = -10 + C$ and C = 12. So the equation is $y = 3x^2 - 13x + 12$.

Answers 199

b) $y = 3x^2 - 13x + 12 = (3x - 4)(x - 3)$. So

$y = 0$ when $x = 3$ or $3x = 4$ so $x = \frac{4}{3}$.
At $x = 0$, $y = 12$.

The x^2 coefficient is positive so
the curve looks like this:

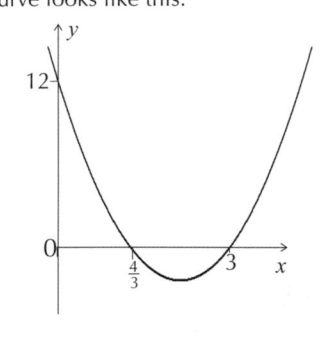

Q6 a) $y = \int \frac{dy}{dx}\, dx = \int (6x^2 + 6x - 5)\, dx$

$$= 6 \int x^2\, dx + 6 \int x\, dx - 5 \int 1\, dx$$
$$= 6\left(\frac{x^3}{3}\right) + 6\left(\frac{x^2}{2}\right) - 5\left(\frac{x^1}{1}\right) + C$$
$$= 2x^3 + 3x^2 - 5x + C$$

When $x = 0$, $y = 0$.
So $0 = 2(0^3) + 3(0^2) - 5(0) + C = C$ and
$C = 0$. So the equation is $y = 2x^3 + 3x^2 - 5x$.

b) $y = 2x^3 + 3x^2 - 5x = x(2x^2 + 3x - 5)$.
$$= x(x - 1)(2x + 5)$$

This is a cubic graph with a positive x^3 coefficient
so the curve will go from bottom–left to top–right.
If $y = 0$, $x(x - 1)(2x + 5) = 0$ so $x = 0$, $x = 1$ and
$x = -\frac{5}{2}$ are x-intercepts. If $x = 0$, $y = 0$ so the only
y-intercept is the origin. The graph looks like this:

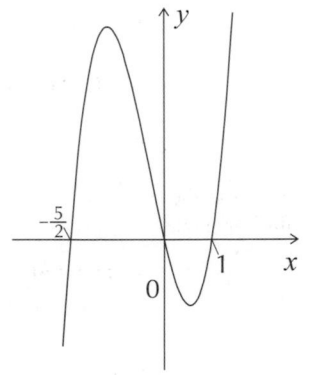

Q7 a) $\dfrac{dy}{dx} = \dfrac{(x + 2)(x - 2)}{\sqrt{x}} = \dfrac{x^2 + 2x - 2x - 4}{\sqrt{x}}$

$$= \frac{x^2 - 4}{\sqrt{x}} = \frac{x^2}{\sqrt{x}} - \frac{4}{\sqrt{x}} = \frac{x^2}{x^{\frac{1}{2}}} - \frac{4}{x^{\frac{1}{2}}}$$
$$= x^2 x^{-\frac{1}{2}} - 4x^{-\frac{1}{2}} = x^{\frac{3}{2}} - 4x^{-\frac{1}{2}}$$

So $A = 1$ and $B = -4$.

b) $y = \int \dfrac{dy}{dx}\, dx = \int (x^{\frac{3}{2}} - 4x^{-\frac{1}{2}})\, dx$

$$= \int x^{\frac{3}{2}}\, dx - 4 \int x^{-\frac{1}{2}}\, dx$$
$$= \frac{x^{\frac{5}{2}}}{\left(\frac{5}{2}\right)} - 4\left(\frac{x^{\frac{1}{2}}}{\left(\frac{1}{2}\right)}\right) + C$$
$$= \frac{2}{5}x^{\frac{5}{2}} - 8x^{\frac{1}{2}} + C = \frac{2}{5}(\sqrt{x})^5 - 8\sqrt{x} + C$$

When $x = 1$, $y = \frac{7}{5}$.
So $\frac{7}{5} = \frac{2}{5}(\sqrt{1})^5 - 8\sqrt{1} + C = -\frac{38}{5} + C$ and
$C = 9$.
So the equation is $y = \frac{2}{5}(\sqrt{x})^5 - 8\sqrt{x} + 9$.

Q8 $f(x) = \int f'(x)\, dx = \int \left(6x^2 - 12 - \dfrac{8}{x^2}\right) dx$

$$= \int (6x^2 - 12 - 8x^{-2})\, dx$$
$$= 6 \int x^2\, dx - 12 \int 1\, dx - 8 \int x^{-2}\, dx$$
$$= 6\left(\frac{x^3}{3}\right) - 12\left(\frac{x^1}{1}\right) - 8\left(\frac{x^{-1}}{-1}\right) + C$$
$$= 2x^3 - 12x + \frac{8}{x} + C$$

When $x = -2$, $y = 5$ and $y = f(x)$ so $f(x) = 5$.
So $5 = 2(-2)^3 - 12(-2) + \dfrac{8}{(-2)} + C = 4 + C$ and
$C = 1$.

So the equation is $y = 2x^3 - 12x + \dfrac{8}{x} + 1$.

Q9 $f(x) = \int f'(x)\, dx = \int \left(\dfrac{5x^2 + 1}{x^{\frac{1}{2}}} - 10\right) dx$

$$= \int \left(\frac{5x^2}{x^{\frac{1}{2}}} + \frac{1}{x^{\frac{1}{2}}} - 10\right) dx$$
$$= \int \left(5x^{\frac{3}{2}} + x^{-\frac{1}{2}} - 10\right) dx$$
$$= 5 \int x^{\frac{3}{2}}\, dx + \int x^{-\frac{1}{2}}\, dx - 10 \int 1\, dx$$
$$= 5\left(\frac{x^{\frac{5}{2}}}{\left(\frac{5}{2}\right)}\right) + \left(\frac{x^{\frac{1}{2}}}{\left(\frac{1}{2}\right)}\right) - 10\left(\frac{x^1}{1}\right) + C$$
$$= 2x^{\frac{5}{2}} + 2x^{\frac{1}{2}} - 10x + C$$
$$= 2(\sqrt{x})^5 + 2\sqrt{x} - 10x + C$$

When $x = 1$, $y = -9$ and $y = f(x)$ so $f(x) = -9$.
So $-9 = 2(\sqrt{1})^5 + 2\sqrt{1} - 10(1) + C = -6 + C$
and $C = -3$.
So the equation is $y = 2(\sqrt{x})^5 + 2\sqrt{x} - 10x - 3$.

Exam-Style Questions — Chapter 7

Q1 a) Multiply out the brackets and simplify the terms:

$(5 + 2\sqrt{x})^2 = (5 + 2\sqrt{x})(5 + 2\sqrt{x})$

$= 25 + 10\sqrt{x} + 10\sqrt{x} + 4x$

$= 25 + 20\sqrt{x} + 4x$

So $a = 25$, $b = 20$ and $c = 4$

[3 marks — one for each constant]

b) Integrate your answer from a), treating each term separately:

$\int (25 + 20\sqrt{x} + 4x)\,dx$

$= 25x + 20\left(\dfrac{x^{\frac{3}{2}}}{(\frac{3}{2})}\right) + 4\left(\dfrac{x^2}{2}\right) + C$

$= 25x + \dfrac{40\sqrt{x^3}}{3} + 2x^2 + C$

[3 marks available — 1 for each term. Lose one mark if C missing or answers not simplified (surds not necessary)]

Q2 To find f(x) you integrate f$'(x)$, but it helps to write all terms in powers of x, so

$5\sqrt{x} = 5x^{\frac{1}{2}}$ and $\dfrac{6}{x^2} = 6x^{-2}$ *[1 mark]*

Now integrate each term:

$f(x) = \int\left(2x + 5x^{\frac{1}{2}} + 6x^{-2}\right)dx$

$= \dfrac{2x^2}{2} + 5\left(\dfrac{x^{\frac{3}{2}}}{(\frac{3}{2})}\right) + \left(\dfrac{6x^{-1}}{-1}\right) + C$

$f(x) = x^2 + \dfrac{10\sqrt{x^3}}{3} - \dfrac{6}{x} + C$

[2 marks for correct terms, 1 mark for +C]

You've been given a point on the curve so you can calculate the value of C:

If $y = 7$ when $x = 3$, then

$3^2 - \dfrac{6}{3} + \dfrac{10\sqrt{3^3}}{3} + C = 7$ *[1 mark]*

$9 - 2 + 10\sqrt{3} + C = 7$

$7 + 10\sqrt{3} + C = 7$

$C = -10\sqrt{3}$

$f(x) = x^2 + \dfrac{10\sqrt{x^3}}{3} - \dfrac{6}{x} - 10\sqrt{3}$ *[1 mark]*

Q3 a) Rearrange the terms so each is written as a power of x, showing your working:

$\dfrac{1}{\sqrt{36x}} = \dfrac{1}{\sqrt{36}\sqrt{x}} = \dfrac{1}{6} \times \dfrac{1}{\sqrt{x}} = \dfrac{1}{6}x^{-\frac{1}{2}}$ *[1 mark]*

$2\left(\sqrt{\dfrac{1}{x^3}}\right) = 2\left(\dfrac{1}{x^3}\right)^{\frac{1}{2}} = 2(x^{-3})^{\frac{1}{2}}$

$= 2\left(x^{(-3 \times \frac{1}{2})}\right) = 2x^{-\frac{3}{2}}$ *[1 mark]*

This shows that f$'(x) = \dfrac{1}{6}x^{-\frac{1}{2}} - 2x^{-\frac{3}{2}}$ — so $A = \dfrac{1}{6}$ and $B = 2$ *[1 mark]*

b) Integrate f$'(x)$ to find f(x):

$f(x) = \left(\dfrac{1}{6}\left(\dfrac{x^{\frac{1}{2}}}{(\frac{1}{2})}\right)\right) - \left(2\left(\dfrac{x^{-\frac{1}{2}}}{(-\frac{1}{2})}\right)\right) + C$ *[1 mark]*

$= \dfrac{1}{3}x^{\frac{1}{2}} + 4\left(\dfrac{1}{\sqrt{x}}\right) + C$

$= \dfrac{\sqrt{x}}{3} + \dfrac{4}{\sqrt{x}} + C$ *[1 mark]*

Now use the coordinates $(1, 7)$ to find the value of C:

$7 = \dfrac{\sqrt{1}}{3} + \dfrac{4}{\sqrt{1}} + C$ *[1 mark]*

$7 - \dfrac{1}{3} - 4 = C$

$C = \dfrac{8}{3}$

So $y = \dfrac{\sqrt{x}}{3} + \dfrac{4}{\sqrt{x}} + \dfrac{8}{3}$ *[1 mark]*

Q4 a) The tangent at $(1, 2)$ has the same gradient as the curve at that point, so use f$'(x)$ to calculate the gradient:

$f'(1) = 1^3 - 2$ *[1 mark]*

$= -1$ *[1 mark]*

Put this into the straight-line equation $y - y_1 = m(x - x_1)$:

$y - 2 = -1(x - 1)$ *[1 mark]*

$y = -x + 1 + 2$

$y = -x + 3$ *[1 mark]*

b) $f(x) = \int\left(x^3 - \dfrac{2}{x^2}\right)dx$

$= \int(x^3 - 2x^{-2})\,dx$ *[1 mark]*

$= \dfrac{x^4}{4} - 2\left(\dfrac{x^{-1}}{-1}\right) + C$

$= \dfrac{x^4}{4} + 2x^{-1} + C$ *[1 mark]*

$= \dfrac{x^4}{4} + \dfrac{2}{x} + C$

Now use the coordinates $(1, 2)$ to find the value of C:

$2 = \dfrac{1^4}{4} + \dfrac{2}{1} + C$ *[1 mark]*

$2 - \dfrac{1}{4} - 2 = C$

$C = -\dfrac{1}{4}$ *[1 mark]*

So $f(x) = \dfrac{x^4}{4} + \dfrac{2}{x} - \dfrac{1}{4}$ *[1 mark]*

Q5 a) Multiply out the brackets in $f'(x)$
$(x-1)(3x-1) = 3x^2 - x - 3x + 1$
$= 3x^2 - 4x + 1$ *[1 mark]*
Now $f(x) = \int (3x^2 - 4x + 1)\,dx$
$= \dfrac{3x^3}{3} - \dfrac{4x^2}{2} + \dfrac{x}{1} + C$ *[1 mark]*
$= x^3 - 2x^2 + x + C$ *[1 mark]*
Input the x and y coordinates to find C:
$10 = 3^3 - 2(3^2) + 3 + C$ *[1 mark]*
$10 - 27 + 18 - 3 = C$
$C = -2$ *[1 mark]*
So $f(x) = x^3 - 2x^2 + x - 2$ *[1 mark]*

b) First calculate the gradient of $f(x)$ when $x = 3$:
$f'(3) = 3(3^2) - (4 \times 3) + 1$
$= 27 - 12 + 1$
$= 16$ *[1 mark]*
Use the fact that the tangent gradient multiplied by the normal gradient must equal -1 to find the gradient of the normal (n):
$16 \times n = -1$ therefore $n = -\dfrac{1}{16}$ *[1 mark]*.
Put n and P(3, 10) into the formula for the equation of a line and rearrange until it's in the form $y = \dfrac{a-x}{b}$:
$y - 10 = -\dfrac{1}{16}(x - 3)$ *[1 mark]*
$16y - 160 = -x + 3$
$y = \dfrac{163 - x}{16}$
So $a = 163$ and $b = 16$. *[1 mark]*

Q6 a) First, simplify expression for $f'(x)$:
$f'(x) = 2x - 3\sqrt{x} + \dfrac{16}{x^2}$
$= 2x - 3x^{\frac{1}{2}} + 16x^{-2}$ *[1 mark]*
Now $f(x) = \int (2x - 3x^{\frac{1}{2}} + 16x^{-2})\,dx$
$= 2\dfrac{x^2}{2} - 3\dfrac{x^{\frac{3}{2}}}{(\frac{3}{2})} + 16\dfrac{x^{-1}}{-1} + C$ *[1 mark]*
$= x^2 - 2(\sqrt{x})^3 - \dfrac{16}{x} + C$ *[1 mark]*

Input the x and y coordinates to find C:
$1 = 4^2 - 2(\sqrt{4})^3 - \dfrac{16}{4} + C$ *[1 mark]*
$1 = 16 - 16 - 4 + C$
$C = 5$ *[1 mark]*
So $f(x) = x^2 - 2(\sqrt{x})^3 - \dfrac{16}{x} + 5$ *[1 mark]*

b) The tangent at (4, 1) has the same gradient as the curve at that point, so use $f'(x)$ to calculate the gradient:
$f'(4) = 2(4) - 3\sqrt{4} + \dfrac{16}{4^2}$ *[1 mark]*
$= 3$ *[1 mark]*

Put this into the straight-line equation $y - y_1 = m(x - x_1)$:
$y - 1 = 3(x - 4)$ *[1 mark]*
$y = 3x - 12 + 1$
$y = 3x - 11$ *[1 mark]*

Q7 a) Square both sides to get y on the left:
$y = (1 + 3\sqrt{x})^2$ *[1 mark]*
$= 9x + 6\sqrt{x} + 1$
$= 9x + 6x^{\frac{1}{2}} + 1$ *[1 mark]*

b) $\int y\,dx = \int (9x + 6x^{\frac{1}{2}} + 1)\,dx$
$= 9\left(\dfrac{x^2}{2}\right) + 6\left(\dfrac{x^{\frac{3}{2}}}{(\frac{3}{2})}\right) + x + C$
$= \dfrac{9}{2}x^2 + 4(\sqrt{x})^3 + x + C$
[3 marks available — 1 for each term. Lose a mark if C is missing.]

Q8 a) $\dfrac{dy}{dx} = 3\sqrt{x} - \dfrac{5}{\sqrt{x}} = 3x^{\frac{1}{2}} - 5x^{-\frac{1}{2}}$ *[1 mark]*
Now integrate each term to find y:
$y = \int \dfrac{dy}{dx}\,dx = \int (3x^{\frac{1}{2}} - 5x^{-\frac{1}{2}})\,dx$
$= 3\left(\dfrac{x^{\frac{3}{2}}}{(\frac{3}{2})}\right) - 5\left(\dfrac{x^{\frac{1}{2}}}{(\frac{1}{2})}\right) + C$ *[1 mark]*
$= 2(\sqrt{x})^3 - 10\sqrt{x} + C$ *[1 mark]*
Use the coordinates to find the value of C:
$-6 = 2(\sqrt{4})^3 - 10\sqrt{4} + C$
$= 16 - 20 + C$
$= -4 + C$
So $C = -2$ *[1 mark]*
So the equation of the curve is
$y = 2(\sqrt{x})^3 - 10\sqrt{x} - 2$. *[1 mark]*

b) First calculate the gradient of $f(x)$ when $x = 4$:
$\dfrac{dy}{dx} = 3\sqrt{4} - \dfrac{5}{\sqrt{4}} = (3 \times 2) - \dfrac{5}{2} = \dfrac{7}{2}$ *[1 mark]*

Use the fact that the tangent gradient multiplied by the normal gradient must equal -1 to find the gradient of the normal (n):
$\dfrac{7}{2} \times n = -1$ therefore $n = -\dfrac{2}{7}$ *[1 mark]*.
Put n and P(4, –6) into the formula for the equation of a line and rearrange until it's in the form $y = ax + by + c$:
$y + 6 = -\dfrac{2}{7}(x - 4)$ *[1 mark]*
$7y + 42 = -2x + 8$
$7y = -2x - 34$
$2x + 7y + 34 = 0$ *[1 mark]*

Index

C1 Formula Sheet

These are the formulas you'll be given in the exam, so make sure you know exactly when you need them and how to use them.

Measurement

Surface area of a sphere = $4\pi r^2$

Area of the curved surface of a cone = $\pi r \times$ (slant height)

Arithmetic Series

$$u_n = a + (n - 1)d$$

$$S_n = \frac{1}{2}n(a + l) = \frac{1}{2}n[2a + (n - 1)d]$$

As you can see, they don't give you many formulas for the C1 exam — you really do have to learn all the others off by heart, I'm afraid. They are a little more generous in later modules if that's any consolation...

Finally, don't forget that C1 is a non-calculator exam. So make sure you're completely happy doing basic arithmetic without your calculator — you really don't want to throw away marks in the exam because you're a bit rusty on long division...

All the questions in this book can be done without a calculator (well, except for a handful of questions which are clearly highlighted), so put away your calculator and use this book to get plenty of practice.

MEC1T51